STATISTICS: AN INTRODUCTION TO QUANTITATIVE ECONOMIC RESEARCH

Daniel B. Suits
UNIVERSITY OF MICHIGAN

STATISTICS:

AN INTRODUCTION TO QUANTITATIVE ECONOMIC RESEARCH

RAND McNALLY & COMPANY : Chicago

RAND McNALLY ECONOMICS SERIES

Walter W. Heller *and* **Dale W. Jorgenson**, *Advisory Editors*

Baldwin, et al., *Trade, Growth, and the Balance of Payments*
Barger, *The Management of Money*
Barger, *Money, Banking and Public Policy*
Dewey, *Monopoly and Economics in Law*
Duesenberry, Fromm, Klein, and Kuh, eds., *The Brookings Quarterly Econometric Model of the United States*
Frisch, *Theory of Production*
Holzman, ed., *Readings on the Soviet Economy*
Kenen, *Giant Among Nations*
Kirschen, ed., *Economic Policy in Our Time,* **3 volumes**
Nerlove, *Estimation and Identification of Cobb-Douglas Production Functions*
Quade, ed., *Analysis for Military Decisions*
Solow, *Capital Theory and the Rate of Return*
Spengler and Allen, eds., *Essays in Economic Thought: Aristotle to Marshall*
Suits, *Statistics: An Introduction to Quantitative Economic Research*
Theil, ed., *Studies in Mathematical and Managerial Economics*
    Boot, *Quadratic Programming*
    Ijiri, *Management Goals and Accounting for Control*
    Theil, *Optimal Decision Rules for Government and Industry*
Whittaker, *Schools and Streams of Economic Thought*

Copyright © 1963 by Rand McNally & Company
All rights reserved
Printed in U.S.A. by Rand McNally & Company
Book design by Georgette Roux
Library of Congress Catalog Card Number 63:8246
Second printing, 1966

To my father and mother,

Hollis E. and Dorothy D. H. Suits

PREFACE

This book is designed to serve as the text for a one-semester beginning course in economic or business statistics. The number of similar books currently available is large, and, since all are intended for the same purpose, the amount of material in common is necessarily substantial. This book differs from the others, then, not so much in content as in its basic organization and method of exposition. In this it is sufficiently novel to merit a few words of explanation.

The central problem of quantitative analysis in any social science arises from the complex and multivariate character of individual human and institutional behavior. A realistic approach to the subject requires that the student be introduced to this problem in its most general and complicated form as soon as possible. While many specialized multivariate techniques are far beyond the scope of a single semester, the most general and inclusive method is fortunately also the easiest. The cross-tabulation of cell means and their standard errors is easily understood, applied, and interpreted by the student as soon as he understands the nature of the arithmetic mean and its sampling distribution.

Not only is this method the easiest, it is also—given sufficient data— the most sophisticated. Indeed, the student immediately meets such concepts as multiple correlation, interaction, and multivariate relationships combining numerical and categorical variables. Moreover he learns to know nonlinearity, heteroskedasticity, estimating bias, unequal cell sizes, and so on, as facts of research life rather than as vague threats lurking somewhere behind simplifying assumptions.

This book is tightly organized around the multivariate function analyzed as a table. Its focus is to be found in Chapter V where the concept of the multivariate stochastic function is introduced and its analysis set forth. The first four chapters lead directly into this focus; the last five chapters lead away from it to specialized problems. For example, the need for formal significance testing arises, in most cases, purely from the insufficiency of data. The use of regression for significance testing arises from the same source, but it is more often called on to approximate a function by a particular mathematical form.

The problem of quantitative research is that of finding a statistical method that yields a useful approximation to reality. Thus wherever possible, ideas are introduced by specific, real, or at least realistic, examples. The idea is then generalized by its application to several different problems. The number that can be included for this purpose is necessarily small, however, and I consider one of the most important parts of classroom discussion to be the consideration of a wide variety of additional examples.

Throughout the exposition mathematics has been assigned to its proper role as a support and enrichment of the subject for those who can benefit from it. Mathematical proofs and derivations are kept concise and are located in footnotes out of the way of students insufficiently trained to use them. Moreover, the attempt is made to develop the theory in concrete, rather than abstract, terms. Many students—including some who had elected a beginning course in economic statistics as a cognate for concentration in mathematical statistics—have commented on the insight provided by the simple concrete expression of sampling theory in terms of a houseful of 3×5 cards. In a somewhat similar vein, one of my favorite teaching devices is to have students toss a number of N-coin samples and study the distribution of the proportion of heads. By assigning a different value of N to each student, the formula $\sigma_{\hat{P}}^2 = \dfrac{P(1-P)}{N}$ can be empirically explored in an unforgettable way in no more than an hour of class or laboratory time.

Above all, I think the student learns research technique by manipulating actual data and interpreting actual results. Real problems necessarily involve a lot of data processing, and access to a statistics laboratory or a desk machine is invaluable. Even so, calculation can be a burden unless efficient data layout, computing, and checking routines are used. The work sheets accompanying each technique are the product of research experience and are used as standard procedure for hand calculation in my Research Seminar in Quantitative Economics. Concentrating on standard machine procedure, of course, means that the methods embodying shortcuts for use without a machine are omitted. If a calculating machine is unavailable, the instructor will doubtless want to supplement the text by a discussion of other calculating procedures.

Although much is to be said for laboratory exercise manuals, I have never used them. They seem to me to impose still another barrier—if not actually, at least psychologically—between the student and economic reality. Ideally the student should be sent to sources for his own data, but for obvious reasons this is generally infeasible. My own solution is to provide mimeographed problems containing data and instructions. Interesting and pertinent examples are sometimes hard to find, however, and I have included some of my own favorite laboratory exercises among the questions and problems at the end of each chapter.

Hundreds of people have contributed, one way or another, to this book. The ideas, point of view, organization, and method of exposition are the product of twenty years of teaching and quantitative economic research with students at all levels. Their responses, questions, and performances guided the development of my thinking. I am particularly indebted to the two beginning classes who, in the spring of 1961 and of 1962, participated in the dry run of the first two versions of the book. The treatment of the topics has benefited greatly from discussion with my colleagues at the University of Michigan, Professors Leslie Kish, John B. Lansing, James N. Morgan, and Eva Mueller. I am particularly indebted to Professor W. H. Locke Anderson for his active interest and many suggestions, and to my good friend and erstwhile colleague Professor Arthur Goldberger of the University of Wisconsin, who kindly read the first draft. I did not always follow the advice I was given; in any case the full responsibility for errors is my own. Special recognition is due to Mrs. Vivian Finley for her speedy and careful typing—often under pressure of time—of the many versions and revisions of the manuscript.

I am indebted to Sir Ronald A. Fisher, F.R.S., Cambridge and to

Preface

Dr. Frank Yates, F.R.S., Rothamsted, also to Messrs. Oliver & Boyd Ltd., Edinburgh, for permission to reprint Tables III and IV from their book *Statistical Tables for Biological, Agricultural and Medical Research*.

Finally, particular thanks are due to my wife, Adelaide, both for her help with the manuscript and for her patience in suffering through its long preparation.

DANIEL B. SUITS

Athens, September 1962.

CONTENTS

Contents

LIST OF TABLES

List of Tables

LIST OF FIGURES

STATISTICS: AN INTRODUCTION TO
QUANTITATIVE ECONOMIC RESEARCH

CHAPTER I

Introduction

1.1 MEASUREMENT AND THEORY

Quantitative economics deals with the disciplined observation and measurement of economic phenomena. Its objective is twofold: to test economic theories by comparing them with facts and, where theories are found to be valid, to measure the economic relationships implied by them. Our ability to understand economic behavior, to predict its response to changed conditions, to forecast its course in the future, and to alter or control it as a matter of business or public policy depends on the union of valid theory with accurate measurement.

The familiar demand schedule of the beginning economics course is a good example. Economic theory selects price and quantity sold as two important facts of market activity. These are then fitted together in a demand schedule showing how much will be bought at each price. This schedule can be represented by a table in which high prices are matched with small quantities and low prices with large quantities, or we can draw a graph of the demand curve and discuss market behavior in terms of its shape, its elasticity, and the way it shifts on the chart. The student learns, for example, that an increase in supply lowers price, and, for a given increase, price will fall more, the lower the elasticity of demand.

This theory establishes a basis for the analysis and prediction of market conditions, but we need more than abstract theory. In the first place, theories can be wrong. The wrong factors can be assigned to important roles, or key factors can be overlooked, or the theory can push

1

the correct factors into a distorted pattern of relationship. Thus, before we can use them as guides for action, theories must be tested against experience to see that they really work.

In the second place, the theoretical magnitudes must be measured. With a given reduction in corn crops, prices will rise more the smaller the elasticity of demand, but to establish sound farm policy a congressional committee needs to know *how much* of a price increase to expect from given circumstances. An automobile manufacturer is perfectly aware that a larger number of cars can be sold at lower than at higher prices. To formulate intelligent price policy he needs to know *how many* more. A 50 per cent reduction in federal excise taxes will lower retail prices and will stimulate purchase of the goods taxed. But before the Secretary of the Treasury can bring forward a sound tax proposal he needs to know *how much* stimulation in sales to expect. In other words, to bring theoretical market demand to the point where it can be applied, the magnitudes implied by the theory, that is, the elasticity of demand, must actually be measured.

What is true of demand is equally true of all other economic theory. To help in understanding events, in forecasting their future course, and in policy formation to modify, control, or adapt to this course, theory must be completed by observation, test, and measurement.

1.2 SOCIAL SCIENCE AND STATISTICS

What is true of economic theory is true of science in general, but theories in some sciences are easier to test and measure than in others. The great power of laboratory science—of which physics is the outstanding example—lies in the use of the experimental method. The scientist in the laboratory can produce, at will, the conditions that he wants to study. He can explore any desired variation in those conditions, to the exclusion of variation in almost any other factor, in a laboratory in which temperature, air currents, vibrations from outside, electric field, lighting intensity, noise level, and other factors that might affect the outcome are held constant.

The position of the economist is quite different. The phenomena he wants to isolate and study cannot be brought into a laboratory and

2

manipulated at will. He cannot put a family in a test tube and observe its behavior when various levels of income are injected, nor can he manipulate prices to see how a market responds. To measure the relationship of, say, consumption expenditure to family income he cannot compare the behavior of families that differ only in income. There are thousands of differences between any pair of families, and the variation in their consumption patterns reflects a great deal more than a simple difference in income. The successful exploration of such relationships requires the careful use of data from a large number of families, and account must be taken of many variables in addition to income. Statistics is the body of tools and methods for conducting these tests and making these measurements.

1.3 STATISTICS IN OTHER SCIENCES

Statistics is the everyday tool of the professional economist in college, business, labor union, consulting firm, or government agency. Economic forecasting, market research, econometric model-building, and general economic analysis demand professional competence in the use of statistics, but understanding statistical method is essential to everyone who comes into contact with data in quantity or the conclusions drawn from them. The doctor, social worker, lawyer, teacher, or engineer needs a working knowledge of statistical methods if he is to use tests of drugs, casework methods, evidence, student performance, or electronic components, or even to interpret their results intelligently. The business executive, congressman, or legislator, his advisors and staff members, need enough familiarity with statistical tools to evaluate reports and to avoid the more common fallacies in statistical reasoning. Indeed, it is almost impossible to pick up a daily newspaper or hear a television news broadcast without encountering some kind of analysis of medical, political, educational, social, engineering, business, or economic data whose interpretation is a statistical problem.

In this book we are concerned with economic relationships, and our discussion will be centered on these, but the statistical techniques required in sociology, psychology, or education differ but little. Indeed, the differences among sciences is one of degree rather than kind. Al-

3

though physics and chemistry are characterized by the maximum of laboratory control, it is by no means true that they can proceed without statistical tools. Any single physical observation might be unduly influenced by accidental factors, even in a laboratory. Consequently, any physical experiment is conducted a number of times and the variation in results treated statistically.

Biological sciences like agronomy, botany, zoology, and physiology, while often characterized by some measure of experimental control, also involve a large number of uncontrollable factors. For example, the physiologist attempting to evaluate the effect of a drug can administer controlled doses to a number of white rats of given weight, age, and sex. He can even control the diet of the rats, but he cannot control the inner biological variation from one rat to another. In these sciences experimental design requires a careful combination of laboratory controls with statistical technique.

In the social sciences like economics, sociology, social psychology, and anthropology, experimental controls are virtually absent, and the verification of theory and the measurement of relationships depend almost entirely on statistical analysis of data in quantity.

1.4 THE ORGANIZATION OF THIS BOOK

Our study of statistical methods begins with the problem of summarizing large quantities of data, first by means of tables and charts (Chapter II), then (Chapter III) by means of calculated averages and measures of dispersion. In Chapter IV we meet the problem of sampling and learn how to draw conclusions from sample material and to evaluate the accuracy of the results.

In Chapter V the methods and ideas developed in the earlier chapters are focused on the study of relationships. We meet here a formal discussion of such concepts as *variable*, *function*, and *correlation* and develop the most widely useful method of multivariate analysis. Chapter VI deals with significance tests to be used when it is not already clear that the data depict a relationship. Chapters V and VI form the heart, not only of this book, but of all statistical analysis. A student who thoroughly understands these two chapters will find that not only the remaining chapters of this volume, but even the most advanced statistical methods are, at bottom, variations developed for special cases or for special purposes.

Linear regression—the problem of representing a statistical relationship by a linear equation—is the topic of Chapter VII, and elementary problems of curvilinear relationships are taken up in Chapter VIII. Chapter IX is devoted to the trend and seasonal behavior of time series, while aggregation and index numbers are explored in Chapter X.

1.5 STATISTICS AND MATHEMATICS

The purpose of this book is to help the reader to genuine insight into statistical methods: to see what each procedure is supposed to do and to understand how it does it. A working knowledge of mathematics contributes greatly to this end. There is a rich mathematics to statistics, and probability theory, statistical decision-making, and related topics are important branches of modern mathematics. But intelligent application of statistical methods is not a mathematical matter—at least not beyond the demands of knowing how to substitute numbers in a formula and to carry out arithmetic with accuracy.

Knowing the mathematics of statistical formulas is generally useful to their understanding. Their derivations have been included in footnotes for the reader with the interest and equipment to use them, but they do not occupy the center of attention. Mathematical derivation should not be confused with insight and understanding.

1.6 UNDERSTANDING STATISTICAL METHODS

A good help toward understanding a statistical theory is to "test it out" several times using a few simple numbers. For example, in studying the properties of deviations from the arithmetic mean, the reader is invited to pick a few numbers, calculate the mean, and see for himself that the sum of their squares is a minimum. Examples are given in the text for this purpose, but the reader is urged to try others for himself.

Secondly, before a new technique is applied to a realistic problem, the student should make a "dry run," duplicating one or more of the examples given in the text. This will bring to light any misunderstanding of the mechanical procedure and assist in understanding the operations.

Finally, each procedure should be applied to one or more real problems, preferably with the aid of a desk calculator. It is a useful habit to stop after each step of the procedure and think about what the step means in terms of the problem. This not only serves to keep the research "target" constantly in mind, but is also a useful check on results. A copying error, a misplaced decimal point, or an incorrect computation is often easily spotted simply because the result is absurd.

Particular attention should be paid to the interpretation of the final result. The object of quantitative research is to gain knowledge of the world around us. The most elaborate manipulation of data by the most sophisticated techniques is wasted effort unless we know what the answer means.

CHAPTER II

Summarizing
a Large Quantity of Data:
Tables and Charts

To yield useful information, a mass of data must first be summarized and reduced to understandable proportions. Imagine sending a large crew of interviewers to ask each family in the United States the size of its annual income. Each income could be recorded, perhaps together with the name of the family, on a 3 × 5 card, and the cards assembled in a central location. Some idea of the mass of this data can be had from the fact that 45 million 3 × 5 cards, one for each family in the United States, would solidly fill three rooms in a typical house.

Imagine this mountain of cards neatly stacked in a big warehouse. The warehouse contains all the information there is on the subject of United States family incomes, but the unorganized mountain of data is too vast to be informative. The first task of statistics is to reduce the mountain of raw data to a form that can yield useful information. This can be done in three ways: (1) The data can be reduced to a table; (2) they can be plotted as a chart; and (3) averages and other descriptive key numbers, called *statistics*, can be calculated. This chapter is devoted to the first two of these: the construction and use of frequency tables and charts.

2.1 THE FREQUENCY TABLE

The first step in the summarization of data is to reduce the mountain of cards to a frequency table showing the 45 million families classified by income brackets. The entire range of income is partitioned into a number of convenient subdivisions, and the families in each bracket counted.

7

The resulting frequency table summarizes the mountain of data on a single sheet of paper, reducing 45 million individual family incomes to frequency of occurrence in a dozen or so income brackets, as in Table 2.1.

Table 2.1 Number of Families by Family Income, U.S., 1960

Family Income	Number of Families (millions)
Under $1,000	2.285
$1,000–1,999	3.613
$2,000–2,999	3.970
$3,000–3,999	4.456
$4,000–4,999	4.773
$5,000–5,999	5.839
$6,000–6,999	4.889
$7,000–7,999	3.973
$8,000–9,999	5.135
$10,000–14,999	4.795
$15,000 or more	1.707
Total	45.435

Source: *Current Population Reports: Consumer Income* (Washington, D.C.: U.S. Department of Commerce, Bureau of the Census, June 1961).

The brackets into which the data are classified are generally designated as *classes*. The number of items in a class is called the *class frequency*. There is no rule for the number of classes to be used, the choice largely depending on what is to be done with the resulting table. The larger the number of classes, and the narrower each income bracket, the more detailed is the information in the table. At the same time, the larger the number of classes, the less summary is obtained of the original data.

2.1.1. Class Limits

Each class in a frequency table is demarked by *lower* and *upper class limits* so assigned that there is one and only one possible place for each item to be counted. For example, in the case of family incomes, the table must cover the entire income range, and there must be no ambiguity about which income class any particular family belongs to. With a continuous variable like income, classes can be designated as "$1,000 but less than $2,000," "$2,000 but less than $3,000," and so on. This leaves

8

no gaps in the classification; each family belongs unambiguously to a unique class, and the class limits are clearly stated. In practice, however, the notational convention of Table 2.1 is often employed. By this convention income brackets like "$1,000 but less than $2,000," "$2,000 but less than $3,000" are designated "$1,000–1,999," "$2,000–2,999," and so on. It is to be emphasized that this is merely a notational convenience; the actual class limits are identical in the two cases.

Where the magnitudes involved are discrete units, the class designations should reflect the fact. In Table 2.2, size classes of retail es-

Table 2.2   Distribution of U.S. Retail Trade Establishments, by Number of Employees, November 15, 1958

Number of Paid Employees	Number of Establishments (thousands)
None	591
1	231
2	214
3	151
4 or 5	163
6 or 7	88
8 or 9	52
10 to 14	65
15 to 19	30
20 to 49	48
50 to 99	10
100 or more	4
Total	1,647

Source: *U.S. Census of Business, 1958*, Vol. 1, *Retail Trade* (Washington, D.C.: U.S. Department of Commerce, Bureau of the Census, 1959).

tablishments are designated as "4 or 5 paid employees," "6 or 7 paid employees," and so on. Since no shop employs, say 5.6 people, the classification is unambiguous.

2.1.2   Concentration Points and Class Limits

In compiling a frequency table it is important to designate class limits so they will reveal any important concentrations of data. A natural variable

9

like weight or height is likely to have a smooth distribution, that is, there is no particular height or weight that shows a striking concentration of frequency. But economic data often exhibit points of high concentration associated with institutional factors. Data on the number of years of schooling show high concentration at eight years, produced by the large number of students who finish grammar school but do not enter high school. Frequency distributions of people by hours worked per week show heavy concentration at 40 and 48 hours, corresponding to exactly five and six eight-hour days, with smaller concentrations at 36 and 44 hours.

Table 2.3 Persons 45 Years Old and Over, by Years of School Completed, U.S., 1959

Years of School Completed	Number of Persons (thousands)
/ None	1,725
2 1 to 4	4,337
3 5 to 7	8,394
4 8	11,779
5 9 to 11	8,023
6 12	8,815
7 13 to 15	3,389
8 16 or more	3,124
Total	49,586

Source: *Statistical Abstract of the United States* (Washington, D.C.: U.S. Department of Commerce, Bureau of the Census, 1961), Table 138, p. 109.

Concentration points should either be singled out as separate classes, or the class limits should be set so that the concentration points tend to fall in the middle of their classes. Note how concentration at 8 and 12 years is shown in Table 2.3. In Table 2.4, 40 and 48 hours are designated as special classes, while 44 hours falls at the midpoint of the class.

2.1.3 Class Intervals

The difference between the upper and the lower limits of a class is the *class interval*. The class interval of the class "$1,000–1,999" in Table 2.1 is one thousand dollars. Although class intervals are sometimes equal in width throughout the table, it is often useful to have the intervals at some part of the range wider than those at another. In Table 2.1, for example, narrow class intervals are desirable at the lower end of the income range

Table 2.4 Persons at Work by Number of Hours Worked: Week of March 8–14, 1959, U.S.

Hours Worked	Per Cent of Total Workers
1–34	19.8
35–39	6.3
40	41.8
41–47	7.9
48	7.3
49 or more	16.9
Total	100.0

Source: *Current Population Reports*, Series P-57, No. 201 (Washington, D.C.: U.S. Department of Commerce, Bureau of the Census, April 1959).

(where most families are concentrated) in order to preserve as much detail as possible. Further up the income scale, however, the density of families becomes so thin that some high income classes would have few, if any, members, unless class intervals were widened.

2.1.4 Open-End Classes

Often the density of a distribution becomes so thin near the end of the range that classification, even by wide intervals, is uninformative. Situations of this kind require *open-end classes* to include all items larger or smaller than a specified amount. Thus, the highest income bracket in Table 2.1 is designated "$15,000 and over"; the lowest, open ended to include those with business losses, is "under $1,000."

2.1.5 Frequency Density

The *frequency density* of a class is the class frequency divided by the class interval. If we think of the class interval as a physical area and the class frequency as the number of its inhabitants, frequency density is the "population density" of the class. A class with high frequency density has a thick concentration of items in it. In a class with low density the items are thinly spread out. The derivation of frequency densities for the data of Table 2.1 is shown in Table 2.5. In this case, frequency density

11

Table 2.5 Derivation of Frequency Densities
from Data of Table 2.1

Income Class	Number of Families (millions)	Class Interval (thousands of $)	Frequency Density (millions of families per $1,000 interval)
Under $1,000	2.285	1.0	2.285
$1,000–1,999	3.613	1.0	3.613
$2,000–2,999	3.970	1.0	3.970
$3,000–3,999	4.456	1.0	4.456
$4,000–4,999	4.773	1.0	4.773
$5,000–5,999	5.893	1.0	5.893
$6,000–6,999	4.889	1.0	4.889
$7,000–7,999	3.973	1.0	3.973
$8,000–9,999	5.135	2.0	2.568
$10,000–14,999	4.759	5.0	0.952
$15,000 or more	1.707	–	–
Total	45.435	–	–

rises steadily with income, reaching a peak somewhere in the "$5,000–5,999" class. At higher incomes, frequency density declines and in the "$7,000–7,999" class the concentration of families is the same as in the "$2,000–2,999" class. Note that although the total frequency in the "$8,000–9,999" class exceeds that of the "$7,000–7,999" class, the frequency *density* continues to decline with income; the 5.135 million families with incomes in the "$8,000–9,999" class are spread out over an interval twice as wide as the preceding classes.

2.1.6 Frequency Density in Special Cases

When the basis of classification is a discrete variable like "Number of paid employees" in Table 2.2, the class interval is best measured by the number of discrete values covered by the class. The classes "no paid employees," "1," "2," and "3" include only one possible value, and, as shown in Table 2.6, the class interval is 1. A firm in the "4 or 5" class, on the other hand, may have either exactly four or exactly five paid employees; the class includes two possible values, and the class interval is 2. Similarly the interval of the class "20 to 49" is 30, and so on.

Where a continuous variable has been so classified as to single out points of concentration (as in the "years of school completed" of Table

Table 2.6   Computation of Frequency Density
for Data of Table 2.2

Number of Paid Employees	Number of Establishments (thousands)	Class Interval	Frequency Density
None	591	1	591
1	231	1	231
2	214	1	214
3	151	1	151
4 or 5	163	2	81.5
6 or 7	88	2	44
8 or 9	52	2	26
10 to 14	65	5	13
15 to 19	30	5	6
20 to 49	48	30	1.6
50 to 99	10	50	.2
100 or more	4	–	–

2.3 or "hours worked per week" of Table 2.4), the calculation of frequency density is generally best carried out by treating the variable *as if* it were discrete. Thus, the class "1–34 hours" is treated as having a class interval of 34, while the class "40 hours" is treated as having a class interval of 1.

Frequency density cannot be calculated for an open-end class, but since these occur at the extremes of the distribution, it is not generally necessary to do so.

2.2   FREQUENCY CHARTS

Although the frequency table reduces a houseful of 3 × 5 cards to a single page, it still presents the information in a form that is to be studied in some detail. The purpose of the frequency *chart* is to carry simplification a stage further and present the information as a picture giving a quickly obtained and easily remembered general impression. The important considerations in the construction of a frequency chart are related to the problem of providing an accurate picture of class-to-class variation in frequency density.

Figure 2.1 Bar Chart: Incomes of U.S. Families, 1960

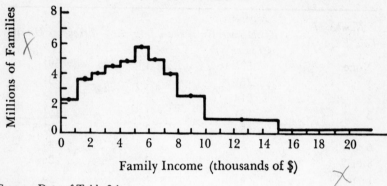

Source: Data of Table 2.1.

2.2.1 Chart Construction

Since a chart is a picture, its construction is more a matter of art than of technical science, and it is to be expected that practice will vary from person to person and from case to case. The following suggestions are intended only as a general guide to the layout of a good chart.

The relationship of frequency density to income can be graphically depicted in either of two ways: by a *frequency histogram* (*bar chart*) or by a *frequency polygon* (*line chart*). In the bar chart, frequency densities are plotted as vertical bars standing on the class interval, as in Figure 2.1. The frequency polygon is formed by locating a point in the center of each class interval whose height on the vertical scale represents frequency density in the class. The points are then connected by ruled lines as in Figure 2.2. The two methods of plotting show essentially the same facts, and choice between them is largely a matter of personal taste.

2.2.1.1 SELECTION OF SCALES Charts are usually drawn on commercially ruled "graph paper" to facilitate plotting. One division of the paper might represent one, five, ten, fifty, or any other convenient number of units so long as points can be quickly and easily located. In addition the selection of scales should be governed by two factors:

1. The scale should permit the chart to be drawn on a single page, leaving ample room for labels, scales, title, and margins.

Figure 2.2   Line Chart: Incomes of U.S. Families, 1960

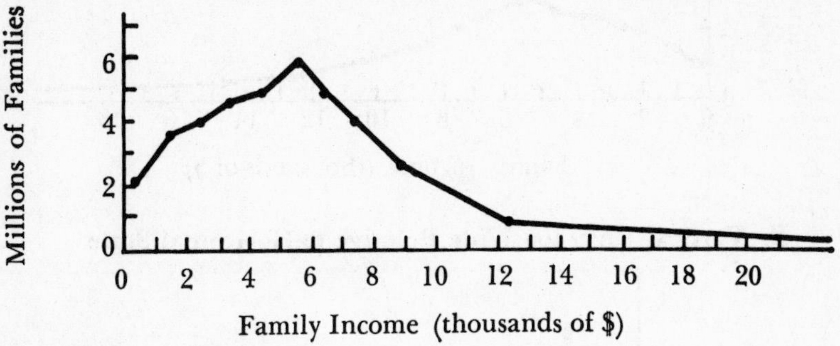

Source: Data of Table 2.1.

2. The horizontal and vertical scales should be so proportioned that the main slope of the finished chart will rise or fall at an angle of about 45°. The data of Table 2.1, properly plotted in Figure 2.2, are plotted in Figure 2.3A with the units on the vertical axis too narrow in proportion to those on the horizontal scale; in Figure 2.3B the vertical units are relatively too wide. The exaggerated smoothness of Figure 2.3A and the sharp peak of Figure 2.3B are unsatisfactory representations of the data.

2.2.1.2   LABELS   The axes should be clearly labeled, and, if necessary, the unit indicated in parentheses. Enough numbers should be put on the axes to enable the reader to make quick, rough comparisons, but the chart should not be crowded with lines. The title should be conspicuously placed in bold letters.

2.2.1.3   PLOTTING   Once the axes are drawn and scales assigned, the actual drawing of the chart is relatively simple. Mark the class limits on the horizontal axis. At the center of each class interval locate a point whose height on the vertical scale is the frequency density of the class. For a line chart, these points are connected by a ruled line. For a bar chart, the top of the bar is ruled through the point, extending across the

15

Figure 2.3   Influence of Choice of Scale on Appearance of Chart

A. Vertical Units too Narrow Relative to Horizontal Scale

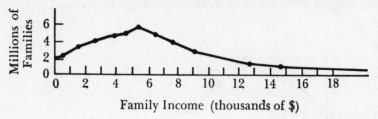

B. Vertical Units too Wide Relative to Horizontal Scale

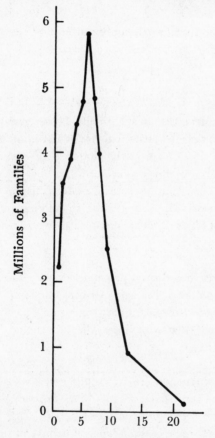

Source: Data of Table 2.1.

16

class interval. The edges of the bars are then drawn in to complete the chart.

2.3 THE CUMULATIVE DISTRIBUTION

Sometimes the *cumulative* properties of data are important. How many people have had *at least* a given amount of schooling may be a more meaningful question than how many have been to school any particular number of years. Information about the number of firms *below* any given size may be critical for evaluating the possible impact of a change in, say, unemployment tax laws. In these cases, data are best summarized in tables and charts drawn up on a cumulative basis.

2.3.1 The Cumulative Table

It is a simple matter to accumulate a frequency table. Table 2.7 shows the number of people who have completed at least each specified number of years of school, as derived from the data of Table 2.3. Each lower

Table 2.7 Number of Persons 45 Years Old and Over Who Completed at Least the Indicated Number of Years of School

Years of School Completed	Accumulated Number of People (thousands)
Total	49,586
At least 1	47,861
At least 5	43,524
At least 8	35,130
At least 9	23,351
At least 12	15,328
At least 13	6,513
At least 16	3,124

Source: Accumulated from Table 2.3.

class limit in Table 2.3 is a specified number of years. Since there is no such thing as a negative amount of schooling, everybody has "at least no schooling," and the total, 49,586, is found opposite "Total" in Table 2.7. Of all these people, 1,725 had no schooling; the remaining 47,861

17

had at least one year. Among the latter group, 4,337 had from one to four years; the remaining 43,524 had at least five years schooling, and so on. As in the parent table 2.3, of course, these figures are all in thousands of persons.

Table 2.8   Number of U.S. Retail Establishments Employing Fewer than the Indicated Number of Paid Employees

Number of Paid Employees	Accumulated Number of Establishments (thousands)
Fewer than 1	591
Fewer than 2	822
Fewer than 3	1,036
Fewer than 4	1,187
Fewer than 6	1,350
Fewer than 8	1,438
Fewer than 10	1,490
Fewer than 15	1,555
Fewer than 20	1,585
Fewer than 50	1,633
Fewer than 100	1,643
Total (including those with 100 or more paid employees)	1,647

Source: Accumulated from Table 2.2.

Table 2.8 shows the number of establishments with fewer than each specified number of employees. The 591 establishments with fewer than one paid employee are those with no paid employee in Table 2.2. These, together with the 231 establishments having one paid employee, constitute the establishments with fewer than two paid employees, and so on. No specified maximum number of employees can be assigned to the establishments having 100 or more paid employees, but these are included in the total number of establishments. Again, of course, figures are in thousands.

2.3.2 The Cumulative Chart or Ogive

Like any other chart, the purpose of the cumulative chart or *ogive* is to provide a quick and accurate picture of the data, and general rules for its construction are, therefore, similar to those given above. It is drawn as follows: At each lower class limit on the horizontal scale, a point is located whose height on the vertical scale corresponds to the accumulated frequency given in the table. These points are then connected with ruled lines to form the chart.

Figure 2.4 Number of Persons 45 Years Old or Over Who Have Completed at Least the Indicated Number of Years of Education

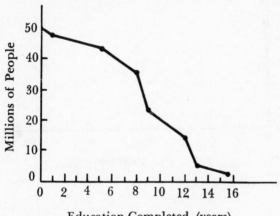

Education Completed (years)

Source: Data of Table 2.3.

As shown in Figure 2.4, when the chart shows the accumulated number of items with "at least" a given magnitude, its curve falls to zero from a height corresponding to the total; when, as in Figure 2.5, the chart shows the number of items with "less than" a given magnitude, its curve rises from zero to the height of the total. A cumulative chart is constructed without direct calculation of frequency density. The slope of the curve over any range is automatically proportional to the frequency density in that range, that is, the curve rises or falls most sharply where the frequency density is greatest. In Figure 2.4, for example, the sharp drop in the curve at 8 years and again at 12 years marks the relatively

Figure 2.5 Number of Retail Establishments Having Fewer than the Indicated Number of Employees

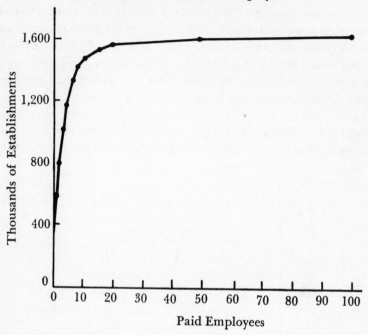

Source: Data of Table 2.2.

high frequency density at these points. The curve of Figure 2.5 indicates the frequency density is a maximum at zero employees and smoothly declines as size increases.

2.4 SUMMARY

The most elementary step in summarizing a large quantity of data is to reduce it to a frequency table made by setting mutually exclusive, exhaustive class limits and tallying the frequency with which items fall in each class.

Charts provide an even greater summarization by reducing the data to a picture that can be comprehended at a glance.

Questions and Problems

1. Look in a copy of the *Statistical Abstract of the United States* and find a frequency table (for example, "Population by Age"; "Old Age and Survivors Insurance—Percentage Distribution of Workers by Wage Credits"; "Number of Banks by Total Deposits," or some other table). Identify the class limits, the class intervals, and the open-end classes, if any. Calculate the frequency density in each class and plot the data as a frequency chart. Write a short paragraph describing the distribution.

2. Take 25 pennies and a cup to shake them in. Shake the pennies thoroughly, dump them out on the table, count and record the number of heads. Repeat the experiment 50 times. Compile the data into a frequency table and plot it as a line chart. Accumulate the data and plot it as an ogive. Write a short paragraph describing the results. Save the data for future use.

3.

**Distribution of Employees by Straight-Time Earnings,
Three Occupations, Toledo, March 1962**

Earnings	Janitors, Porters, and Cleaners	Laborers	Truck Drivers
Under $1.10	3	–	–
$1.10–1.29	34	–	–
$1.30–1.49	20	33	–
$1.50–1.69	108	47	2
$1.70–1.89	91	72	27
$1.90–2.09	145	151	36
$2.10–2.29	160	340	80
$2.30–2.49	309	226	130
$2.50–2.69	71	136	102
$2.70–2.89	2	163	597
$2.90–3.10	–	101	180
Total	943	1,269	1,154

Source: *Occupational Wage Survey, Toledo, Ohio*, BLS Bulletin 1303-47 (Washington, D.C.: U.S. Department of Labor, Bureau of Labor Statistics, March 1962).

To make these three distributions comparable, calculate each class frequency as a percentage of total number in the occupation. Plot the three percentage distributions on the same chart, using a distinctive line for each. Write a short paragraph comparing the wages earned in the three occupations.

References

1. Frederick E. Croxton and Dudley J. Cowden. *Applied General Statistics.* 2nd Ed. New York: Prentice-Hall, 1955. Chs. 3, 4, 5, and 6, pp. 50–135. An extensive treatment of table and chart construction for the beginning student.

2. Herbert Arkin and Raymond R. Colton. *Graphs: How to Make and Use Them.* New York: Harper and Brothers, 1940.

3. Calvin F. Schmidt. *Handbook of Graphic Presentation.* New York: The Ronald Press Company, 1954.

The last two references are comprehensive treatments of the technical and esthetic aspects of chart construction.

CHAPTER III

Summarizing
a Large Quantity of Data:
Statistics

The most important summary of a quantity of numerical data consists of the calculation of key numbers, called *statistics*, to describe its distribution. This chapter takes up the two most useful kinds of statistics: measures of *central tendency* and *dispersion*.

3.1 MEASURES OF CENTRAL TENDENCY

A statistic of *central tendency*, often called an *average*, is a single number used to represent the general magnitude of all items in a distribution. It is "typical" of the observed magnitudes. Three averages are in general use: the *mode*, the *median*, and the *arithmetic mean*. While these averages have important properties in common, they differ in many respects and involve different definitions of what is "typical." In selecting the average theoretically appropriate to any particular purpose this definition is the controlling factor.

3.1.1 The Mode (Mo)

The mode is the point in a frequency distribution at which the frequency density reaches a maximum. It takes as "typical" that value which occurs more frequently than any other single magnitude. The mode is, in a sense, the most "popular" value in the frequency distribution, and is clearly the average to use to express, say, the "typical" length of women's dresses. Indeed, the term "mode" is derived from the French word for "fashion." As a point of maximum density, the mode is sometimes used in the study of traffic congestion and peak loads on transportation, power, telephone, and similar facilities. For example, in a distribution of employees by time of day they quit work, the modal time is the period of greatest addition to traffic.

3.1.1.1 LOCATING THE MODE Since the mode is the value at which the frequency distribution reaches a maximum, it is located on the horizontal axis directly beneath the peak of a frequency chart. For example, the modal income of United States families can be seen in Figure 2.1 above to be about $5,500. It is clear, however, that accurate estimation of the mode requires a chart drawn with considerable care from a table with small class intervals. Moreover, some data (for example, the size distribution of firms in Table 2.2) fail to exhibit a clearly defined mode, while some distributions (for example, Table 2.3) are *bimodal* with two, or *multimodal* with several distinct peaks of frequency density. Fortunately, economic problems are rarely concerned with the definition of "typical" implied by the mode, and the problem of accurate estimation seldom arises.

3.1.2 The Median (Md)

The median is the midpoint of a frequency distribution: the value that is exceeded by half the items while the other half are smaller. The median income is the number of dollars such that half of all families have incomes higher, and the other half lower than this. As defined by the median, then, "typical" implies "middle" or "center." The median income is the income of the true middle class of the community.

3.1.2.1 LOCATING THE MEDIAN In principle, the midpoint of a frequency distribution can be found by ranking all the items by size and picking out the one in the center of the array; the magnitude of this item is the median.[1] If there are relatively few items in the distribution this is easy, but a warehouse full of data would pose formidable difficulties, and the median must be estimated in other ways. If an ogive has been drawn, the median can be estimated by finding the point where

---

1. When there are an even number of items, the median is taken midway between the two in the center.

the accumulated frequency equals half the total. For example, the total number of items in Figure 2.4 is about 50,000. The accumulated frequency reaches 25,000 at about 8¾ years of education. Similarly, Figure 2.5 involves a total of 1,647 establishments; the curve reaches 823.5 at about 2½ employees.

Estimating the median by linear interpolation in the frequency table is both more accurate and avoids the need to draw an ogive. This method is illustrated in Table 3.1. To find the point at which the cumulative

Table 3.1 Interpolating for the Median

Class	Frequency	
0 – 3.99	5	
4.0 – 7.99	10	
8.0 – 11.99	15	*Median estimated at 5/15 of class interval above the lower limit of this class, that is,*
12.0 – 16.0	10	
Total	40	$Md = 8.0 + 4.0 \times \frac{5}{15} = 9\frac{1}{3}.$

frequency reaches half of the total of 40 items, start accumulating from the lowest class. Counting past the first 5 items takes us through the first class to 4.0, the lower limit of the next class. Counting past the next 10 items takes us through the second class to 8.0, the lower limit of the third class, and makes a total of 15 items counted. When we count past the next 5 items to complete the required 20, we will be somewhere in the class marked "8.0–11.99." The class that contains the median item is called the *median class*. Obviously, there is no way to tell exactly where the median item lies within this class, but it is reasonable to suppose that counting past 5 out of 15 items in the class will take us about 5⁄15 of the way along the median class interval. Since the interval of this class is 4.0, we estimate that the required item lies $\frac{5}{15} \times 4.0 = 1\frac{1}{3}$ units from the lower limit of the median class. Thus the median is estimated as

$$Md = 8.0 + 1\frac{1}{3} = 9\frac{1}{3}.$$

Designate by "required number" the number of items that must be counted in the median class to reach the median item. Then the estimated median is summarized in a general formula:

Md = Lower limit of Md class

$$+ \text{ Md class interval} \times \frac{\text{required number}}{\text{frequency of Md class}}.$$

Estimating the median family income from Table 2.1: the median family is located $45.435/2 = 22.7175$ from the end. The first five classes contain 19.097 items, so the median class is "$5,000–5,999." The required number of items in the median class is 3.6205 million, and the class interval is $1,000. The median income as estimated by the formula is

$$Md = \$5,000 + \$1,000 > \frac{3.6205}{5.839} = \$5,620.$$

3.1.3 The Arithmetic Mean ($\bar{X}$)

The arithmetic mean is the figure most commonly implied in everyday use of the term "average." It is obtained by summing the values and dividing by the number of items. Thus, if three men weigh respectively 150, 200, and 280 pounds, their mean weight is $(150 + 200 + 280)/3 = 210$ pounds. The arithmetic mean, usually referred to simply as the mean, defines "typical" in a Robin Hood fashion. If amounts are taken away from the larger items and added to the smaller so that all are equal, the common magnitude is the mean. The mean weight of the three men is the amount each would weigh if the total poundage were equally distributed among them.

Put in another way, the mean defines as "typical" that amount which, when multiplied by the number of items, gives the total for the group. Because of this property, the mean of a small sample can be used to estimate the total of a much larger group. To estimate the total crop of apples in a large orchard, pick out a small sample of trees. The mean yield per tree in this sample can then be multiplied by the number of trees in the entire orchard to get an estimate of the total yield.

3.1.3.1 CALCULATION OF THE ARITHMETIC MEAN The mean is calculated from raw data by summing the values and dividing by the number of items. Symbolically, let N be the number of items and X_i be the value of the ith item $(i = 1, 2, \ldots N)$. The formula for the mean is then

$$\bar{X} = \frac{\Sigma X_i}{N}$$

where $\bar{X}$ is the generally accepted symbol for the mean of X.

3.1.3.2 CALCULATING THE ARITHMETIC MEAN FROM CLASSI-FIED DATA Even in this day of high-speed electronic computers, the calculation of the mean family income from a warehouse full of data would be time consuming and expensive, and it is important to be able to calculate the mean from a frequency table. This would be easily done if we knew the mean income in each income bracket: It could be multiplied by the class frequency to get the total income of all families in the bracket. These totals when added up and divided by the over-all number of families would give the mean.

Unfortunately, the mean incomes of families in the different income brackets is generally unknown, and we resort to an approximation. We suppose that families are evenly distributed within each class. If this is the case, the mean income in the class will be at the class midpoint or *class mark*, and we can estimate total income in each bracket by multiplying the class mark by the class frequency. The bracket totals can be added up and divided by the total frequency to get the arithmetic mean.

This method of approximating the mean is summarized by the following formula. Where the frequency table contains k classes, let m_j be the mark, and f_j the frequency, of the jth class. The formula for the mean then becomes

$$\bar{X} = \frac{\Sigma m_j f_j}{\Sigma f_j} \cdot$$

27

Table 3.2 Work Sheet for Hand Calculation of $\bar{X}$ from Classified Data

Class	Class Mark (m)	Frequency (f)	mf
0– 5.9	3.0	5	15.0[a]
6.0–11.9	9.0	10	90.0
12.0–17.9	15.0	15	225.0
18.0–24.0	21.0	10	210.0
Total		$\Sigma f_j = 40$	$\Sigma m_j f_j = 540.0$

$$\bar{X} = \frac{540}{40} = 13.5$$

[a] When using an automatic desk calculator, the figures in this column are not recorded, but are allowed to accumulate in the machine.

Table 3.2 shows a sample work sheet for the calculation of the mean from data contained in a frequency table. Table 3.3 shows the work sheet as it appears when mean family income of Table 2.1 is calculated, using a desk calculator.

Note that, since f_j appears in both the numerator and denominator of the formula for the mean, its units cancel out. This means that class frequency can be expressed in any convenient unit without affecting the average. The frequencies in Table 3.3 are expressed in millions of families. They could equally well be in thousands, hundreds, or in percentage of total. The calculation would proceed exactly the same way and yield identical results.

3.1.3.3 CALCULATION OF MEAN WITH OPEN-END CLASSES Since an open-end class does not have a class mark, the mean can be calculated from a table containing such a class only if some other information is available about the values in the class. Sometimes the mean or the median of the class is given in a footnote to the table and can be used in place of the nonexistent class mark.

Sometimes an approximate class mark can be supplied from knowledge of the data. Great care must be used in doing this, however. One is usually guessing about numbers at the large end of the scale, and a poor guess can swamp the final result. Such guesses must be supplied only on the basis of actual familiarity with the material, and even so a reasonable

Table 3.3 Work Sheet for Calculation of
Mean Family Income from Table 2.1

Income Class	m ($)	f (millions)	mf
Under $1,000	500	2.285	
$1,000–1,999	1,500	3.613	
$2,000–2,999	2,500	3.970	
$3,000–3,999	3,500	4.456	
$4,000–4,999	4,500	4.773	
$5,000–5,999	5,500	5.839	
$6,000–6,999	6,500	4.889	
$7,000–7,999	7,500	3.973	
$8,000–9,999	9,000	5.135	
$10,000–14,999	12,500	4.795	
$15,000 or more	22,500[a]	1.707	

$$\Sigma f_j = 45.435$$
$$\Sigma m_j f_j = \$291,812^{b}$$
$$\bar{X} = \frac{\$291,812}{45.435} = \$6,423$$

[a] Approximate value.
[b] Individual products not recorded; sum accumulated in machine.

range of guesses should be explored to determine how much it might alter the estimated mean.

3.1.3.4 A PROPORTION AS A MEAN Although the mean is usually thought of in connection with numerical data like heights, weights, and incomes, the concept is equally applicable to categorical data like unemployment, sex, marital status, occupation, and so on. With categorical data each item either belongs to a designated category or does not, that is, every person in the labor force is unemployed or not; every student in a university is a male or not; every official time at bat results in a hit or not; every 15 ampere fuse inspected is judged acceptable or not.

Categorical data are summarized by a proportion or percentage: 4 per cent of the labor force is unemployed; .6 of the students are male, and so on, but a proportion is actually a special case of the arithmetic

29

mean. To see this, define a "magnitude" X with the property that $X = 1$ for all people in the category and $X = 0$ for all who are not. In any group of people, the total, ΣX_i, is simply the number in the category, and the mean, $\bar{X} = \dfrac{\Sigma X_i}{N}$, is equal to P, the proportion of the group belonging to the category.

This is illustrated by the following table. $X = 1$ has been assigned

Worker No.	Status	X
1	Employed	0
2	Unemployed	1
3	Employed	0
4	Employed	0
5	Unemployed	1

to unemployed workers and $X = 0$ to those with jobs. Among the workers shown, the proportion of unemployment is:

$$\bar{X} = \frac{\Sigma X_i}{N} = \frac{2}{5} = .4 .$$

The fact that proportions can be treated as arithmetic means brings them under a unified sampling theory in Chapter IV.

3.1.3.5 FOUR IMPORTANT PROPERTIES OF THE MEAN Because of its definition, the mean has four important properties:

1. *The sum of the deviations from the mean is zero.* Here, and throughout the rest of this book, deviations from means will be represented by lower-case letters, *i.e.*, where X_i is the value of the ith item in the distribution, and $\bar{X}$ is the mean of all items, the deviation of the ith item from the mean is

$$x_i = X_i - \bar{X}.$$

By the property of the mean,

$$\Sigma x_i = 0.$$

This follows from the "cut-and-fill" nature of the mean. The (positive) amounts by which high values exceed the mean are just exactly enough to equal the (negative) amounts by which those below the mean fall short.[2] The proposition can be explored with a few simple trials. The numbers 1, 2, 9 have $\bar{X} = 4$. The three deviations $x_1 = -3$, $x_2 = -2$, $x_3 = 5$ total zero.

2. *The sum of the squares of the deviations from the mean is a minimum.* That is, let k be a constant whose value is to be chosen later. Subtract k from each value X_i, square the deviations and sum:

$$\Sigma(X_i - k)^2.$$

The magnitude of this sum depends on the value chosen for k; when $k = \bar{X}$, the sum is a minimum.[3]

This property of the mean is also explored with the three numbers 1, 2, 9. Since $\bar{X} = 4$, the sum of the squared deviations from the mean is

$$\Sigma(X_i - \bar{X})^2 = (-3)^2 + (-2)^2 + (5)^2 = 38.$$

Using some other value for k, say $k = 5$, in place of $k = \bar{X}$, gives a larger total.

$$\Sigma(X_i - 5)^2 = (-4)^2 + (-3)^2 + (4)^2 = 41.$$

Because of this property, the mean is called a *least squares* measure of central tendency. The importance of this fact will appear later in the discussion of linear regression.

3. *The mean of the sum of two values is the sum of their individual means.* For example, total family income (X) consists of the income (Y) of the principal earner plus any income (Z) earned by secondary earners. Then $\bar{X} = \bar{Y} + \bar{Z}$, regardless of how these incomes are distributed among the individual families.[4] Given the following five primary in-

---

2. Mathematical proof:
$$\Sigma x_i = \Sigma(X_i - \bar{X}) = \Sigma X_i - N\bar{X} = \Sigma X_i - N\frac{(\Sigma X_i)}{N} = 0.$$

3. Mathematical proof: Set the derivative (with respect to k) of the sum of squares equal to zero and solve for the value of k producing a minimum:
$$\frac{d(\Sigma(X_i - k)^2)}{dk} = 2\Sigma(X_i - k) = 0.$$
So
$$\Sigma X_i - Nk = 0, \text{ and}$$
$$k = \frac{\Sigma X_i}{N} = \bar{X}.$$

4. Mathematical proof: Let Y_i and Z_i be the primary and secondary incomes of the ith family, and represent its total income by $X_i = Y_i + Z_i$. Then mean total income is clearly
$$\bar{X} = \frac{\Sigma X_i}{N} = \frac{\Sigma(Y_i + Z_i)}{N} = \frac{\Sigma Y_i}{N} + \frac{\Sigma Z_i}{N} = \bar{Y} + \bar{Z}.$$

comes with a mean of $3,000, and five secondary incomes with a mean of $600, experiment shows that the mean total income is $3,600 regardless of how the primary and secondary incomes are paired up. No corresponding statement can be made for the median or the mode.

	Primary Incomes ($)	Secondary Incomes ($)	Total Income ($)
	1,000	0	1,000
	2,000	600	2,600
	3,000	700	3,700
	4,000	800	4,800
	5,000	900	5,900
Mean	3,000	600	3,600

4. *The mean of two or more combined distributions can be calculated from their individual means.* Suppose Group A consists of 3 families with a mean income of $5,000; B consists of 9 families with a mean income of $4,000. If the 12 families are combined in a single group what will the mean income be?

By the nature of the mean, we know the total income in Group A is $3 \times \$5,000 = \$15,000$. In Group B the total income is $9 \times \$4,000 = \$36,000$. The combined groups, therefore, have a total of $15,000 + $36,000 = $51,000, which, when divided by the combined number of families gives $\bar{\bar{X}}$, the grand mean of the combined samples as

$$\bar{\bar{X}} = \frac{\$51,000}{12} = \$4,250.$$

In general, the grand mean, $\bar{\bar{X}}$, of a distribution made up of the combination of Groups A, B, C, . . . , composed of N_A, N_B, N_C, . . . items respectively, and with means equal to $\bar{X}_A$, $\bar{X}_B$, $\bar{X}_C$, . . . is given by

$$\bar{\bar{X}} = \frac{N_A \bar{X}_A + N_B \bar{X}_B + N_C \bar{X}_C + \ldots}{N_A + N_B + N_C + \ldots}.$$

Note in particular that the mean of two or more groups combined is not the simple average of their means, but that each mean is *weighted* by the number of items in its group. Thus the expression on the right is frequently called a *weighted mean* of group means. Weighted means are taken up again in the chapter on index numbers.

3.1.4 Summary Comparison of Mode, Median, and Mean

The relationship among the three measures of central tendency is shown graphically in Figure 3.1: A line erected at the mode intersects the frequency curve at its point of maximum frequency density. A line erected at the median divides the area under the frequency curve into two regions of equal area. A line erected at the mean marks the center of gravity of the figure: drawn on sheet metal and cut out following the frequency curve and the horizontal axis, the resulting figure would balance on a knife edge placed along this line.

The mode takes as "typical" the point of maximum concentration of items and is rarely useful as a measure of central tendency in economic research.

The median takes as "typical" the true middle-class item. It is the best average to use in evaluating the performance or status of individuals. The median incomes of two communities will give a better comparison of how individuals fare in the two places than can be had from the mean, which is influenced by extremes of wealth or poverty.

The mean is the most useful central tendency in applications where totals are important. Mean output per man multiplied by the number of men to be employed gives expected output. In addition, the special properties of the mean make it particularly adapted for use in connection with samples. Use of median and mean is contrasted in the following examples:

1. A firm increases wages. The *median* increase shows how employees fared as individuals. A median raise of five cents an hour tells us that half of the workers in the plant received at least this increase, while half received less. This would be important in evaluating the possible effect of the raise on worker morale, union activity, and so on. The *mean* increase, on the other hand, shows the impact on production cost. If mean output is two units per man-hour, and the mean raise is eight cents an hour, unit labor cost will rise by four cents.

2. The price of grapefruit declines by 15 per cent, and as a result people eat more. The *median* increase in family consumption tells us something about the influence of the price change on individual diets and on community health. The *mean* increase in consumption reflects the effect of the price change on total consumption, and hence is essential for the measurement of price elasticity of demand.

33

Figure 3.1   Comparison of Mean, Median, and Mode

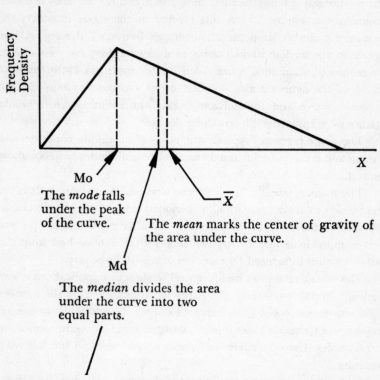

Mo

The *mode* falls
under the peak
of the curve.

$\overline{X}$

The *mean* marks the center of gravity of
the area under the curve.

Md

The *median* divides the area
under the curve into two
equal parts.

The *median* of a single-peaked distribution *always lies between
the mode and the mean* unless the distribution is symmetrical. In a
symmetrical distribution the mode, median, and mean are all equal.

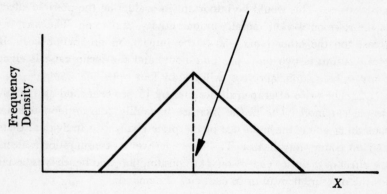

3.1.5 Central Tendency and Skewness

A *symmetrical* distribution is one in which the half of the frequency curve above the median is a mirror image of the half below the median. In a symmetrical distribution with a single mode, the mean, median, and mode are equal. A distribution that is not symmetrical is *skewed*. In a skewed distribution with a single mode, the mean, median, and mode differ, with the median always lying between the mode and the mean. A distribution whose tail is skewed out to the right (as in Figure 3.1) has a *right* or *positive* skew. The mode is the smallest and the mean the largest of the three measures of central tendency. In a distribution whose tail is skewed out to the left (*left* or *negative* skew) the mode is the largest, and the mean the smallest of the three.

3.2 MEASURES OF DISPERSION

The items in a frequency distribution vary in magnitude, that is, their values are not equal, but are *dispersed*. A large metropolitan area has high dispersion of income; there are extremes of wealth and poverty. With low dispersion of income, families are more nearly alike, as in a middle-class suburban development. Statistics of *dispersion* measure the extent of this scattering of values.

One of the most important uses of a statistic of dispersion is to indicate how well the average represents the individual items in a distribution. If there were no dispersion at all, everybody would have exactly the same income, and the average would exactly represent everybody. Because of dispersion the average is not exactly representative; the greater the dispersion, the less representative the average becomes. The greater the dispersion of a distribution, the larger the proportion of items that differ from the average by more than any specified amount. If the weights of a group of men are much alike in magnitude (low dispersion), relatively few men will differ either way from the average by more than, say, 5 pounds. If weights vary widely from man to man (high dispersion), a larger proportion will differ from the average by this amount or more. Looked at another way, the greater the dispersion, the wider the interval around the average needed to contain any specified proportion of the total number of items. For example, in the group of men whose weights

35

are much alike, ⅔ of the weights might lie within limits set, say, 8 pounds above and below the mean, while to contain ⅔ of a more dispersed group the limit might have to be set, say, 15 pounds above and below the mean (see Figure 3.2).

Figure 3.2   Implications of Dispersion

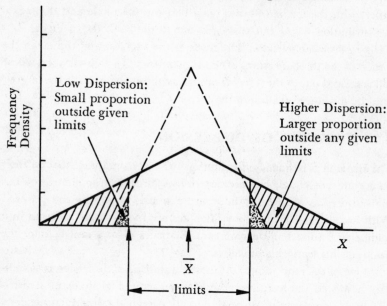

The most important statistics of dispersion are the *range*, the *interquartile range*, and the *variance*, together with its square root, the *standard deviation*.

3.2.1   The Range

The *range* of a frequency distribution is the difference between the largest and the smallest magnitudes. If the lowest number of years of education in Table 2.3 is 0 and the highest is, say, 24, the range of the distribution is $24 - 0 = 24$ years. Although easy to calculate, the range depends on the two extremes of atypical behavior and rarely gives a useful impression of the dispersion of the distribution as a whole. Even in everyday speech we reduce the range to what will include only the "bulk" of the items, that is, we might say that "most people" go to school from 5 to 16 years.

3.2.2 The Interquartile Range

The *interquartile range* is the range that includes the center half of all the items. One-fourth of the items fall beyond the upper, and one-fourth beyond the lower limits of the interquartile range. Thus it follows the everyday practice of expressing a range that includes the "bulk" of the items, defining "bulk" as the central 50 per cent.

The quartiles of a distribution are similar to the median in that they are *partition values*, that is, magnitudes that partition the distribution into equal parts. The three quartiles split the distribution into four quarters: One quarter of all items have magnitudes below the first quartile (Q_1); one quarter lie between the first and the second quartile (Md); one quarter between the second and third quartiles (Q_3) and the remaining quarter have magnitudes larger than the third quartile. It is clear that the second quartile is also the median.

3.2.2.1 LOCATING QUARTILES Like the median, quartiles are estimated either from an ogive or by linear interpolation in a frequency table. In Table 3.1 the first quartile is $40/4 = 10$ items from the lower end. Counting past the first 5 items brings us to 4.0, the lower limit of the first quartile class. Since we must count past 5 of the 10 items in this class, the first quartile must lie about 5/10 of the class interval above the lower limit. That is:

$$Q_1 = 4.0 + 4 \times \frac{5}{10} = 6.0.$$

The upper quartile is estimated in similar fashion:

$$Q_3 = 12.0.$$

The interquartile range is then

$$Q_3 - Q_1 = 12.0 - 6.0 = 6.0.$$

Although the interquartile range is a more useful measure of dispersion than the range, it leaves out of account the 50 per cent of the items lying outside the quartiles. The two distributions of Figure 3.3, for example, have the same interquartile range, yet the items in the lower

Figure 3.3 Two Distributions with the Same Interquartile Range

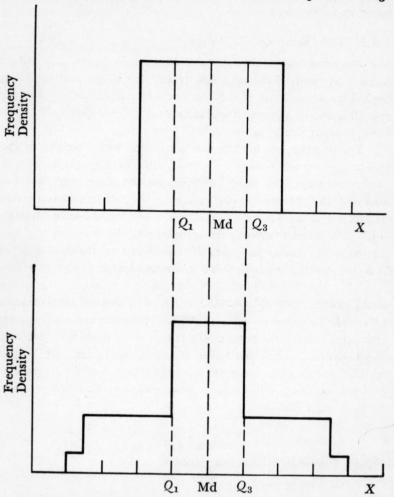

figure are clearly more disperse than in the upper. Many purposes, especially in connection with sampling, require a measure of dispersion that takes account of *all* items in the distribution.

3.2.3 The Variance and the Standard Deviation

The *variance* and its square root, the *standard deviation*, are the measures of dispersion almost universally employed in formal statistical work.

Since they take into account every item in the distribution, they are free of the difficulties encountered with the range and the interquartile range.

The variance is found by calculating the deviation of each item from the mean, squaring these deviations. and calculating the mean square deviation. The symbol employed for the variance is σ^2. Recalling that the deviation of the ith item from the mean is represented by $X_i - \bar{X} = x_i$, we can write the formula for the variance as

$$\sigma^2 = \frac{\Sigma x_i^2}{N} = \frac{\Sigma (X_i - \bar{X})^2}{N}.$$

The standard deviation, σ, is the square root of the variance. They are, therefore, essentially the same measure of dispersion, but as we shall see later, the standard deviation is more convenient for some purposes and the variance for others.

3.2.3.1 CALCULATION OF THE VARIANCE AND STANDARD DEVIATION

One way to calculate the variance is to follow literally the procedure in the formula given above. This would be done in five steps, as shown in Table 3.4.

Table 3.4   Calculation of σ^2 and σ

X	x	x^2
1	$1 - 3 = -2$	4[a]
2	$2 - 3 = -1$	1
3	$3 - 3 = 0$	0
4	$4 - 3 = 1$	1
5	$5 - 3 = 2$	4
$\Sigma X_i = 15$		$\Sigma x_i^2 = 10$

$$\bar{X} = \frac{15}{5} = 3$$

$$\sigma^2 = \frac{\Sigma x_i^2}{N} = \frac{10}{5} = 2$$

$$\sigma = \sqrt{\sigma^2} = \sqrt{2} = 1.4$$

[a] When using an automatic calculator the individual values of x_i^2 are not recorded, but are allowed to accumulate to the total in the machine.

1. Calculate the mean.
2. Subtract the mean from each item X_i to get its deviation, x_i.

3. Square the deviations.
4. Add them up.
5. Divide by the number of items.

Unless the number of items is small, however, this is a roundabout and tedious procedure. In actual practice a short-cut method is used. Instead of calculating the squared *deviations*, calculate the sum of the squared magnitudes themselves. It can be shown that the sum of the squared deviations from the mean can then be calculated by the formula[5]

$$\Sigma x_i^2 = \Sigma (X_i - \bar{X})^2 = \frac{N \Sigma X_i^2 - (\Sigma X_i)^2}{N}.$$

Table 3.5 Work Sheet for Calculation of σ^2 and σ, Short Method

X	X^2
1	1[a]
2	4
3	9
4	16
5	25
$\Sigma X_i = 15$	$\Sigma X_i^2 = 55$

$$\Sigma x_i^2 = \frac{N(\Sigma X_i^2) - (\Sigma X_i)^2}{N} = \frac{5(55) - (15)^2}{5} = 10.0$$

$$\sigma^2 = \frac{\Sigma x_i^2}{N} = \frac{10.0}{5} = 2.0$$

$$\sigma = \sqrt{2.0} = 1.4$$

[a] When using an automatic calculator the values of X_i^2 are not recorded, but are allowed to accumulate to the total in the machine.

Calculation by the short-cut method is shown in Table 3.5.

5. This formula is derived as follows:
$$\Sigma x_i^2 = \Sigma (X_i - \bar{X})^2 = \Sigma (X_i^2 - 2\bar{X}X_i + \bar{X}^2) = \Sigma X_i^2 - 2\bar{X} \Sigma X_i + N\bar{X}^2.$$
Substituting

$$\bar{X} = \frac{\Sigma X_i}{N} \text{ and simplifying:}$$

$$\Sigma x_i^2 = \frac{N \Sigma X_i^2 - (\Sigma X_i)^2}{N}.$$

40

3.2.3.2 CALCULATION OF VARIANCE AND STANDARD DEVIATION FROM TABULATED DATA It is often necessary to calculate the variance and standard deviation from tabulated data, using the class mark in place of the (unknown) actual values of the individual items. This procedure is similar to that used for the mean. As before, let the number of classes be k and represent by m_j and f_j respectively the mark and frequency of the jth class. Record m_j^2, the square of the class mark, next to m_j on the work sheet. Then,

$$N = \Sigma f_j,$$

$$\Sigma x_i^2 = \frac{N \Sigma m_j^2 f_j - (\Sigma m_j f_j)^2}{N}$$

and

$$\sigma^2 = \frac{\Sigma x_i^2}{N}.$$

This calculation is illustrated in Table 3.6.

Table 3.6 Work Sheet for Calculation of Variance and Standard Deviation from Tabulated Data

Class	m	m^2	f	mf	m^2f
0–1.9	1.0	1.0	5	5.0[a]	5.0[a]
2.0–3.9	3.0	9.0	15	45.0	135.0
4.0–6.0	5.0	25.0	10	50.0	250.0

$$N = \Sigma f_j = 30 \quad \Sigma m_j f_j = 100.0 \quad \Sigma m_j^2 f_j = 390.0$$

$$\Sigma x_i^2 = \frac{N(\Sigma m^2 f) - (\Sigma m f)^2}{N} = \frac{30 \times 390 - (100)^2}{30} = 56.67$$

$$\sigma^2 = \frac{\Sigma x_i^2}{N} = \frac{56.67}{30} = 1.89$$

$$\sigma = \sqrt{1.89} = 1.37$$

[a] When using an automatic calculator the individual products are not recorded, but are allowed to accumulate to the total in the machine.

Note that when results are allowed to accumulate in the calculating machine, the work sheet provides a compact format for the systematic calculation of both the mean and the variance of a classified frequency distribution. The application of this format to the calculation of the mean, variance, and standard deviation of family income is shown in Table 3.7.

Table 3.7 Work Sheet for Calculation of Mean, Variance, and Standard Deviation of Family Income

Income Class	m (thousands of $)	m²	f (millions)
Under $1,000	.5	.25	2.285
$1,000–1,999	1.5	2.25	3.613
$2,000–2,999	2.5	6.25	3.970
$3,000–3,999	3.5	12.25	4.456
$4,000–4,999	4.5	20.25	4.773
$5,000–5,999	5.5	30.25	5.839
$6,000–6,999	6.5	42.25	4.889
$7,000–7,999	7.5	56.25	3.973
$8,000–9,999	9.0	81.00	5.135
$10,000–14,999	12.5	156.25	4.795
$15,000 or more	22.5[a]	506.25	1.707

$$N = \Sigma f_j = 45.435$$
$$\Sigma m_j f_j = 291.812$$
$$\Sigma m_j^2 f_j = 2,820.746$$

$$\bar{X} = \frac{\Sigma m_j f_j}{N} = \frac{291.812}{45.435} = \$6.423 \text{ (thousand)}$$

$$\Sigma x^2 = \frac{N\Sigma m_j^2 f_j - (\Sigma m_j f_j)^2}{N}$$

$$= \frac{(45.435)(2,820.746) - (291.812)^2}{45.435} = 946.5467$$

$$\sigma^2 = \frac{\Sigma x^2}{N} = \frac{946.5467}{45.435} = 20.833$$

$$\sigma = \sqrt{\sigma^2} = \sqrt{20.833} = \$4.564 \text{ (thousand)}$$

[a] Approximate value.
Source: Data of Table 2.1.

3.2.3.3 VARIANCE AND STANDARD DEVIATION OF CATEGORICAL VARIABLES We have seen that a categorical variable like employment can be treated as a special case of a number X whose values are restricted to 0 and 1, the mean $\bar{X}$ being the proportion P of items belonging to the category. The variance of a categorical variable can be calculated by the simple formula[6]

$$\sigma^2 = P(1 - P).$$

If employment is designated by $X = 1$ and unemployment by $X = 0$, in a group in which 80 per cent are employed:

$$X = P = .8$$
$$\sigma^2 = P(1 - P) = .8 \times .2 = .16$$
$$\sigma = \sqrt{P(1 - P)} = \sqrt{.16} = .4 .$$

The variance and standard deviation of a categorical variable have important applications in the theory of sampling in the following chapter.

3.2.4 Four Important Properties of the Variance and Standard Deviation

1. *If a constant is added to every value in a distribution, the values of σ^2 and σ are unaffected.* If every family is given an additional $100, the variance and standard deviation of incomes remain the same as before. This is because the mean rises by $100 along with the individual incomes, and deviations from the mean are the same as before. Symbolically,

$$\sigma^2_{X+k} = \sigma^2_X; \ \sigma_{X+k} = \sigma_X.$$

2. *If every value in a distribution is multiplied by a constant, the standard deviation is multiplied by the absolute value of the constant, and the variance is multiplied by the square of the constant.* The effect of a 20 per cent increase in all incomes is to multiply each family income by 1.2. If the standard

6. Mathematical proof: Of a total of N items, N_1 belong to the category and N_0 do not. Sum the squared deviations from the mean ($P = N_1/N$) for the two groups separately:

First group: $\Sigma x_i^2 = \Sigma(X_i - P)^2 = \Sigma(1 - P)^2 = N_1(1 - P)^2$

Second group: $\Sigma x_i^2 = \Sigma(X_i - P)^2 = \Sigma(- P)^2 = N_0 P^2$

Total: $\Sigma x_i^2 = N_1(1 - P)^2 + N_0 P^2$

so

$$\sigma^2 = \frac{\Sigma x_i^2}{N} = \frac{N_1}{N}(1 - P)^2 + \frac{N_0}{N} P^2$$

$$= P(1 - P)^2 + (1 - P)P^2$$

Expanding and simplifying:

$$\sigma^2 = P - P^2 = P(1 - P).$$

43

deviation of income initially was $1,000, it becomes $1,200 after the raise. The variance, which before tax was 1,000,000, becomes 1,440,000 after the increase.[7] Symbolically:

$$\sigma^2_{kX} = k^2 \, \sigma^2_X; \ \sigma_{kX} = |k|\sigma_X.$$

3. *The variance of the sum of two* independent *values* X *and* Y *is the sum of their variances.* This is the counterpart of the proposition that the mean of $(X + Y)$ is $\bar{X} + \bar{Y}$; but while the latter *always* holds, the variance of $(X + Y)$ depends on the relationship between X and Y. X and Y are *independent* when the value of $\bar{X}$ is constant for all values of Y, and the value of $\bar{Y}$ is constant for all values of X. This definition needs to be explained more fully.

Suppose income of the ith family consists of husband's earnings (X_i) and wife's earnings (Y_i), entered on the ith card in our warehouse. Now classify families by husband's income (X) and form a frequency distribution in the usual way. Although the families in a given bracket have approximately the same husband's income, the wives have, in general, different incomes. Within each X bracket, make a frequency distribution of families by wife's income (Y). The result is a bivariate distribution like that shown in Table 3.8.

Table 3.8 Distribution of Families by Husband's and Wife's Income (Tabulated figures are number of families.)

Husband's Income (X)	Wife's Income (Y)				
	$0– 1,999	$2,000– 3,999	$4,000– 5,999	$6,000– 8,000	Y
$ 0–1,999	10	30	50	10	$4,200
$2,000–3,999	20	60	100	20	$4,200
$4,000–5,999	30	90	150	30	$4,200
$6,000–8,000	20	60	100	20	$4,200
X̄	$4,500	$4,500	$4,500	$4,500	

Each row of the table is the distribution by wives' incomes of those families having a specified husband's income (for example, the first row

7. Mathematical proof:

$$\frac{\Sigma(kX_i - k\bar{X})^2}{N} = \frac{k^2\Sigma(X_i - \bar{X})^2}{N} = k^2\sigma^2.$$

is the distribution, by wife's income, of families where the husband's income is in the $0–1,000 bracket). Each column of the table is the distribution by husbands' incomes of those families having a specified wife's income (for example, the second column shows that of the 240 families in which the wife's income is in the $2,000–3,999 bracket, 30 husbands had incomes of $0–1,999; 60 had incomes of $2,000–3,999, and so on).

Incomes of husbands and wives are *independent* if, as in Table 3.8, the mean husband's incomes of each column are all equal to $\bar{X}$, the grand mean of husbands' incomes, and the means of each row are all equal to $\bar{Y}$, the grand mean of wives' incomes. The proposition states that, under these circumstances, the variance of total family incomes equals the variance of husbands' incomes plus the variance of wives' incomes.[8] Symbolically:

$$\sigma^2_{X+Y} = \sigma^2_X + \sigma^2_Y.$$

This proposition is central to the theory of sampling developed in Chapter IV. It can be tested by simple examples.[9] The values of X and

8. If $\bar{X}$ and $\bar{Y}$ vary among columns and rows, the variables are not independent, but are *correlated*. The variance of the sum of two correlated variables differs from the sum of their variances by an amount that depends on the direction and extent of the correlation.

9. Mathematical proof:

$$\sigma^2_{X+Y} = \frac{\Sigma[(X_i + Y_i) - (\bar{X} + \bar{Y})]^2}{N} = \frac{\Sigma(x_i + y_i)^2}{N}$$

$$= \frac{\Sigma(x_i^2 + y_i^2 + 2x_iy_i)}{N}$$

$$= \sigma^2_X + \sigma^2_Y + \frac{2\Sigma x_iy_i}{N}.$$

We must show that the last term is zero. This is done as follows: Class together all items with $x_i = a$, all those with $x_i = b$, and so on, and call these classes A, B, ... and so on. Let the number of items in the classes be N_A, N_B, ... The last term can then be written

$$2\frac{\Sigma x_iy_i}{N} = \frac{2}{N}[a\underset{A}{\Sigma}y_i + b\underset{B}{\Sigma}y_i + \ldots]$$

$$= \frac{2}{N}[aN_A\bar{y}_A + bN_B\bar{y}_B + \ldots],$$

where $\underset{A}{\Sigma}y_i$ and $\bar{y}_A$ are respectively the total and mean of the values of y_i in Class A, and so on. Since x and y are independent, $\bar{y}_A = \bar{y}_B = \bar{\bar{y}} = \frac{\Sigma y_i}{N} = 0$, and the proof is complete.

Y in the following pairs are clearly independent: $\bar{Y} = 3$ for both values of X, and $\bar{X} = 6$ for both values of Y.

X	Y	X+Y
3	2	5
3	4	7
9	2	11
9	4	13

Calculation shows $\sigma_X^2 = 9$, $\sigma_Y^2 = 1$, $\sigma_{X+Y}^2 = 10$.

In contrast, the following values of X and Y not independent but are *correlated:*

X	Y	X+Y
3	2	5
3	4	7
9	6	15
9	8	17

$\bar{Y} = 3$ for $X = 3$, but $\bar{Y} = 7$ for $X = 9$. Since the larger values of X are accompanied by the larger values of Y, X and Y are *positively correlated*, and σ_{X+Y}^2 is larger than $\sigma_X^2 + \sigma_Y^2$. By calculation:

$$\sigma_X^2 = 9, \; \sigma_Y^2 = 5, \; \sigma_{X+Y}^2 = 26.$$

4. *The variance of two or more combined distributions can be calculated from their individual means and variances.* Given samples A and B containing N_A and N_B items with means $\bar{X}_A$ and $\bar{X}_B$ and variances σ_A^2, σ_B^2. When the two samples are combined into one, the grand mean will be

$$\bar{\bar{X}} = \frac{N_A \bar{X}_A + N_B \bar{X}_B}{N_A + N_B}.$$

The sum of the squared deviations from $\bar{\bar{X}}$ will be

$$\Sigma x^2 = N_A \sigma_A^2 + N_B \sigma_B^2 + N_A(\bar{X}_A - \bar{\bar{X}})^2 + N_B(\bar{X}_B - \bar{\bar{X}})^2.$$

Hence the variance of the combined sample will be

$$\sigma^2 = \frac{\Sigma x^2}{N} = \frac{N_A \sigma_A^2 + N_B \sigma_B^2 + N_A(\bar{X}_A - \bar{\bar{X}})^2 + N_B(\bar{X}_B - \bar{\bar{X}})^2}{N_A + N_B}.$$

This property of the variance can be mathematically demonstrated.[10] It can easily be tested by two small samples:

Sample A: 25   27   29   31; $\bar{X}_A = 28$ $\sigma_A^2 = \dfrac{10}{4}$

Sample B: 6   7   8; $\bar{X}_B = 7$ $\sigma_B^2 = \dfrac{2}{3}$

According to our formula, when combined into one sample, we should have

$$\bar{\bar{X}} = \frac{4 \times 28 + 3 \times 7}{3 + 4} = 19$$

$$\sigma^2 = \frac{(4 \times 10/4) + (3 \times 2/3) + 4(28 - 19)^2 + 3(7 - 19)^2}{3 + 4} = 109\frac{5}{7}.$$

This agrees with results obtained when samples are combined:

Combined Sample: 6   7   8   25   27   29   31; $\bar{\bar{X}} = 19$, $\sigma^2 = 109\frac{5}{7}$.

This property of the variance holds for the combination of any number of individual samples into one. It will have important application to the analysis of variance and correlation in later chapters.

10. Mathematical proof: Consider the items formerly in Group A:

$$\sum_A (X_i - \bar{\bar{X}})^2 = \sum_A [(X_i - \bar{X}_A) + (\bar{X}_A - \bar{\bar{X}})]^2$$

$$= \sum_A (X_i - \bar{X}_A)^2 + \sum_A (\bar{X}_A - \bar{\bar{X}})^2$$

$$+ 2 \sum_A (\bar{X}_A X_i - \bar{\bar{X}} X_i - \bar{X}_A^2 + \bar{X}_A \bar{\bar{X}})$$

$$= N_A \sigma_A^2 + N_A (\bar{X}_A - \bar{\bar{X}})^2$$

$$+ 2 [\bar{X}_A \sum_A X_i - \bar{\bar{X}} \sum_A X_i - N_A \bar{X}_A^2 + N_A \bar{X}_A \bar{\bar{X}}].$$

But since $\sum_A X_i = N_A \bar{X}_A$, the expression in brackets is zero:

$$[N_A \bar{X}_A^2 - N_A \bar{\bar{X}} \bar{X}_A - N_A \bar{X}_A^2 + N_A \bar{X}_A \bar{\bar{X}}] = 0,$$

so for items formerly in Group A:

$$\sum_A (X_i - \bar{\bar{X}})^2 = N_A \sigma_A^2 + N_A (\bar{X}_A - \bar{\bar{X}})^2.$$

Repeating for B, and combining:

$$\sigma^2 = \frac{\sum_A (X_i - \bar{\bar{X}})^2 + \sum_B (X_i - \bar{\bar{X}})^2}{N_A + N_B}$$

$$= \frac{N_A \sigma_A^2 + N_B \sigma_B^2 + N_A (\bar{X}_A - \bar{\bar{X}})^2 + N_B (\bar{X}_B - \bar{\bar{X}})^2}{N_A + N_B}.$$

Figure 3.4 Proportion of Items Within One and Two Standard Deviations of the Mean in Distributions of Various Shapes

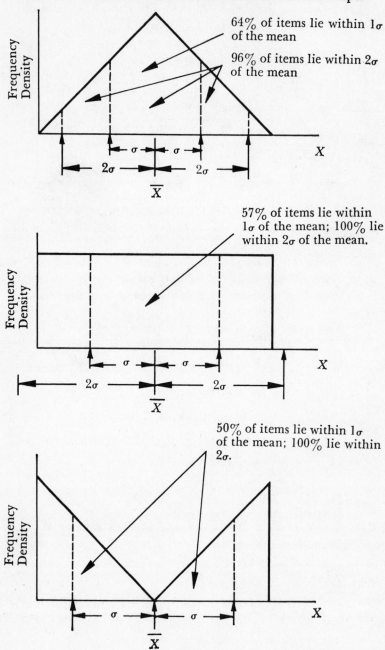

64% of items lie within 1σ of the mean

96% of items lie within 2σ of the mean

57% of items lie within 1σ of the mean; 100% lie within 2σ of the mean.

50% of items lie within 1σ of the mean; 100% lie within 2σ.

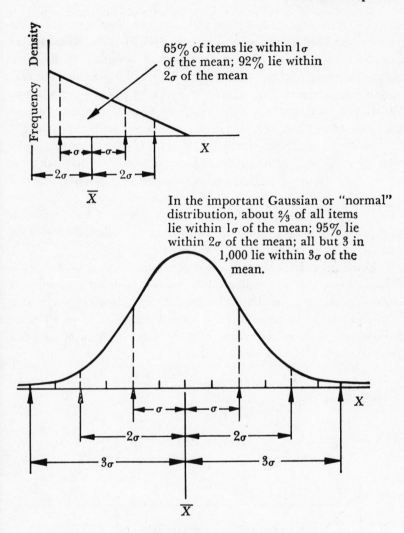

65% of items lie within 1σ of the mean; 92% lie within 2σ of the mean

In the important Gaussian or "normal" distribution, about ⅔ of all items lie within 1σ of the mean; 95% lie within 2σ of the mean; all but 3 in 1,000 lie within 3σ of the mean.

3.2.5 The Standard Deviation and the Proportion of Items Near the Mean

Regardless of the shape of a frequency distribution, all of the items lie within its range, and exactly 50 per cent lie within its interquartile range. In contrast, the proportion of items that fall within one standard deviation of the mean depends on the shape of the distribution. In

49

Figure 3.4 the proportion of items within one standard deviation of the mean varies from 67 per cent to as low as 50 per cent. Similarly, the proportion of items lying within two standard deviations of the mean varies from about 90 to 100 per cent. In the Gaussian or "normal" distribution, whose importance will be seen later, about $\frac{2}{3}$ of all items lie within 1σ of the mean, about 95 per cent lie no farther than 2σ from the mean, and all but three in one thousand lie within 3σ of the mean.

But while the exact proportion of items in given intervals varies with the shape of the distribution, it is rare to find fewer than half lying within 1σ of the mean. In fact, a proportion this small is found only in a V-shaped distribution. If the distribution is "humped" rather than "troughed," the proportion of items falling within 1σ of the mean tends to be more than 60 per cent, while more than 90 per cent lie within 2σ, and almost 100 per cent within 3σ of the mean.

Finally, regardless of the shape of the distribution, the definition of σ^2 and σ fixes $1/k^2$ as a mathematical maximum to the proportion of items that can lie *farther* than $k\sigma$ from the mean. In other words, it is mathematically impossible to have more than $\frac{1}{2^2} = \frac{1}{4}$ of all items farther than 2σ from the mean, or more than $\frac{1}{3^2} = \frac{1}{9}$ of all items farther than 3σ from the mean, and so on.[11]

11. Mathematical proof of this proposition, known as the *Tchebycheff inequality*, is quite simple.

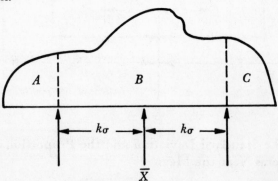

In any frequency distribution locate the mean and the two points $k\sigma$ on either side of the mean. These two points divide the items into three classes: A, containing N_A items lying $k\sigma$ or more below the mean; B, containing N_B items lying within $k\sigma$ of the mean; C, containing N_C items lying $k\sigma$ or more above the mean.

In Table 3.7 we calculated the mean income of United States families to be \$6,423 and the standard deviation to be \$4,564. The families within one standard deviation of the mean are those whose incomes lie between \$6,423 − 4,564 = \$1,859 at the lower limit, and \$6,423 + 4,564 = \$10,987 at the upper limit. Setting these limits roughly at \$2,000 and \$10,000, we see that about 33 million families, or over 70 per cent of the total, have incomes within one standard deviation of the mean.

3.3 SUMMARY

Measures of central tendency and dispersion summarize two important properties of frequency distributions. Central tendency can be measured by mode, median or mean; dispersion is measured by range, inter-quartile range, or variance and standard deviation. Of these, the mean and the variance and standard deviation are the most often used. The full importance and usefulness of the mean, variance, and standard deviation will appear only later in the discussion of sampling, statistical

---

The inequality says that $\dfrac{N_A + N_C}{N} \leq \dfrac{1}{k^2}$. In calculating the variance, sum the squared deviations of the groups separately:

$$\frac{\underset{A}{\Sigma}(X_i - \bar{X})^2 + \underset{B}{\Sigma}(X_i - \bar{X})^2 + \underset{C}{\Sigma}(X_i - \bar{X})^2}{N} = \sigma^2 .$$

In A and C, the absolute value of the smallest deviation from the mean is $k\sigma$. Hence

$$N_A k^2 \sigma^2 \leq \underset{A}{\Sigma}(X_i - \bar{X})^2$$

and

$$N_C k^2 \sigma^2 \leq \underset{C}{\Sigma}(X_i - \bar{X})^2 ,$$

so

$$\frac{N_A k^2 \sigma^2 + \underset{B}{\Sigma}(X_i - \bar{X})^2 + N_C k^2 \sigma^2}{N} \leq \sigma^2 .$$

Dropping out the center term only makes the left side of this expression smaller, so

$$\frac{(N_A + N_C)}{N} k^2 \sigma^2 \leq \sigma^2 .$$

Dividing both sides by $k^2 \sigma^2$ gives

$$\frac{N_A + N_C}{N} \leq \frac{1}{k^2} ,$$

and the proof is complete.

51

testing, and related topics. It is already clear, however, that these statistics summarize important properties of a large quantity of data.

The mean is a value calculated to be "typical" (in a special sense) of the magnitudes in the distribution. The standard deviation indicates the extent to which items differ from this "typical" value. Without further knowledge of the shape of the distribution it is impossible to say exactly what proportion of items falls within a given number of standard deviations of the mean. But in the humped distributions generally encountered, about 60 per cent of all items lie within 1σ and about 90 per cent lie within 2σ of the mean. Only the rare item differs from the mean by more than 3σ.

As will be seen later, in the most important cases enough is known about the shape of the distribution to permit much more exact statements of proportions.

Questions and Problems

1. Which measure of central tendency is most easily estimated by:
   (a) a quick glance at a frequency table?
   (b) a quick glance at a histogram?
   (c) a quick glance at an ogive?

2. (a) Suppose items are recorded on 3×5 cards and filed in order of size in a file drawer. How could you locate the approximate median without even counting the cards?

   (b) Suppose items are filed alphabetically in a file drawer. How would you get a quick estimate of the mean?

   (c) Suppose the items are stacked in piles, each containing all the items of a given size. What is the fastest way to estimate the mode?

3. A sportsman writing about a certain lake asserts that the adult bass "average from one to three pounds." What does he probably mean? A biologist studying the same lake says that the adult bass have a mean weight of 2.15 pounds and standard deviation of 1.21 pounds. What does this mean?

4. In area A the mean family income is $10,000 and the standard deviation is $5,000. In area B, the mean is $9,000 and the standard deviation is $1,000. Describe these two areas.

5. Calculate the mean, median, mode, range, interquartile range, variance, and standard deviation of each of the wage distributions of Chapter II, problem 3. What proportion of the workers have straight time earnings within 1σ of the mean? Within 2σ of the mean?

Combine the three occupations into one frequency distribution. Calculate the mean and variance of this distribution and verify the properties of the mean given in section 3.1.3.5 (4) and of the variance given in section 3.2.4.

6. Calculate the mean, variance, and standard deviation of the penny-tossing experiment of Chapter II, problem 2. What proportion of the 50 tosses comes within 1σ of the mean? Within 2σ?

7. Select one of the distributions from Tables 2.2, 2.3, or 2.4 of Chapter II, calculate its mean and standard deviation, and estimate the proportion of items lying within one standard deviation of the mean.

References

1. Darrell Huff. *How to Lie with Statistics.* New York: W. W. Norton & Co., 1954. An amusing account of the uses and abuses of statistics, especially measures of central tendency.

2. Frederick E. Croxton and Dudley J. Cowden. *Applied General Statistics.* 2nd Ed. New York: Prentice-Hall, 1955. Chapter 9, "Measures of Central Tendency," contains a good comparison of the mean, median, and mode, and also deals with a number of minor averages such as the harmonic and quadratic mean. Chapter 10, "Dispersion, Skewness, Kurtosis," contains a formal treatment of measures of the shape of a frequency distribution.

CHAPTER IV

The Use of Samples: Statistical Inference

4.1 POPULATION AND SAMPLE

The objective of any scientific inquiry is to make measurements and to establish relationships that hold for a broad class of objects. The physicist attempts to derive a law for the period of pendulums, applicable to all pendulums of a certain description. The botanist attempts to find the relationship between plant hormone and growth in a wide class of plants. The economist hopes to find a relationship between family income and consumption that will hold among all families of a given description. The broad class of objects to which the measurement or relationship is applicable will be called the *population* or the *universe*.

4.1.1 The Need for Samples

One way to be sure that a measurement applies to an entire population is to examine every item in the population. Unfortunately, this is often impossible for several reasons:

1. Much of the population may not yet exist. For example, understanding the effect of plant hormone on growth leads to improvement in the yield of crops as yet unplanted. Knowledge of the properties of a drug will help to cure people not yet ill and, for that matter, still unborn.

2. Exploration of the relationship may be destructive. A piece of cable whose strength has been tested by breaking it under measured conditions cannot be used again.

3. Finally, we generally have neither the time nor the resources to examine the entire population, even where physically possible to do so.

For these reasons it is usually necessary to resort to a small sample of a population to get information applicable to the whole.

4.1.2 Representative Samples

In order to yield exact information about a population, a sample would have to be precisely representative: a small-scale image of the population from which it was drawn, with all of its frequencies proportional to those of its parent. Unfortunately, we can get representative samples only from populations with characteristics already known; thus, since the population of all the possible tosses of a coin consists of half heads and half tails, it can be completely represented by a sample of only two coins, one a head and one a tail. Similarly, the population of numbers resulting from throwing a pair of dice can be exactly represented by a sample of 36 throws consisting of one "2" and "12," two "3's" and "11's," three "4's" and "10's," and so on. Means, standard deviations, variances, or other statistics calculated from such a sample will exactly represent the population.

Since it can be constructed only after the properties of the population are known, it is impossible to draw on a representative sample to learn anything new. In exploring the unknown, the most we can do is assure ourselves that the sample used is not systematically *un*representative or *biased*.

4.1.3 Biased Samples

There are several common sources of bias in selecting samples. The most common bias arises when the composition of the sample is influenced by the (conscious or unconscious) preconceptions of the researcher about the nature of the population to be investigated. It is impossible to obtain an unbiased sample of a population by deliberately selecting the items to be included. For example, one cannot obtain an unbiased sample of the crowd at a football game by walking up and down the aisles and deliberately picking out the people to be included. The sampler would be very likely either to select too many people somewhat like himself or, conscious of this predisposition, to lean over backward and select a sample that overrepresents people unlike himself.

An interesting experiment that illustrates this point is to ask a number of your friends to think of a number between 1 and 10 "at random" and write it down on a slip of paper. You will find that there is a systematic tendency for people to avoid numbers near the end such as 1 and 9. These are apparently "not random enough." On the other hand, there is a strong disposition to choose the number 7. As another illustration, unsuspecting people given a "random" choice among the numbers 1, 2, 3, and 4 almost invariably select the number 3.

A second important kind of bias arises when members of the population are allowed to decide for themselves whether to belong to the sample or not. A mail survey usually exhibits this kind of bias. People with strong interest in the subject will answer the questions and return the questionnaire. Other people will drop the letter in the wastebasket and forget about it. For example, a mail inquiry about performance of a household product will elicit responses overrepresenting women who are enthusiastic about its performance and—probably even more so— women for whom it performed especially poorly.

4.1.4 Random Samples

To avoid these sources of bias a sample must be so selected that whether a given item is included is a matter of chance, independent of the will or judgment of the researcher or the nature of the item. Such a sample is known as a *random sample*. There are a wide variety of techniques for drawing such samples, and the science of sample design is an important specialized branch of statistics. In this book, however, we shall limit attention to theory of inferences from the *simple random sample*.

4.1.4.1 SIMPLE RANDOM SAMPLES A simple random sample is one in which the items are independently selected with equal probabilities, that is, (1) all items in the population have an equal chance to be drawn into the sample, and (2) each item is selected independently of whether any other item is drawn into the sample. Taken together, these conditions mean that any one combination of items has as good a chance to occur in the sample as any other. The nature of the simple random sample can best be understood in contrast to two other important random sample types.

4.1.4.2 STRATIFIED SAMPLES Essentially, a *stratified* random sample consists of a set of simple random subsamples, each drawn from a designated subpopulation or *stratum*, the sizes of the several subsamples being chosen to give maximum reliability to the final result. In a study of firms we would stratify the sample to ensure that firms of all industries and all sizes would be represented. This means that certain combinations—for example a sample of firms all from the same industry—cannot occur. Thus the result is not a simple random sample. Because it incorporates facts already known about the population, a stratified sample is generally more accurate than a simple random sample of the same size.

4.1.4.3 CLUSTERED SAMPLES A *clustered sample* is one in which the items are drawn into the sample in groups, or clusters, rather than independently. In interviewing households in a city, we often select a random sample of city blocks and visit every household in the chosen blocks. This minimizes the interviewer time and transportation cost of the study. The result is not a simple random sample since no household can appear except in combination with all its neighbors. A clustered sample is somewhat less accurate than a simple random sample of the same size, since the clusters tend to be somewhat more homogeneous than the population at large. On the other hand, a clustered sample is usually more accurate than a simple random sample of the same total cost.

4.1.5 Selecting a Simple Random Sample

The proper way to draw a simple random sample depends on the population being sampled. In relatively simple cases—coins, dice, cards, and so on—the sample can be drawn by actually tossing the coins, throwing the dice, or dealing the cards the required number of times. Even here, however, the difficulties are somewhat greater than might first be imagined. For example, a simple random sample of the population of all possible bridge hands requires that the deck be shuffled with much greater care than would ordinarily be the case in the course of a bridge game. The technique of shuffling ordinarily employed is not a very good mixer of the cards, and the sequence of bridge hands obtained is not a simple random sample but a clustered sample, since the hands dealt on one deal are partly related to those dealt on the preceding deal.

Some populations can be sampled by physical devices. A random sample from a carload of wheat can be obtained by inserting a long tube through the contents of the car. A random sample of coffee beans in a hundred-pound bag can be obtained by a special device inserted into the bag. A sample of the output of a particular machine may consist of every hundredth item produced during a particular period, and so on.

Sampling human and institutional populations is somewhat more difficult. If a list or *frame* of the population is available, assign every member a number, and then draw a sample of these numbers by some chance mechanism. Since setting up and operating a properly functioning chance mechanism is a complicated matter, we often resort to random number tables, obtained as the output of a carefully constructed and operated random drawing device. Published tables of these numbers are available and can be used by the researcher to draw a sample from the frame. Table 4.1 is a small random number table. To

Table 4.1 A Table of Four-Digit Random Numbers

7205	6698	7167	8954	3717	5544
5312	9571	5703	6362	7891	3719
6459	0661	7273	1708	7897	1188
8700	2365	0045	0027	1391	4910
4546	2421	7302	7453	0012	2877
9085	7915	4122	0007	1866	5167
0134	8185	5062	8886	4197	7898
0405	5227	9949	6659	5418	6358
2465	9752	2594	4427	0688	3654
3923	5930	3122	0281	9957	1065

get a sample of 30 items drawn at random from a frame of 1,000, number the items in the frame from 000 to 999. Beginning with an arbitrary start in the table, record the first three digits of a sequence of 30 numbers, and draw the items with corresponding numbers into the sample. For example if we start at the top of the second column of Table 4.1 and read down, we would select items numbered 669, 957, 66, 236, 242, 791, and so on, until the required sample has been selected.

4.2 STATISTICAL INFERENCE

Statistical inference is the process of estimating properties of a population from evidence furnished in a random sample. It consists of two steps.

1. The data in a random sample are processed to produce the best single estimate of the required population characteristic. This number is called a *point estimate*.

2. A point estimate will vary from sample to sample. Rarely will a sample be sufficiently representative to furnish an exactly correct estimate of the population characteristic. If the estimate is to be useful, we must be able to assign some kind of limits to its probable deviation. These limits form a *confidence interval* around the estimate.

For example, if we are given a random sample of business firms and the number of employees in each, the task of estimating the mean number of employees in the entire population of such firms entails first using the sample to produce a single best estimate of the mean number of employees. This point estimate might be, let us say, 126.8 employees. This implies that if we must settle on one single number as the estimate of the mean number of employees in the population of firms, the best choice is 126.8. The trouble is that while this is the best choice, it may or may not be very accurate. Before we can employ the estimate, we need to know something about its probable limits of error. Is it likely to be accurate within 2 employees? Could it be off by as much as 50? 100? In other words, given 126.8 as a single best *estimate*, within what range would we expect the *true* value to lie?

The discussion is facilitated by the following notation. A subscript p will designate a population characteristic whose value is to be estimated. Thus $\bar{X}_p$ is the true value of the population mean. Placing a hat ($\wedge$) above a symbol will designate a point estimate. Thus, $\hat{X}_p$ is a point estimate of the population mean. Sample statistics will be designated by the subscript s; $\bar{X}_s$ is the mean of a random sample.

Table 4.2   The Two-Item Samples from the Population (1, 2, 3)
($\bar{X}_p = 2.0$; $\sigma_p^2 = .67$)

X_1	X_2	$\bar{X}_s$	σ_s^2	$(\bar{X}_s - \bar{X}_p)$	$(\bar{X}_s - \bar{X}_p)^2$
Sample					
1	1	1.0	.00	−1.0	1.00
1	2	1.5	.25	− .5	.25
1	3	2.0	1.00	.0	.00
2	1	1.5	.25	− .5	.25
2	2	2.0	.00	.0	.00
2	3	2.5	.25	.5	.25
3	1	2.0	1.00	.0	.00
3	2	2.5	.25	.5	.25
3	3	3.0	.00	1.0	1.00

Mean of 9 samples 2.0   .33

$$\sigma_{\bar{X}}^2 = \frac{\Sigma(\bar{X}_s - \bar{X}_p)^2}{k} = \frac{3}{9} = .33$$

The mean of sample means equals the population mean

The variance among sample means is
$$\sigma_{\bar{X}}^2 = \frac{\sigma_p^2}{N} = \frac{.67}{2} = .33$$

The mean σ_s^2 underestimates σ_p^2 until multiplied by $\dfrac{N}{N-1}$:
$$.33\left(\frac{2}{2-1}\right) = .67 = \sigma_p^2$$

4.2.1   Point Estimate of the Population Mean

The sample mean $\bar{X}_s$ is the best point estimate of the population mean. Although individual sample means deviate more or less from $\bar{X}_p$, the *mean* of sample means is identical with $\bar{X}_p$.[1] This can be demonstrated

1. Mathematical proof: Let the set of all samples of size N consist of k samples with means $\bar{X}_1, \bar{X}_2, \ldots, \bar{X}_k$. Pool all k samples into a single big sample G. The mean is given by

$$\bar{X}_G = \frac{N\bar{X}_1 + N\bar{X}_2 + \ldots + N\bar{X}_k}{Nk} = \frac{\bar{X}_1 + \bar{X}_2 + \ldots + \bar{X}_k}{k},$$

that is, $\bar{X}_G$ is the mean of sample means.

Now each item in the population appears in the same number of samples, and hence each item in the population is represented the same number of times in G. Thus G is a representative sample and mathematically but it is useful to verify it in a simple case. The proposition holds regardless of the population being sampled or the sample size, therefore consider all possible two-item samples from a population consisting only of the values 1, 2, and 3 in equal proportions. The 9 possible samples and their means are shown in Table 4.2; the equality between the mean of the sample means and $\bar{X}_p$ is obvious.

In other words, given a sample of firms, the best estimate of the mean number of employees in the entire population of such firms is simply the mean of the sample. The virtue of this estimate is that while individual samples give individual estimates that are more or less accurate, the method is still exact on the average. The estimate of 126.8 might be too high; another sample might yield 94.7, which may be too low. But while individual estimates are in error, these errors are not systematic and average zero over all possible samples.

4.2.2 Point Estimate of the Population Variance

If $\bar{X}_p$ were known, the point estimate of the population variance would be

$$\hat{\sigma}_p^2 = \frac{\Sigma\,(X_i - \bar{X}_p)^2}{N}\,.$$

Since $\bar{X}_p$ is generally unknown, we use $\bar{X}_s$ in its place, but this introduces a bias. As shown in Chapter III, the sample mean has the property of minimizing the sum of squares in the expression above. Thus, use of $\bar{X}_s$ produces an estimate that is systematically lower than would be had from $\bar{X}_p$, and an upward adjustment is required to remove the bias. The adjustment depends on sample size N, and it can be shown that an unbiased point estimate of σ_p^2 is given by[2]

$$\hat{\sigma}_p^2 = \left(\frac{N}{N-1}\right)\sigma_s^2\,.$$

$$\bar{X}_G = \bar{X}_p.$$

So

$$\bar{X}_p = \frac{\bar{X}_1 + \bar{X}_2 + \ldots + \bar{X}_k}{k}.$$

2. Mathematical proof: Consider all possible samples of size N, drawn from a population. Let there be k such samples, with sample variances $\sigma_1^2, \sigma_2^2, \ldots, \sigma_k^2$ and

This is tested on the 9 two-item samples of Table 4.2. The nine sample variances appear in the fourth column. Their mean, .33, is only half the true population variance. When the mean is multiplied by $N/N - 1$, however, the result is .67, the true value.

The variance in employment among a sample of firms is not the best estimate of the variance of employment in the population of such firms, since not only is any individual sample result likely to be somewhat in error, but even on the average the method yields an estimate that is incorrect. The sample estimate is improved, therefore, by adjusting it by a factor that depends on sample size. If a random sample of 20 firms had a variance in employment of, say, 380, the best estimate of the population variance would be

$$\hat\sigma_p^2 = \frac{20}{19} \times 380 = 400.$$

Again, the figure 400 may be too large. Another sample might give 300, perhaps too small. But again, although individual sample estimates are in error, these errors are not systematic and exactly average to zero over all possible samples.

4.2.3 Degrees of Freedom

The number $N - 1$ in the formula for $\hat\sigma_p^2$ is the number of *degrees of freedom* associated with the N deviations x_i. This important concept,

---

means $\bar X_1, \bar X_2, \ldots, \bar X_k$. If all k samples are combined, they will have mean equal to $\bar X_p$ and variance σ_p^2, given by

$$\sigma_p^2 = \frac{N\sigma_1^2 + N\sigma_2^2 + \ldots N\sigma_k^2 + N(\bar X_1 - \bar X_p)^2 + N(\bar X_2 - \bar X_p)^2 + \ldots + N(\bar X_k - \bar X_p)^2}{kN}$$

$$\sigma_p^2 = \frac{\sigma_1^2 + \sigma_2^2 + \sigma_k^2}{k} + \frac{(\bar X_1 - \bar X_p)^2 + (\bar X_2 - \bar X_p)^2 + \ldots + (\bar X_k - \bar X_p)^2}{k}.$$

The first term on the right is the average sample variance, $\bar\sigma_\bullet^2$. The second term is clearly $\sigma_{\bar X}^2$. But, as will be shown below (note 3),

$$\sigma_{\bar X}^2 = \frac{\sigma_p^2}{N}.$$

Whence

$$\sigma_p^2 = \bar\sigma_\bullet^2 + \frac{\sigma_p^2}{N}$$

and

$$\sigma_p^2 = \bar\sigma_\bullet^2 \frac{N}{N-1}.$$

which will have many applications later, is the number of items that can be freely chosen in forming a designated group. The fact that the first two items in a three-item simple random sample are $X_1 = -5$ and $X_2 = 12$, tells nothing about the value of X_3; by the nature of a simple random sample, X_3 is chosen specifically without reference to the values of the other members of the sample. The three items involve three free choices and three degrees of freedom.

Contrast this with the deviations from the *mean* of a three-item sample. If $x_1 = -5$ and $x_2 = 12$, it follows mathematically that $x_3 = -7$, for the sum of the deviations must be zero. In any set of N deviations from a sample mean, all but one could be chosen arbitrarily, but the Nth must bring the total to zero. Thus the N deviations involve only $N - 1$ degrees of freedom.

The fact that $\sigma_s^2 = \dfrac{\Sigma x_i^2}{N}$ systematically underestimates σ_p^2 can be explained in terms of degrees of freedom. N is too large a divisor because it exaggerates the number of independent residuals. When the number of degrees of freedom, $N - 1$, is used as a divisor, the larger result is an unbiased estimate, that is,

$$\hat{\sigma}_p^2 = \sigma_s^2 \frac{N}{N-1} = \frac{\Sigma x_i^2}{N} \left(\frac{N}{N-1} \right) = \frac{\Sigma x_i^2}{N-1}.$$

Among other things, this means that $\hat{\sigma}_p^2$ can be directly estimated without first calculating σ_s^2. The alternative calculations are shown in Table 4.3.

4.3 CONFIDENCE INTERVALS

4.3.1 Definition and Interpretation of Confidence Intervals

Everyday expressions reveal the varying confidence placed in the accuracy of estimates. One figure is "very probably within $10 of the truth, one way or the other." A less reliable one could "easily be off by as much as a thousand dollars." Both statements involve two things: a stated error limit and an evaluation of "how likely" it is that the actual error in the estimate is within the limit. In a scientific confidence interval,

Table 4.3   Estimating Population Variance from a Sample

Class	m	m^2	f
0–1.9	1	1	6
2.0–3.9	3	9	10
4.0–6.0	5	25	5

$$\Sigma f = 21 \quad \Sigma mf = 61 \quad \Sigma m^2 f = 221$$

$$\Sigma x_i^2 = \frac{21 \times 221 - (61)^2}{21} = 43.81$$

Direct calculation: $\quad \hat{\sigma}_p^2 = \dfrac{\Sigma x_i^2}{N-1} = \dfrac{43.81}{20} = 2.19$

Indirect calculation: $\sigma_s^2 = \dfrac{\Sigma x_i^2}{N} = \dfrac{43.81}{21} = 2.086$, then

$$\hat{\sigma}_p^2 = \sigma_s^2 \frac{N}{N-1} = (2.086)\left(\frac{21}{20}\right) = 2.19$$

stated error limits are accompanied by a precise measurement of the level of confidence to be placed in them.

A measured confidence level is the probability that the stated limits are correct. The assertion that "the estimate is within $10 of the true value" is either true or false; we don't know which. But suppose that when a large number of samples are drawn and the data processed in the same way, such an assertion will be true of, say, 90 per cent of them. We still don't know whether our sample is one of those of which the statement is true, or one of the 10 per cent of which it is false, but the probability of drawing one of the samples that make the statement true is clearly .90. This probability is the *confidence level* associated with the stated limits.

The statement that "at a .90 level of confidence the estimate is in error by less than $10" implies three things: (1) I assert that the estimate does not deviate from the true value by more than $10. (2) I do not really know whether this assertion is true or false, but (3) in 90 per cent of the cases in which this estimating procedure is used, such a statement turns out to be true. To assign confidence limits to the mean we need to know what proportion of sample means come within a specified distance of the population mean $\bar{X}_p$.

4.3.2   The Distribution of Sample Means

Consider all the possible samples of N items that can be drawn from the population of 45 million United States families. If N is at all large, say

100, the total number of samples is astronomical, but we can imagine a representative distribution of a billion or so sample means transcribed onto cards and stored in our warehouse. Now imagine the information consolidated into a frequency table, plotted as a chart, and its mean and variance calculated. This frequency distribution will have the following three important properties:

1. *The mean of all sample means is the population mean.* We have already noted this property of sample means in the discussion of the point estimate of $\bar{X}_p$.

2. *The variance $\sigma_{\bar{X}}^2$ of the distribution of sample means is directly proportional to σ_p^2, and inversely proportional to N, the size of the sample, that is,*

$$\sigma_{\bar{X}}^2 = \frac{\sigma_p^2}{N}.$$

This formula combines two rather obvious facts. The greater the dispersion of individuals in the population being sampled, the greater the variance among sample means. On the other hand, the larger the samples, the more individual peculiarities are averaged out and the lower the variance among sample means. The formula itself can be mathematically demonstrated.[3] It is tested against the two-item samples of Table 4.2. The variance of the population (1, 2, 3) is $\sigma_p^2 = .67$; the theoretical value $\sigma_{\bar{X}}^2 = \frac{.67}{2} = .33$ agrees with the figure calculated from the nine sample means. Since it is used as a standard in setting confidence limits to estimating errors, the standard deviation $\sigma_{\bar{X}}$ is called a *standard error*.

3. By definition $\bar{X}_s = \frac{1}{N}(X_1 + X_2 + \ldots + X_N)$. Thus $\bar{X}_s$ consists of a constant, $\frac{1}{N}$, times a variable $(X_1 + X_2 + \ldots + X_N)$. By the property of the variance:

$$\sigma_{\bar{X}}^2 = \frac{1}{N^2} \text{[variance of } (X_1 + X_2 + \ldots + X_N)].$$

But by the nature of a random sample, the values of $X_1, X_2 \ldots X_N$ are independent: the variance of their sum is the sum of their variances. Moreover, all are drawn from the same population and therefore all have variance σ_p^2. Hence

$$\sigma_{\bar{X}}^2 = \frac{1}{N^2} (N\sigma_p^2) = \frac{\sigma_p^2}{N}.$$

3. *If* N *is large (30 or more), the charted frequency distribution closely approximates the bell-shaped normal distribution.* We have seen that the proportion of items lying within any given number of standard deviations of the mean varies with the shape of the distribution. Since sample means follow a normal distribution, it is possible to calculate the proportion of sample means lying between given limits by the proportion of the area under the normal curve between these limits. A table of areas under the normal curve, or a *normal table*, shows the proportion of area lying between the mean and an ordinate erected $t\sigma$ above the mean.

4.3.3 The Normal Curve and the Normal Table

Regardless of the underlying population, if samples are reasonably large, the frequency distribution of their means approaches a bell-shaped curve with known mathematical properties. This normal curve, shown in Figure 4.1, was extensively analyzed by the mathematician Gauss, and is often known as a Gaussian distribution. Its great importance lies in the fact that once its mathematical properties are known, the proportion of samples whose means lie within any specified distance of the population mean can be calculated by mathematical measurement of areas under the curve.

4.3.4 Use of the Normal Table

The detailed normal table is found in Appendix F, but to illustrate we use the short normal table of Table 4.4. Corresponding to each value of t, the table gives the proportion of area included under the curve between an ordinate erected at the mean, $\bar{X}_p$, and one erected t standard deviations $(t\sigma)$ from the mean. This area is shown by the shaded part of the chart at the head of Table 4.4. To find the area included between the mean and, say, $.6\sigma$ above the mean, locate $t = .6$ and find opposite it .226. That is, .226 or 22.6 per cent of all items in a normal distribution fall between the mean and $.6\sigma$ above the mean.

To find the proportion of items that fall within $.6\sigma$ of the mean either way, the figure .226 is doubled to give .452. Thus, .452 or 45.2 per cent of all items in a normal distribution fall within $.6\sigma$ of the mean: 22.6 per cent lie between the mean and $.6\sigma$ above the mean, and 22.6 per cent lie between the mean and $.6\sigma$ below the mean.

Figure 4.1 The Meaning of Confidence Intervals

(1) $\overline{X}_p = \overline{X}_s \pm \sigma_{\overline{X}}$ is true of the samples in A_1A_2, but false for all others.

(2) $\overline{X}_p = \overline{X}_s \pm 2\sigma_{\overline{X}}$ is true of samples in $B_1A_1A_2B_2$, but false for all others.

(3) $\overline{X}_p = \overline{X}_s \pm 3\sigma_{\overline{X}}$ is true of samples in $C_1B_1A_1A_2B_2C_2$, and false only for the few samples in D_1, or D_2.

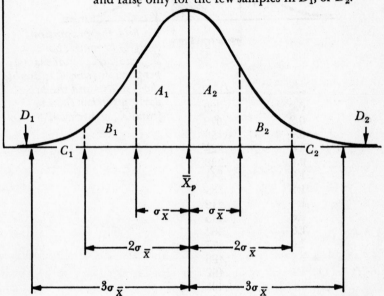

The table can also be used to find the proportion of items lying farther than $t\sigma$ from the mean. Since the distribution is symmetrical, 50 per cent of all items lie above, and 50 per cent lie below the mean. Between the mean and $.6\sigma$ above the mean lie 22.6 per cent of all items. Therefore, the proportion which is found more than $.6\sigma$ above the mean is $.500 - .226 = .274$ or 27.4 per cent. Doubling this, we find 54.8 per cent beyond $.6\sigma$ in both tails of the distribution together.

It is useful to memorize three approximate values in the normal table:

Table 4.4 Areas Under the Normal Curve

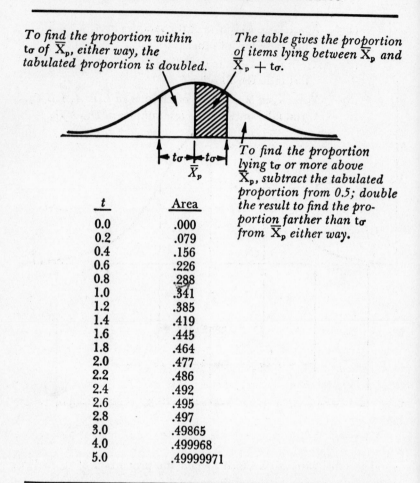

To find the proportion within $t\sigma$ of $\overline{X}_p$, either way, the tabulated proportion is doubled.

The table gives the proportion of items lying between $\overline{X}_p$ and $\overline{X}_p + t\sigma$.

To find the proportion lying $t\sigma$ or more above $\overline{X}_p$, subtract the tabulated proportion from 0.5; double the result to find the proportion farther than $t\sigma$ from $\overline{X}_p$ either way.

t	Area
0.0	.000
0.2	.079
0.4	.156
0.6	.226
0.8	.288
1.0	.341
1.2	.385
1.4	.419
1.6	.445
1.8	.464
2.0	.477
2.2	.486
2.4	.492
2.6	.495
2.8	.497
3.0	.49865
4.0	.499968
5.0	.49999971

1. Approximately ⅔ of all items lie within 1σ of the mean.
2. Approximately 95 per cent of all items lie within 2σ of the mean.
3. All except about 3 in 1,000 items lie within 3σ of the mean.

These key points correspond to the areas indicated in Figure 4.1. A_1A_2 contains about ⅔ of the area under the curve; $B_1A_1A_2B_2$ contains about 95 per cent of the total area. Almost the entire area is contained in $C_1B_1A_1A_2B_2C_2$; only .003—three items in 1,000—lie in the combined areas of D_1 and D_2.

4.3.5 The Confidence Interval for the Mean

The logic of assigning confidence intervals is now easily developed. From a sample of N items we obtain a point estimate of the population mean $\hat{X}_p = \bar{X}_s$, and of the population variance $\hat{\sigma}_p^2 = \sigma_s^2 \dfrac{N}{N-1}$. Moreover, we know that the frequency distribution of all means of such samples forms a normal curve whose mean is the (unknown) population mean $\bar{X}_p$, and whose standard deviation is $\sigma_{\bar{X}} = \sqrt{\dfrac{\sigma_p^2}{N}}$.

Although the population variance σ_p^2 is unknown, we can substitute for it the estimate $\hat{\sigma}_p^2$. This enables us to calculate an approximate standard error:

$$\sigma_{\bar{X}} = \sqrt{\frac{\hat{\sigma}_p^2}{N}}.$$

We are now in the following position. We have in hand one mean, $\bar{X}_s$, representing one item drawn at random from a normal distribution whose true mean $\bar{X}_p$ is unknown and whose standard deviation is $\sigma_{\bar{X}}$. Our $\bar{X}_s$ may be one of those in A_1A_2 of Figure 4.1 that are quite close to $\bar{X}_p$ and hence a very accurate estimate. Or, our $\bar{X}_s$ may be one of those in D_1D_2 that are far out in the tail of the distribution and a very poor estimate of $\bar{X}_p$. We don't know which and must fall back on probabilities.

The area $C_1B_1A_1A_2B_2C_2$ contains about 99.7 per cent of all samples. This means that the chance that a sample mean comes within $3\sigma_{\bar{X}}$ of the true $\bar{X}_p$ is 997 out of 1,000. These are good odds for almost all purposes; we might say that we are "virtually certain" that the sample estimate is in error by no more than $3\sigma_{\bar{X}}$.

In fact, since 95 per cent of all random samples fall in the area $B_1A_1A_2B_2$ in Figure 4.1, the chances that any given random sample will come within $2\sigma_{\bar{X}}$ of the true $\bar{X}_p$ are 95 out of 100. This is 19 to 1, and while somewhat short of "virtual certainty," it is still pretty good, and for most practical purposes we have "considerable confidence" that the estimate is in error by less than $2\sigma_{\bar{x}}$.

The estimate may, of course, be even more accurate. $\frac{2}{3}$ of the sample means fall in the area A_1A_2. This means that the odds are 2 to 1 that the sample mean is accurate to within $1\sigma_{\bar{x}}$ of the true $\bar{X}_p$. These are relatively short odds, and we would say that while there is a "good chance" that the estimate is within $1\sigma_{\bar{x}}$ of $\bar{X}_p$, we do not have great confidence in this degree of accuracy.

In scientific work we dispense with such vague terms as "virtual certainty" and "considerable confidence" and replace them with calculated confidence levels, expressed by the proportion of samples for which the stated error limit holds. Thus, the statement "$\bar{X}_s$ estimates $\bar{X}_p$ with an error less than $3\sigma_{\bar{x}}$" is true of .997 of all samples and is assigned a confidence level of .997. Or, the .997 confidence interval for $\bar{X}_p$ is (approximately)

$$\bar{X}_p = \bar{X}_s \pm 3\sigma_{\bar{x}}.$$

Similarly, the .95 interval is approximately

$$\bar{X}_p = \bar{X}_s \pm 2\sigma_{\bar{x}}$$

and the .67 interval is

$$\bar{X}_p = \bar{X}_s \pm \sigma_{\bar{x}}.$$

Any other desired confidence level can be obtained by consulting the normal table. It can be seen in the enlarged table of Appendix F that .25 of all items lie between the mean and $\frac{2}{3}\sigma$ above the mean. Thus, the 50 per cent confidence interval is given by

$$\bar{X}_p = \bar{X}_s \pm \frac{2}{3}\sigma_{\bar{x}}.$$

In the physical sciences, $\frac{2}{3}\sigma_{\bar{x}}$ is called the *probable error* and is used to specify the accuracy of a physical measurement. The chance that a measurement is off by less than one probable error is 50 per cent.

4.3.6 Calculating Procedure and Example

A systematic calculating procedure for preparing an estimate from a classified sample is shown in Table 4.5. A random sample of new car

4.3 · Confidence Intervals

Table 4.5 Prices Paid by a Sample of 101 New Car Buyers, 1959

Price	m (thousands)	m^2	Number of Buyers
Under $1,400	1.0	1.00	2
$1,400–1,999	1.6	2.56	7
$2,000–2,599	2.3	5.29	14
$2,600–2,999	2.8	7.84	21
$3,000–3,399	3.2	10.24	28
$3,400–3,999	3.7	13.69	17
$4,000 and over	5.0	25.00	12
Total			$\Sigma f = 101$
			$\Sigma mf = 316.7$
			$\Sigma m^2 f = 1,078.07$

$$\bar{X}_s = \$3.136 \text{ (thousand)}$$

$$\Sigma x^2 = \frac{101(1,078.07) - (316.7)^2}{101} = 85.0117$$

$$\hat{\sigma}_p^2 = \frac{\Sigma x^2}{N-1} = \frac{85.0117}{100} = .85012$$

$$\sigma_{\bar{X}}^2 = \frac{\hat{\sigma}_p^2}{N} = \frac{.85012}{101} = .00842$$

$$\sigma_{\bar{X}} = \sqrt{.00842} = \$.092 \text{ (thousand)}$$

.95 confidence interval = $\$3,136 \pm 2(92) = \$3,136 \pm 184$

buyers is classified by the price paid for the car. We are to use the sample to estimate the average price paid by all new car buyers. Note that once the usual calculations required for sample mean and variance have been completed, it is a simple matter to calculate $\hat{\sigma}_p^2$, $\sigma_{\bar{X}}^2$, and $\sigma_{\bar{X}}$.

The .95 confidence interval for the population mean is

$$\bar{X}_p = \$3,136 \pm 184 .$$

This is a statement that the mean price paid for all cars was no lower than $\$3,136 - 184 = \$2,952$, and no higher than $\$3,136 + 184 = \$3,320$. The statement is true or false. We don't know which, but of statements made in similar circumstances, 95 per cent are true. Hence we make the assertion with 95 per cent confidence.

71

Since the procedure of Table 4.5 is used in most calculations in the chapters following, there is no need to multiply examples at this point.

4.3.7 Calculated Risk

It is clear from the foregoing that in any action taken on the basis of a statistical measurement we run a risk that the confidence interval may be obtained from one of the samples for which it is false. Before taking any action, therefore, it is important to calculate this risk.[4]

Consider the following example. Suppose that a test of the breaking point of a sample of nylon filaments used for parachute cord gives a mean breaking strength of 5, with $\sigma_{\bar{X}} = .5$. To arrest the fall of a man these filaments must have a minimum strength of 3.5. What is the risk in using a parachute made of the filaments?

First we note that the minimum required strength falls just outside a $3\sigma_{\bar{X}}$ confidence interval. If our sample is one of the 99.7 per cent within $3\sigma_{\bar{X}}$ of $\bar{X}_p$, the parachute is safe. But among the samples that are more than $3\sigma_{\bar{X}}$ from $\bar{X}_p$, half are too low. If a sample mean, observed to be 5.0, is actually $3\sigma_{\bar{X}}$ too *low*, the true value must be *above* $5 + 3 (.5) = 6.5$. In this case, $\bar{X}_p$ is actually stronger than the confidence interval states, and this is all to the good. The only *risk* is associated with the possibility that our sample is one of the .0015 samples in the *upper* tail of the distribution that are 3σ or more too high. For if our sample is one of those in D_2 of Figure 4.1, its mean dangerously exaggerates the strength of filaments and the parachute is actually unsafe.

Thus, to use the parachute entails a calculated risk of about .0015. Should we chance it? The evaluation of a risk depends on what is at stake. A pilot who has just lost a wing at 10,000 feet would be happy to trade the .0015 calculated risk (or for that matter, one of .5 or even .99) for the certainty of his prospects without a parachute. But if the choice is between making parachutes of this material or using a slightly more

---

4. The term *calculated risk* is often abused. Oddly, in its everyday use, it usually means a risk recognized to exist but *not* calculated. A driver starting on a trip without changing a weak tire may say he is "taking a calculated risk." The risk is obvious. Equally obviously, no calculation has been made. In statistical usage the term means literally a risk that has been calculated.

expensive material that reduces the risk several thousand times, we would probably choose the latter.

4.3.8 Sample Size Required for Specified $\sigma_{\bar{X}}$

Before embarking on any research in which a sample must be drawn, it is important to estimate in advance, at least approximately, how many items will be required for any specified confidence interval. Drawing samples and careful collection of data is an expensive matter, and we want to be sure we can afford the required accuracy before we start. At the same time it would be wasteful to draw and explore a larger sample than necessary.

Suppose, for example, we want to estimate the mean income of New York families within $100 either way, at .95 confidence. How many families would be needed in the sample? To get the answer we turn the formulas around.

At .95 confidence, $100 = 2\sigma_{\bar{X}}$, so $\sigma_{\bar{X}} = \$50$. Substituting this in

$$\sigma_{\bar{X}}^2 = \frac{\sigma_p^2}{N}$$

gives

$$2{,}500 = \frac{\sigma_p^2}{N}$$

or

$$N = \frac{\sigma_p^2}{2{,}500}.$$

To solve for N requires some reasonable estimate of σ_p^2. Often this can be estimated using data from another city, or from New York in past years. For example, the value of $\sigma_s^2 = 20{,}830{,}100$, calculated from the data of Table 2.1 can be inserted in the formula to give

$$N = \frac{20{,}830{,}100}{2{,}500} = 8{,}332$$

that is, a sample of 8 to 9 thousand families should yield the desired accuracy. If no other information is available, the approximate σ_p^2 might be estimated on the basis of information casually available, for example, the dispersion in income status we see around us or read about in newspapers. A pilot study to give a preliminary estimate of σ_p^2 is more expensive but somewhat more accurate.

4.3.9 Confidence Interval for a Proportion

Since proportions are only a special case of arithmetic mean, the same sampling theory applies. The population proportion P_p is estimated by the sample proportion P_s. The variance of the population is estimated by

$$\hat{\sigma}_p^2 = \hat{\sigma}_s^2 \frac{N}{N-1} = P_s (1 - P_s) \frac{N}{N-1}.$$

$\sigma_{\bar{X}}$, the standard error of the proportion, is then given by

$$\sigma_{\bar{X}}^2 = \frac{\hat{\sigma}_p^2}{N} = \frac{P_s (1 - P_s)}{N-1}$$

$$\sigma_{\bar{X}} = \sqrt{\sigma_{\bar{X}}^2} = \sqrt{\frac{P_s (1 - P_s)}{N-1}}.$$

In a recent survey of consumer finances, 47 per cent of the 3,000 families interviewed reported some amount of outstanding installment debt.

Here $P_s = .47$, so the standard error of this proportion is given by

$$\sigma_{\bar{X}}^2 = \frac{P_s (1 - P_s)}{N-1} = \frac{.47 \times .53}{2,999} = 83 \times 10^{-6}$$

$$\sigma_{\bar{X}} = \sqrt{83 \times 10^{-6}} = .009 .$$

Thus, at .95 confidence the proportion in the whole population having some amount of outstanding installment debt is in the range $.47 \pm 2(.009) = .47 \pm .018$.

The interpretation of this interval is exactly like that for the mean. We do not know whether the sample estimate, .47, is within .018 of the true value or not, but the method used results in this accuracy about 95 per cent of the time.

4.3.10 Means of Small Samples: Student's t

Confidence intervals for means are calculated from sample estimates of $\sigma_{\bar{X}}$. In small samples, the great variability in $\hat{\sigma}_p^2$, and hence in $\sigma_{\bar{X}}$, makes the normal curve an unsatisfactory approximation to use in setting confidence intervals. For samples of fewer than 30 items, a distribution is needed that takes account of variation in both $\bar{X}_s$ and in $\sigma_{\bar{X}}$. Student's

t distribution, found in Appendix E, is used for this purpose. The value of t is defined as

$$t = \frac{\bar{X}_s - \bar{X}_p}{\sigma_{\bar{X}}},$$

and it is clear that its value varies from sample to sample not only because of variation in $\bar{X}_s$ but also in $\sigma_{\bar{X}}$. The figures in the body of Appendix E show the value of t, associated with the degrees of freedom at the left, that is exceeded by the proportion of samples shown at the top. For example, if a large number of samples of $N = 8$ are drawn and t calculated for each, the table shows us (opposite $n = 7$ degrees of freedom) that .05 of these t's will exceed 2.36, .02 will exceed 3.00, while only .01 will exceed 3.5.

The t distribution is used much like a normal table. To set a .90 confidence interval for the mean as estimated from a ten-item sample with $\bar{X}_s = 8.0$, $\sigma_{\bar{X}} = 3.0$. Entering the table at 9 degrees of freedom, find that for .05 of all samples, t exceeds 2.24. By symmetry, for another .05 of all samples, t is less than 2.24. The .90 interval is then set as

$$\bar{X}_p = \bar{X}_s \pm 2.24\,\sigma_{\bar{X}}$$
$$\bar{X}_p = 8.0 \pm 6.72\,.$$

As always, we do not know in this particular case whether $\bar{X}_p$ falls within the stated limits or not, but the procedure employed yields correct results for .90 of all samples.

4.4 NONSAMPLING ERRORS

The subject of this chapter is samples and random sampling errors, but it is important to remind ourselves that there are other, often more important, sources of error.

We have referred several times to the collection of family income data. Let us now review a few of the chances for error to arise in the process. In the first place the response to the question "What is your income?" depends on the context in which it is asked. Unless considerable rapport is first established, the interviewer is likely to be told it is none of his business or receive an exaggerated figure intended to impress him or an understatement from caution.

Suppose the respondent tries to give an accurate figure. He may forget part of his income, he may mistake the nature of the question and include gifts or exclude his wife's earnings. The interviewer must ask him to check his memory against his records, and must, through a series of questions, make sure the proper figure is reported. Suppose the respondent gives the figure accurately. It may be misunderstood by the interviewer or incorrectly recorded.

When the interview sheet reaches the central office, the information must be coded. The coder may misread, miscopy, or misclassify the response. Next, the coded data must be copied again onto work sheets or punched onto IBM cards, with further opportunities for mistakes. Finally, the data are processed, with a chance of human or machine error in whatever calculations are done with them.

These are only a few of the sources of error, but they are enough to indicate that, contrary to what one might think, a larger sample is not necessarily a more accurate sample. A larger sample is better than a small sample of data of equal quality, but a small sample of carefully compiled information is better than a large sample of inaccurate material. Proper research design embodies a careful weighing of the several sources of error against each other so as to distribute the total resources devoted to the problem to maximum effect.

4.5 SUMMARY

For several reasons research results applicable to a population must generally be derived from samples. But point estimates will vary from sample to sample, and it is necessary to evaluate the confidence to be placed in them as measurements of population characteristics. The dispersion of sample results varies in proportion to the dispersion of the population and inversely in proportion to the size of the sample. This is summarized in the formula for the standard error of the mean:

$$\sigma_{\bar{X}} = \sqrt{\frac{\hat{\sigma}_p^2}{N}}.$$

Furthermore, the fact that means of large samples are normally distributed permits the assignment of confidence intervals and the calculation of risk.

Proportions are like means, and standard errors can be assigned to them in similar fashion. Means of small samples are not normally distributed and assignment of confidence intervals requires use of Student's distribution.

Other things equal, larger samples are more accurate than smaller, but proper evaluation of a result requires the comparison of sampling errors with many other sources of error.

Questions and Problems

1. Explain how you would draw a random sample of students in your college to get information about their economic status. Would you stratify the sample? If so, on what basis?

2. Tabulate the 27 three-item samples that can be drawn from a population consisting of the numbers 1, 2, 3 in equal proportions. Calculate $\bar{X}_s$ and σ_s^2 for each and show that the mean of the $\bar{X}_s$ equals $\bar{X}_p$, while the mean σ_s^2 underestimates σ_p^2 until multiplied by $\dfrac{N}{N-1} = 1.5$. Calculate $\sigma_{\bar{X}}^2$, the variance of the 27 means, and verify that $\sigma_{\bar{X}}^2 = \dfrac{\sigma_p^2}{N}$.

3. The first four deviations in a five-item sample are $x_1 = -6$, $x_2 = 3$, $x_3 = -5$, $x_4 = 7$. What is the value of x_5?

4. Select any two numbers. How many free choices did you have? Select any two numbers whose sum is zero. How many degrees of freedom were involved in the choice?

5. A random sample of 10 accounting clerks from Des Moines, Iowa, had weekly earnings as follows: $80, $87, $85, $92, $82, $97, $100, $120, $123, $137. Calculate a .95 confidence interval for the mean weekly earnings of all accounting clerks in Des Moines.

6. Using the results of problem 5 as a pilot study, estimate the sample size required to yield a .95 confidence interval of $1.00.

7. A survey of 50,000 people with work experience showed that 16.1 per cent of them had experienced some unemployment or lay-off during the recession year 1958. Calculate a 3σ confidence interval for this estimate and explain what it means.

8. Treat the data of Chapter II, problem 3, as a set of three random samples and estimate a .95 confidence interval for the mean earnings of Des Moines workers in each of the three occupations.

9. In Chapter III, problem 6, you calculated the variance in number of heads found in tossing samples of 25 coins. Use the property of the variance to derive a corresponding value for variance in the *proportion* of heads. (Hint: the proportion of heads is a constant (1/25) times the number of heads.)

10. Calculate the theoretical variance in proportions of heads in random samples of 25 coins and compare with the experimental value of problem 9. How close are the two values? If you had tossed the 25-coin sample 1,000 times instead of only 50, how close do you suppose the agreement would be?

References

1. W. Edwards Deming. *Sample Design in Business Research*. New York: John Wiley & Sons, 1960. A highly useful survey of sampling methods and practical procedures.

2. Leslie Kish. "Selection of the Sample." Chapter 5 in L. Festinger and D. Katz, *Research Methods in the Behavioral Sciences*. New York: Dryden, 1953. A chapter on principles and practices.

3. Morris J. Slonim. *Sampling in a Nutshell*. New York: Simon and Schuster, 1960. A short, amusingly written, nonmathematical treatment of sampling, covering a wide range of types, methods, and applications.

4. Frank L. Wolf. *Elements of Probability and Statistics*. New York: McGraw-Hill Book Co., 1962. Chapter 10 deals with the mathematical nature of the normal distribution and its properties.

5. John B. Lansing and others. *An Investigation of Response Error*. "Studies in Consumer Saving," No. 2, Bureau of Economic and Business Research, University of Illinois, 1961. This careful treatment of the nature and sources of response error in survey data reports the results of several field experiments. It also serves as an excellent introduction to survey methods in general and contains specimen questionnaires, interviewer instructions, and so on.

CHAPTER V

Exploring
Statistical Functions

In this chapter, we shall put to work the tools developed in those preceding. Variables and functions will be carefully defined, and the mechanical aspects of their analysis will be taken up first. After the mechanics are understood, we shall be in a position to take up the more fundamental problems of research design.

5.1 FUNCTIONS AND VARIABLES

5.1.1 Economic Variables

A *variable* is a characteristic or attribute that varies from item to item in a population. "Occupation" is a variable: some men are laborers, some are lawyers, some are doctors. "City type" is a variable: some families live in large cities, some in small cities and towns, some in villages, some in open country. "Sex," "age," "education," "income," "consumption expenditure," "religious preference," "race," "region," "type of farming," "liquid assets," "output," are further examples of variables.

Any variable divides the population into classes, and the *value* of the variable for any member of the population is the class to which he belongs. The values of the variable "sex" are "male," "female"; the variable "region" assumes such values as "New England," "Middle Atlantic," "East North Central," "South East." "Price" has such values as "$1.98," "$4.00," while "automobile production" is "6.2" or "7.0" million cars.

There are two general types of variables: *Numerical* variables are attributes whose values are expressed by numerical magnitudes: income, consumption expenditure, price, liquid asset holdings, employment, output. Variables like occupation, race, region, and so on, whose values are categories, are called *categorical* variables. The distinction between numerical and categorical variables is partly a matter of convenience rather than inherent in the variable itself. Obviously, any numerical variable can be made categorical simply by ignoring its numerical properties. Income brackets, for example, divide the population into classes that can be designated as "poor," "middle class," "rich," and so on. Although the topic extends beyond the scope of this book, it is equally true that categorical variables can be represented by one or more numerical magnitudes. This was done in Chapter II when the category "employment status" was represented by a variable X whose value was 1 for all who were unemployed, and 0 for all who were not. Once defined, X was treated like any other magnitude. By using a set of such variables, X_1, X_2, . . . X_k, this method can be extended to multivalued categorical variables like "occupation," "region," and so on.

5.1.2 Functional Relationships

A variable Y is said to depend on, or be a *function* of, a variable X, whenever knowledge of the value of X enables us to predict the value of Y. X, the predictor, is called an *independent* variable; Y, whose value is to be predicted, is a *dependent* variable. The familiar demand schedule is a function in which quantity bought depends on price; in a production function the volume of output depends on the amount of labor employed; in the consumption function, consumption expenditure depends on income. These examples involve only numerical variables, but either X or Y or both may be categorical. A numerical variable can depend on one or more categorical variables. The postage charged for a letter depends upon whether it is surface or air mail and on its destination; the price of butter depends on the grade sold and whether the transaction is retail or wholesale; the yield of corn varies with soil type, fertilizer used, and type of hybrid grown.

The dependent variable Y can also be categorical. The kind of car a family buys depends on the family income; a man's occupation depends on his educational background; the grade a student receives in a course depends on his study habits.

Economic relationships generally involve many variables. In addition to its own price, the demand for a commodity depends on prices of substitutes, on disposable income, on the relative volume of advertising for this and competing commodities, on the season, and on other factors too numerous to mention. In addition to region, family food preferences vary with age, health, education, ethnic and religious background, income, food prices, season, and—on any particular day—with what the family ate yesterday and whether there are guests for dinner.

In a multivariate function the value of the dependent variable Y is influenced by the values of a set of independent variables X_1, X_2, X_3, . . . X_k. The set may consist entirely of numerical or of categorical variables, or any mixture of the two.

5.1.3 The Function as a Table

Although some can be represented in other ways, all functions can be treated as tables showing various values of the independent variables and the accompanying values of Y. For example, a demand schedule might be:

Price (X)	Quantity (Y)
$10	10,000
$15	9,500
$20	9,000
$25	8,500

The relationship of income to occupation might be:

Occupation (X)	Income (Y)
Wage Earner	$ 3,500
Clerk	$ 4,000
Business & Professional	$10,000

The relationship between the categorical values of the variables "region" and "food preference" might be:

Region (X)	Preferred Starch (Y)
New England	Potatoes
North Central	Potatoes
South East	Hominy
South Central	Rice
West	Potatoes

5.1.4 Correlation

When the tabulated value of the dependent variable varies with the value of the independent variable, the two are said to be *correlated*. In the examples above, quantity bought is correlated with price, income is correlated with occupation, and food preference is correlated with region.

When both variables are numerical, their correlation can be further characterized as to direction. If larger values of Y accompany larger values of X, the variables are said to be *positively* correlated. When smaller values of Y accompany larger values of X, the two are *negatively* correlated. In the example above, price and quantity are negatively correlated.

5.1.5 Multivariate Functions

Multivariate functions can be tabulated in arrays of cells, each cell defined by a combination of values of independent variables and containing the appropriate value of the dependent variable.

Table 5.1 Household Consumption of Purchased Bread as a Function of Income and Region
(Tabulated figures are pounds per week per household)

Household Income	North East	South
Under $1,000	4.02	1.89
$1,000–1,999	4.03	3.06
$2,000–2,999	5.12	3.92
$3,000–3,999	5.22	4.67
$4,000–4,999	5.38	4.83
$5,000–5,999	5.47	5.14
$6,000–7,999	5.50	5.36
$8,000 and over	5.75	5.75

Source: Constructed example roughly based on U.S. Department of Agriculture data.

Table 5.1 shows household consumption of bread as a function of two variables, region and income. To see the effect of region, compare the consumption of families whose incomes are the same but who live in different regions. Table 5.1 shows that bread consumption is correlated with region: southern families consume less bread than families living in the North East. Since, within each region, consumption rises with income, the table also shows positive correlation between income and bread consumption.

5.1.6 Interaction and Additivity

The relationship of the dependent variable to the several independent variables can be further characterized by whether the magnitude of the effect exerted by one independent variable depends on the value of the other. In Table 5.1 the effect of income is different in the two regions. Increasing income from the lowest to the highest bracket raises bread consumption of families in both regions, but the increase amounts to 3.86 pounds per week in the South and only 1.73 pounds per week in the North East. Likewise, the regional differences in bread consumption depend on income level. At the lowest incomes northeastern families consume 2.13 pounds per week more than southern families. This differential is reduced at higher incomes and disappears entirely in the highest bracket.

When the effect of one independent variable depends on the value of another, the two independent variables are said to *interact*. Thus, income and region interact in their effects on bread consumption.

Table 5.2 Quantity Demanded as a Function of Income and Price
(Tabulated figures are quantities bought.)

Price ($)	Disposable Income (billions of $)				
	300	310	320	330	340
10	10,000	13,000	16,000	19,000	22,000
15	9,500	12,500	15,500	18,500	21,500
20	9,000	12,000	15,000	18,000	21,000
25	8,500	11,500	14,500	17,500	20,500

When independent variables do not interact, they are said to be *additive*, since the influence of a change in one can be added to the effect of a change in the other to get the total effect of the two combined. In the demand schedule shown in Table 5.2, price and disposable income are additive variables: increasing price by $5 reduces quantity bought

Table 5.3 Honey Prices as a Function of Region, Class of Sale, Total U.S. Production, and Type of Honey

(Tabulated figures are honey prices, cents per pound.)

Region	Class of Sale	Total U.S. Production (millions of pounds)					
		210–229		230–249		250–270	
		Price of honey		Price of honey		Price of honey	
		Comb	Extracted	Comb	Extracted	Comb	Extracted
North Atlantic	wholesale	33.4	17.0	31.4	16.9	29.4	13.6
	retail	43.0	30.3	42.6	29.6	41.3	28.2
East North Central	wholesale	31.7	15.8	27.7	14.8	25.0	12.8
	retail	35.8	23.7	33.8	22.6	32.1	20.6
West North Central	wholesale	30.4	14.9	29.5	12.9	27.1	12.0
	retail	34.7	22.0	32.7	20.6	31.5	19.0
South Atlantic	wholesale	30.4	18.4	28.3	17.6	26.1	15.5
	retail	36.3	30.7	35.1	29.5	33.6	27.7
South Central	wholesale	29.4	16.8	28.5	16.0	26.1	14.0
	retail	35.3	27.7	35.1	27.5	33.8	26.5
West	wholesale	32.8	13.8	30.0	12.8	25.0	10.0
	retail	37.0	20.3	35.0	18.9	33.5	17.2

Source: Constructed example, roughly based on U.S. Department of Agriculture data.

by 500 regardless of income. Raising aggregate income by $10 billion increases purchases by 3,000, regardless of price. If a $5 price increase and a $10 billion income increase occur simultaneously, the total effect on purchases is an increase of $3,000 - 500 = 2,500$, regardless of the initial levels of price and income.

5.1.7 Functions with Several Independent Variables

More variables can be included by expanding the table. The relationship of the farm price of honey to the four variables "Region," "Class of Sale," "Type of Honey," and "Total United States Production" might appear as in Table 5.3. The effect of any one variable can be seen by comparing cells that are alike in all other respects. For example, a glance at Table 5.3 reveals that price is correlated with class of sale (retail prices are uniformly higher than wholesale), with type of honey (comb honey is more expensive than extracted honey), and negatively correlated with output (a rise in production is associated with a fall in price). Price is also correlated with region (corresponding prices in North Atlantic states are higher than those in the West).

Moreover, the variables are not additive but exhibit complex interactions. For example, retail prices, while always above, tend to differ from wholesale prices by amounts that depend on region, type of honey, and total supply. Similarly, extracted honey is cheaper than comb honey by margins that vary with the other factors. Increasing supply is accompanied by falling prices, but wholesale prices are somewhat more flexible than retail, and again the effect on prices varies by honey type and region. Prices tend to be highest in the North Atlantic region, but this differential is reduced at high levels of supply.

5.1.8 Functions as Graphs and Equations

Simple functions can be plotted as charts, the values of the dependent variable on one axis, those of the independent variable on the other. The relationship between Y and one of the X's is plotted as a curve, with shifts in the level corresponding to the effect of additional variables. Figure 5.1 shows the demand schedule from the table above plotted as a curve that shifts with income.

Negative correlation between quantity and price is indicated by

Figure 5.1 A Demand Function of Two Variables Represented by a Shifting Curve

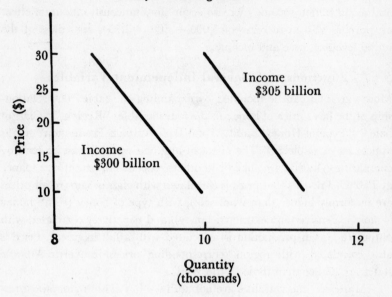

the negative slope of the line; positive correlation between quantity and income is indicated by the fact that the line shifts upward to the right when income rises. The fact that the lines are parallel indicates that income and price are additive in their effect on demand.

Functions of categorical independent variables can be plotted as bar charts, as shown in Figure 5.2 below.

Many functions can be represented by mathematical expressions. The shifting demand schedules above are given by

$$Q = -79,000 + 300\,I - 100\,P.$$

Of course, not all functions are so simply expressed. The function that relates Y, the area under the normal curve, to t is

$$Y = \frac{1}{\sqrt{2\pi}} \int_0^t e^{-\frac{1}{2}t^2}\, dt\,.$$

The proper representation of a function depends on the purpose. The formula for areas under the normal curve is essential for exploring the mathematical properties of the function, but for everyday application the convenience of the normal table is clear. On the other hand, the function expressed as an equation is better adapted for use in an econometric model, for calculating the elasticity of demand at specified prices and incomes, or for estimating demand corresponding to values beyond or in between those shown in the table. Charts are usually employed as auxiliary to tables and formulas.

In general, the function treated as a table is the easiest to understand, and, where adequate data are available, is the most complete and sophisticated representation possible. Once the treatment of tables is understood, other techniques are easily grasped as special cases.

5.2 STATISTICAL OR STOCHASTIC FUNCTIONS

5.2.1 Introduction

Up to this point we have treated functional relationships as though we could actually list and measure all of the factors influencing the dependent variable. In a realistic case, however, the number of independent variables is so large that no matter how many are included in a function, we are bound to omit many. As a result, the value of Y corresponding to a given cell in the table is not unique. For example, we have omitted from Table 5.3 the fact that the price of honey depends on its color, on the kind of container in which it is sold, on the quantity in which the transaction occurs, on the season of the year, on the kind of blossom from which the honey was made, on the amount of advertising by honey growers, on the price of sugar, of strawberry jam, and of other substitutes for honey, and on millions of other factors. In addition, even the few variables included in the table have only crudely defined effects. Each region includes a wide area and prices vary from place to place. Each of the values assigned to "total production" covers a range of 20 million pounds per year, yet variation of supply within these limits will have some effect on price. In such cases, Y is not an exact function of the designated independent variables but is called a *statistical*, or *stochastic*, function.

The stochastic nature of economic functions arises from the vast complexity of human behavior. The demand for automobiles this year is influenced by prices—but prices as perceived by 50 million different families with at least 50 million sets of needs, desires, objectives, anticipations, and values. The kind of car a family buys depends on family income—but income in relation to thousands of other needs, all considered in light of prices, the size of the family, its social position, and the kind of car the neighbors have, as well as the makes, styles, and conditions among which to choose and the credit terms available on each.

5.2.2 Notation for Stochastic Functions

A stochastic function can be represented as

$$Y_{ij} = f(X_1, X_2, \ldots X_k) + u_{ij}.$$

The first term on the right is the systematic relationship or central tendency to be studied, expressed as a function of k variables; the second term is the stochastic impact of the myriad other factors. To fix the meaning of this notation firmly in mind, imagine a set of bins laid out on a warehouse floor, labeled to correspond to the cells of Table 5.3. (The bin in the northwest corner is marked "North Atlantic, wholesale, comb honey, total production 210–229 million pounds." In the opposite corner of the room the bin is marked "West, retail, extracted honey, total production 250–270 million pounds," and so on.) Now locate observers in the various regions of the country to record each honey sale, reporting region, class of transaction, honey type, and price. The cards come into the warehouse, and a clerk stamps on each the total United States production for the period in which the sale was consummated and files it in the proper bin. Imagine the process continued until a substantial sample of cards has accumulated.

All the sales in the same bin have four things in common: region, class of sale, type of honey, and total production. But in thousands of other respects they differ. They occurred at different seasons, they involve honey from various flowers, sold in various quantities, in various containers; people had different incomes, varying tastes, and so on indefinitely. Since the price of honey is a function of all these factors in addition to the four marked on the bin, the result is variation of price from card to card.

In short, each price Y_{ij} consists of two parts: (1) A systematic component depending on the four specified variables, X_1, X_2, X_3, X_4. This component, designated as

$$f(X_1, X_2, X_3, X_4),$$

is the same for all cards in the jth bin, and varies only from bin to bin. (2) A stochastic component, designated u_{ij}, that varies both from bin to bin and from card to card within bins.

The actual price is the sum of these two components. Thus for the ith card in the jth bin:

$$Y_{ij} = f(X_1, X_2, X_3, X_4) + u_{ij}.$$

Table 5.4 Distribution of Employed Women in Three Office Occupations by Straight-Time Weekly Earnings, Salt Lake City, 1961

Weekly Earnings ($)	Secretaries	Typists, Class A	Switchboard Operators	3 Samples Combined
40– 49	0	19	6	25
50– 59	5	52	51	108
60– 69	72	95	39	206
70– 79	66	117	8	191
80– 89	105	17	10	132
90– 99	78	4	6	88
100–110	31	3	0	34
110–120	15	11	0	26
120–130	3	0	0	3
$N =$	375	318	120	813
$\Sigma Y =$	31,595	22,070	7,630	61,295
$\Sigma Y^2 =$	2,740,175	1,592,750	520,600	4,835,525
$\Sigma y^2 =$	78,191	61,036	17,459	214,274
$\bar{Y} =$	84.25	69.40	63.58	75.39
$\hat{\sigma}_p^2 =$	209.07	192.54	146.71	
$\sigma_{\bar{Y}}^2 =$	.5575	.6055	1.2226	
$\sigma_{\bar{Y}} =$	.75	.78	1.11	

$$R^2 = \frac{375(84.25 - 75.39)^2 + 318(69.40 - 75.39)^2 + 120(63.58 - 75.39)^2}{214,274} = .269$$

Source: *Occupational Wage Survey, Salt Lake City, Utah, December 1961*, BLS Bulletin No. 1303-32 (Washington, D.C.: U.S. Department of Labor, Bureau of Labor Statistics, March 1962).

Put into words, this shorthand notation says that the price recorded on the ith card (for example, the sixth from the top) in the jth bin (for example, the one in the northwest corner) is the sum of two parts: a systematic part associated with the particular values of the variables marked on the bin (for example, North Atlantic, wholesale, comb honey, total production 210–229 million pounds) and a stochastic part associated with the way all the other (unspecified) variables happened to alter the price in this particular transaction.

5.2.3 Estimation of a Statistical Function

With statistical functions the problem of analyzing relationships becomes more complicated: In the first place, the systematic behavior of the function must be estimated from sample values and will vary from sample to sample. In the second place, correlation is no longer something that is merely present or absent, but becomes a matter of degree.

Table 5.4 shows the data for weekly straight-time earnings for women in three office jobs. The jobs—secretary, typist, switchboard operator—are three values assumed by the independent categorical variable X, and correspond to bin labels like those described above. The frequency distribution within each occupation is the distribution of $Y_{ij} = f(X) + u_{ij}$ within each bin.

The values of $f(X)$ cannot be directly observed but are estimated from the means of the respective classes. Calculating means in the usual way we have:

When X has the value:	$f(X) =$	with standard error:
Secretary	$84.25	.75
Typist	$69.49	.78
Switchboard operator	$63.58	1.11

Source: Data of Table 5.4.

Like the individual values from which they were calculated, the means are subject to the random impacts of the u_{ij}, and standard errors have been included to indicate the accuracy with which the function has been estimated. From the theory of confidence intervals we know that while the mean will vary from sample to sample, the true value of $f(X)$ for secretaries lies—with almost complete certainty—in the range

$84.25 \pm 3(.75)$. The earnings of individual secretaries vary around this level under the influence of such unspecified variables as skill, experience, seniority, the firm she works for, her particular duties, and so on. All these effects, included in the term u_{ij}, account for the variation in earnings from woman to woman within occupations.

5.2.4 Measuring Correlation: The Determination Ratio and the Correlation Ratio

A glance at Table 5.4 is enough to show that the variation of earnings *within* occupations is more important than that *among* occupations. A qualitative idea of the relative importance of the two sources of variation can be had from the fact that while secretaries as a class are paid 20 per cent more than typists, only 3 out of the 375 secretaries are paid more than the highest paid typist, and fewer than 50 are paid more than the highest paid switchboard operator.

Where accuracy is needed, the relative importance of the variation among classes is measured quantitatively by a statistic called the *determination ratio*, R^2, or by its square root, R, the *correlation ratio*.

The theory on which the calculation of R^2 is based follows directly from a property of the variance already demonstrated in Chapter III: When two or more samples are combined into one, the sum of the squared deviations from the grand mean $\bar{\bar{T}}$ is given by

$$\Sigma y^2 = N_A \sigma_A^2 + N_B \sigma_B^2 + N_C \sigma_C^2 + \ldots$$
$$+ N_A(\bar{T}_A - \bar{\bar{T}})^2 + N_B(\bar{T}_B - \bar{\bar{T}})^2 + N_C(\bar{T}_C - \bar{\bar{T}})^2 + \ldots.$$

This total sum of squares is seen to consist of two parts. One part, $(N_A \sigma_A^2 + N_B \sigma_B^2 + N_C \sigma_C^2 + \ldots)$, consists of the sums of squares within samples. In a stochastic function this is the variation resulting entirely from u_{ij}. The other part of the total, $[N_A(\bar{T}_A - \bar{\bar{T}})^2 + N_B(\bar{T}_B - \bar{\bar{T}})^2 + N_C(\bar{T}_C - \bar{\bar{T}})^2 \ldots]$, is the sum of squares among sample means and is associated with the values of $f(X)$. The determination ratio is the ratio of the sum of squares among means to the total:

$$R^2 = \frac{N_A(\bar{T}_A - \bar{\bar{T}})^2 + N_B(\bar{T}_B - \bar{\bar{T}})^2 + N_C(\bar{T}_C - \bar{\bar{T}})^2 + \ldots}{\Sigma y^2}.$$

If there were no stochastic influence, R^2 would equal 1.0. In this case earnings would vary only among occupations. Everyone in the same occupation would get the same pay, and earnings would be perfectly correlated with occupation. If, on the other hand, there were no correlation between occupation and earnings, R^2 would equal 0. There would be no variation among occupation means. Occupation would count for nothing, and earnings would depend entirely on other factors.

For the data of Table 5.4 we have

$$R^2 = .269.$$

That is, only 26.9 per cent of total variation in earnings is associated with differences in job. Almost 75 per cent of total variation in earnings occurs *within* individual occupations. This finding is in keeping with our qualitative analysis above. There is some correlation between earnings and occupation, but for any given woman, how well she does within her job is of more importance than which of the three jobs she has.

5.2.5 Systematic Calculating Procedure

Calculation of statistical functions entails no new problems, but speed and accuracy are improved if a systematic routine is followed. The systematic procedure in Table 5.5 uses the total frequency of all cells as a check on the calculations and to provide figures needed to calculate the determination ratio. The steps are as follows:

1. Calculate N_j, $\sum_i Y_{ij}$, $\sum_i Y_{ij}^2$ for each cell, j, and for the total. If calculations are correct, the respective figures accumulated over all cells will equal the corresponding totals.

2. Calculate the respective cell means, $\bar{Y}_j$, and the grand mean $\bar{\bar{Y}}$. If these are correct the weighted mean of cell means equals the grand mean:

$$\frac{\sum\limits_j N_j \bar{Y}_j}{\sum\limits_j N_j} = \bar{\bar{Y}}.$$

3. Using the usual formula $\sum y^2 = \dfrac{N_j \sum\limits_i Y_{ij}^2 - (\sum\limits_i Y_{ij})^2}{N_j}$, calculate the sum of squared deviations within each cell and for the total sample. To check these, first define the sum of squared deviations among cell means

Table 5.5   Work Sheet for Tabulating a Statistical Function

Y	m	m^2	A	Values of X B	C	Total
0–1.9	1	1	20	10	0	30
2.0–2.9	3	9	60	50	20	130
4.0–5.9	5	25	20	50	60	130
6.0–8.0	7	49	0	10	20	30

Step (1) $N_j = \Sigma f$ 100   120   100 ⎫ Check: 320
$\Sigma Y_{ij} = \Sigma mf$ 300   480   500 ⎪ These must   1,280
$\Sigma Y^2_{ij} = \Sigma m^2 f$ 1,060 2,200 2,660 ⎭ accumulate to equal these   5,920

Step (2) $\bar{Y}_j =$ 3.0   4.0   5.0 $4.0 = \bar{\bar{Y}}$
check

(Weighted mean $\bar{\bar{Y}} = \dfrac{(100 \times 3) + (120 \times 4) + (100 \times 5)}{100 + 120 + 100} = 4.0$)

Step (3) Sum of squares within cells

Check: 800 = total sum of squared deviations

$\Sigma y^2 =$ 160   280   160 ← These plus this equals this

(Sum of squares among cells

$\Sigma N_j (\bar{Y}_j - \bar{\bar{Y}})^2 = 100(3-4)^2 + 120(4-4)^2 + 100(5-4)^2 = 200$)

Step (4) $\hat{\sigma}^2_p =$ 1.62   2.35   1.62 ⎫ Check by ⎰ 2.51
Step (5) $\sigma^2_{\bar{Y}_j} =$ .0162   .0196   .0162 ⎭ recalculating ⎱ .0078
Step (6) $\sigma_{\bar{Y}_j} =$ .13   .14   .13   Check by squaring .09

as

sum of squares among cells =
$$N_1(\bar{Y}_1 - \bar{\bar{Y}})^2 + N_2(\bar{Y}_2 - \bar{\bar{Y}})^2 + \ldots + N_k(\bar{Y}_k - \bar{\bar{Y}})^2.$$

This can be calculated from figures already available. The check is provided by the identity:

total sum of squares = sum of squares among cells
+ sum of squares within cells.

In addition to providing a check on calculation, these figures are used to measure correlation.

4. Divide the squared deviations within each cell by its degrees of freedom, $N_j - 1$, to obtain $\hat{\sigma}_p^2$.

5. Divide each $\hat{\sigma}_p^2$ by N_j, the number of items in the cell, to get $\sigma_{\bar{Y}_j}^2$.

6. Extract square roots to get $\sigma_{\bar{Y}_j}$.

7. Tabulate the results, giving $\bar{Y}_j$, $\sigma_{\bar{Y}_j}$ and N_j for each cell, as shown in Table 5.6.

Table 5.6 Y Tabulated as a Function of X

X	Y	$\sigma_{\bar{Y}}$	N
A	3.0	.13	100
B	4.0	.14	120
C	5.0	.13	100
Total	4.0	.09	320

8. Calculate $R^2 = \dfrac{\text{sum of squares among cells}}{\text{total sum of squares}}$ and append it to the table.

5.3   EXAMPLES

The following examples illustrate the application of the method to different kinds of functions and give some interpretation to the results.

It will be noted that in all of the examples in this and following chapters, calculations have been carried out far beyond the number of places either needed for the final result or even justified by the accuracy of the original data. A considerable amount of rounding is inevitable, and carrying the calculations beyond the limit that would otherwise appear reasonable helps to minimize its effect on results. Perhaps more important, rounded calculations will not agree exactly with check totals, but only as closely as rounding errors permit. Accuracy therefore demands that calculations be carried out far enough to guarantee that any errors lie beyond the precision needed for the result.

5.3.1   Income as a Function of Occupation and Sex

In this function a numerical variable, income, depends on two categorical variables, occupation and sex of the income receiver. Table 5.7

Table 5.7   Calculation of Income as a Function of Occupation and Sex

Income Class	Class Marks (thousands of $) m	m²	Professional & Technical male	female	Clerical male	female	Sales Workers male	female	Operatives male	female	Total
Under $500	.25	.0625	27	86	56	246	161	159	161	138	1,034
$500–1,499	1.0	1.0	95	180	96	520	113	263	407	352	2,026
$1,500–2,499	2.0	4.0	124	212	142	682	109	255	568	708	2,800
$2,500–3,499	3.0	9.0	140	263	194	1,039	161	127	912	535	3,371
$3,500–4,499	4.0	16.0	240	325	381	964	232	61	1,118	71	3,623
$4,500–4,999	4.75	22.5625	178	137	214	198	116	8	545	302	1,467
$5,000–5,999	5.5	30.25	348	194	541	210	234	8	1,090	43	2,668
$6,000–6,999	6.5	42.25	378	118	219	71	168	3	562	6	1,525
$7,000–7,999	7.5	56.25	327	40	121	24	132	4	241	2	891
$8,000–9,999	9.0	81.0	443	24	69	4	140	–	115	–	795
$10,000–14,999	12.5	156.25	311	16	40	4	111	1	17	–	499
$15,000–24,999	20.0	400.0	70	–	10	–	36	–	–	–	117
$25,000 or more	40.0	1600.0	19	–	–	4	19	–	–	–	42
Σf			2,700	1,595	2,083	3,966	1,732	889	5,736	2,157	20,858
Σmf			19,433.4	5,915.3	10,144.0	11,901.5	9,829.8	1,589.3	24,083.0	5,243.3	88,139.3
Σm^2f			197,476.8	29,239.4	61,601.1	50,557.0	103,422.6	4,586.2	123,326.1	16,108.3	586,317.6
$\bar{Y}$			7.19754	3.70862	4.86990	3.00088	5.67537	1.78768	4.19857	2.43080	4.22569
									(Weighted mean = 4.2257)		
Sum of squares within cells			57,605.3	7,302.1	12,201.9	14,843.0	47,635.8	1,745.2	22,218.5	3,363.0	213,876.3
							(Sum of squares among cells = 46,963.9956)				
σ_p^2			21.34319	4.58099	5.86065	3.7435	27.51922	1.96531	3.87419	1.55983	10.2544
$\sigma_{\bar{Y}}^2$			.00790	.00287	.00281	.00094	.01589	.00221	.00068	.00072	.00049
$\sigma_{\bar{Y}}$			.089	.054	.053	.031	.126	.047	.026	.027	.022

$$R^2 = \frac{46,964}{213,876} = .22$$

Source: Data adapted from *Income of Families and Persons in the United States: 1959, Current Population Reports: Consumer Income,* Series P-60, No. 35 (Washington, D.C.: U.S. Department of Commerce, Bureau of the Census, January 1961).

gives the data for a large sample of workers and shows the calculations. The estimated function, in Table 5.8, shows the relationship of income

Table 5.8   Income as a Function of Occupation and Sex of Receiver[a]

	Occupation			
	Professional & Technical	Clerical	Sales Workers	Operatives
Male Workers				
Mean income	$7,198	$4,870	$5,675	$4,199
Standard error	(89)	(53)	(126)	(26)
Cell size (N)	2,700	2,083	1,732	5,736
Female Workers				
Mean income	$3,709	$3,001	$1,788	$2,431
Standard error	(54)	(31)	(47)	(27)
Cell size (N)	1,595	3,966	899	2,157

[a] For the two variables together, $R^2 = .22$.
Source: Data of Table 5.7.

to occupation for income receivers of the same sex, and the sex differential within occupations. Clearly, women receive lower incomes than men in all occupations. For both sexes, professional and technical workers are the highest paid. Likewise, for both sexes, incomes in clerical occupations are about $700 higher than among operatives. Note, however, the interesting interaction where women sales workers receive substantially lower, and men sales workers substantially higher incomes than either clerks or operatives. When two independent variables interact to this extent, the effect of one cannot be measured without specifying the value of the other. In this instance, it is clearly meaningless to compare incomes of clerical and sales workers until we specify whether we are talking about men or women. Likewise, to compare earnings of the two sexes requires specifying the occupation. Among clerical workers, the incomes of men exceed those of women by less than $2,000; among sales workers the difference is almost $4,000.

The small standard errors in the cells assure us that the cell means are estimated with great accuracy, and that any comparisons made from the table carry a high level of confidence. The determination ratio,

Figure 5.2   Mean Incomes of Men and Women in Four Occupations

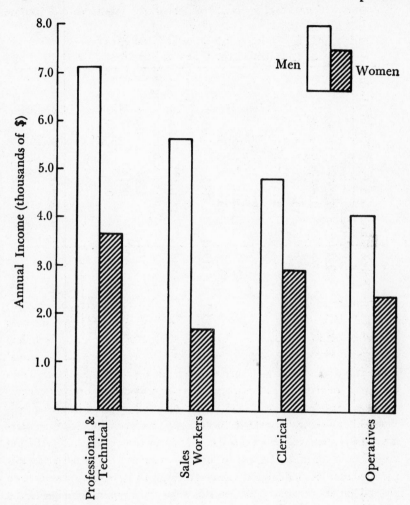

Source: Data of Table 5.7.

$R^2 = .22$, indicates that the two independent variables taken together account for 22 per cent of the observed variation in income.

The function is presented as a chart in Figure 5.2.

Table 5.9 Work Sheet for Calculation of Wife's Labor Force Status as a Function of Husband's Income

	m m^2	Under $3,000	$3,000–4,999	$5,000–6,999	$7,000–9,999	$10,000 or more	All Incomes
				Husband's Income			
Wife in L.F.	1 1	44	67	43	13	3	170
Wife not in L.F.	0 0	78	180	174	76	57	565
N		122	247	217	89	60	735
ΣY		44	67	43	13	3	170
ΣY^2		44	67	43	13	3	170
$\bar{Y}$ = Proportion in L.F. = P		.3607	.2713	.1982	.1460	.0500	.2313 = $\bar{\bar{P}}$
							(Weighted mean = .2313)
Sum of squares within cells		28.1311	48.8259	34.4793	11.1011	2.850	130.6803
					(Sum of squares among cells = 5.2956)		
$\hat{\sigma}_p^2$ =		.2325	.1985	.1597	.1261	.0483	.1780
σ_p^2 =		.00190	.00080	.00074	.0014	.00081	.00024
σ_p =		.043	.028	.027	.038	.028	.015

$$R^2 = \frac{5.2956}{130.6803} = .041$$

Source: Data adapted from *A Social Profile of Detroit, 1955* (Ann Arbor: Detroit Area Study, Survey Research Center, The University of Michigan, 1956).

5.3.2 Wife's Labor Force Status as a Function of Husband's Income

An important influence on labor supply is the fact that whether a wife enters the labor force depends on her husband's income. In the function describing this relationship the dependent variable is categorical (that is, the wife is either in the labor force or not).

In making the calculations in Table 5.9, the categorical variable has been treated as a numerical variable whose value is 1 if wife is a member of the labor force and 0 if she is not. Thus the cell means are proportions of wives in the labor force at various income levels, and their standard errors are standard errors of the sample proportions.

Table 5.10 Wife's Labor Force Participation as a Function of Husband's Income

| | Husband's Income | | | | | |
	Under $3,000	$3,000–4,999	$5,000–6,999	$7,000–9,999	$10,000 or over	All Incomes
Percentage of families with wife in labor force	36.1	27.1	19.8	14.6	5.0	23.1
Standard error	(4.3)	(2.8)	(2.7)	(3.8)	(2.8)	(1.5)
Cell size (N)	122	247	217	89	60	735

$$R^2 = .041$$

Source: Data of Table 5.9.

The function is shown in Table 5.10. When plotted in Figure 5.3 it clearly exhibits a backward sloping function: the higher husbands' incomes, the fewer the wives who want to work. Standard errors are shown on the chart by a bar drawn through each point.

Although the standard errors are large, in only one case do neighboring figures differ by less than two standard errors. The determination ratio, $R^2 = .041$, indicates that about 4 per cent of the total variation in labor force participation depends on the husband's income. At first sight this may appear small, but if we reflect on some of the factors that are omitted—for example, the number of children in the family, the health of the wife, and the attitudes she and her husband have toward working wives—it is surprising that a variable like husband's income can account for as much as it does. In any event, since a categorical variable usually exhibits both of its values in every cell, R^2 should be expected to be low.

99

Figure 5.3   Wife's Labor Force Participation as a Function of Husband's Income
(Width of bar represents one standard error.)

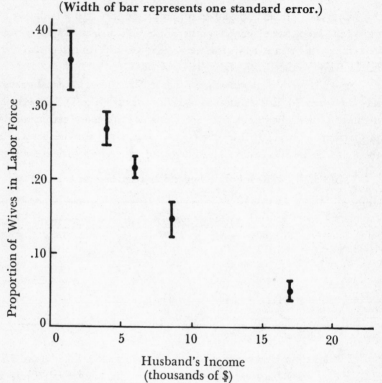

Source: Data of Table 5.9.

5.3.3   New Automobile Demand and Income

The relationship of income to new car sales can be explored with data obtained from a cross-section of states. The number of new cars registered (licensed) during a given year serves to measure new car sales in each state. This is compared with disposable income the same year. Of course, with more people, larger states have both more income and more car sales than smaller states. This fact would tend to bias the measurement unless both variables are expressed on a per capita basis. The question of bias will be taken up in section 5.4.5.2 below.

The examples shown up to this point have all involved data already classified into frequency distributions. In this case the computations are made from unclassified data. Forty-eight states are first ranked by income and divided into 8 cells of 6 states each as shown in Table 5.11. Mean

Table 5.11 Derivation of New Car Registrations as a Function of Per Capita Disposable Income from a Cross-Section of States, 1955

State	Disposable Income X ($ per capita)	New Car Registration Y (cars per 1,000)		
Mississippi	921	29.4	$N = 6$	$\Sigma y^2 = 54.213$
Arkansas	1,009	28.0	$\Sigma Y = 180.4$	$\hat{\sigma}_p^2 = 10.842$
South Carolina	1,046	26.2	$\Sigma Y^2 = 5,478.24$	
Alabama	1,098	33.0		$\sigma_{\bar{Y}}^2 = 1.807$
Kentucky	1,137	28.8	$\bar{Y} = 30.067$	
Tennessee	1,168	35.0	$(\bar{X} = 1,063)$	$\sigma_{\bar{Y}} = 1.35$
South Dakota	1,169	35.5	$N = 6$	$\Sigma y^2 = 67.733$
North Carolina	1,174	30.5	$\Sigma Y = 201.4$	$\hat{\sigma}_p^2 = 13.547$
West Virginia	1,198	28.0	$\Sigma Y^2 = 6,828.06$	
Louisiana	1,228	34.6		$\sigma_{\bar{Y}}^2 = 2.258$
Georgia	1,233	38.2	$\bar{Y} = 33.567$	
North Dakota	1,255	34.6	$(\bar{X} = 1,210)$	$\sigma_{\bar{Y}} = 1.51$
New Mexico	1,312	38.5	$N = 6$	$\Sigma y^2 = 42.533$
Idaho	1,356	39.9	$\Sigma Y = 233.8$	$\hat{\sigma}_p^2 = 8.507$
Oklahoma	1,373	43.0	$\Sigma Y^2 = 9,152.94$	
Utah	1,399	34.2		$\sigma_{\bar{Y}}^2 = 1.418$
Vermont	1,400	40.2	$\bar{Y} = 38.967$	
Virginia	1,408	38.0	$(\bar{X} = 1,375)$	$\sigma_{\bar{Y}} = 1.19$
Arizona	1,412	36.2	$N = 6$	$\Sigma y^2 = 303.868$
Iowa	1,413	39.9	$\Sigma Y = 254.3$	$\hat{\sigma}_p^2 = 60.744$
Nebraska	1,431	42.9	$\Sigma Y^2 = 11,081.95$	
Maine	1,449	32.8		$\sigma_{\bar{Y}}^2 = 10.129$
Texas	1,470	49.0	$\bar{Y} = 42.383$	
Florida	1,496	53.5	$(\bar{X} = 1,445)$	$\sigma_{\bar{Y}} = 3.34$
Kansas	1,505	48.2	$N = 6$	$\Sigma y^2 = 47.153$
Minnesota	1,512	40.6	$\Sigma Y = 253.6$	$\hat{\sigma}_p^2 = 9.431$
New Hampshire	1,539	41.7	$\Sigma Y^2 = 10,765.98$	
Wisconsin	1,565	40.8		$\sigma_{\bar{Y}}^2 = 1.572$
Colorado	1,570	39.7	$\bar{Y} = 42.267$	
Missouri	1,613	42.6	$(\bar{X} = 1,551)$	$\sigma_{\bar{Y}} = 1.25$

(Continued on next page.)

TABLE 5.11 (cont.)

State	Disposable Income X ($ per capita)	New Car Registration Y (cars per 1,000)		
Oregon	1,623	48.1	$N = 6$	$\Sigma y^2 = 89.273$
Wyoming	1,630	48.2	$\Sigma Y = 277.6$	$\delta^2_p = 17.855$
Montana	1,658	43.0	$\Sigma Y^2 = 12,932.90$	
Pennsylvania	1,680	42.6		$\sigma^2_{\bar{Y}} = 2.976$
Indiana	1,704	53.0	$\bar{Y} = 46.267$	
Maryland	1,709	42.7	$(\bar{X} = 1,667)$	$\sigma_{\bar{Y}} = 1.72$
Rhode Island	1,730	39.2	$N = 6$	$\Sigma y^2 = 860.060$
Washington	1,769	34.1	$\Sigma Y = 278.4$	$\delta^2_p = 172.012$
Ohio	1,820	49.4	$\Sigma Y^2 = 13,777.82$	
Massachusetts	1,828	36.6		$\sigma^2_{\bar{Y}} = 28.669$
Michigan	1,885	69.7	$\bar{Y} = 46.400$	
Illinois	1,982	49.4	$(\bar{X} = 1,836)$	$\sigma_{\bar{Y}} = 5.36$
New York	1,988	40.1	$N = 6$	$\Sigma y^2 = 165.568$
Nevada	2,020	49.3	$\Sigma Y = 294.7$	$\delta^2_p = 33.002$
California	2,033	51.3	$\Sigma Y^2 = 14,640.25$	
New Jersey	2,039	48.2		$\sigma^2_{\bar{Y}} = 5.500$
Delaware	2,106	57.9	$\bar{Y} = 49.117$	
Connecticut	2,196	47.9	$(\bar{X} = 2,064)$	$\sigma_{\bar{Y}} = 2.35$

All states combined

$N = 48$
$\Sigma Y = 1,974.2$
$\Sigma Y^2 = 84,658.14$

(Weighted mean = 41.15)

$\bar{Y} = 41.129$
$(\bar{X} = 1,526)$

Total sum of squares $= 3,460.94$

Sum of squares within cells $= 1,630.401$

Sum of squares among cells $= 1,830.505$

$$R^2 = \frac{1,830.505}{3,460.906} = .53$$

Sources: State Per Capita Incomes, 1955, from *Survey of Current Business* (Washington, D.C.: U.S. Department of Commerce, Office of Business Economics, August 1958). Per Capita New Car Registrations are derived from state data given in *Ward's Automotive Yearbook, 1956* (Detroit: Ward's Reports, 1956).

per capita registrations, $\bar{Y}$, its standard error, $\sigma_{\bar{Y}}$, and the sum of squares within cells, Σy^2, are computed for each cell as shown. Mean income, $\bar{X}$, is likewise calculated.

The total sum of squares is obtained from N, ΣY, ΣY^2, accumulated over all states. The agreement of this total with the sum of squares within cells plus the sum of squares among cells checks the calculation. R^2 is then computed in the usual way.

The function is tabulated in Table 5.12 and plotted in Figure 5.4.

Table 5.12   New Car Registrations Per Capita as a Function of Per Capita State Income

Mean Per Capita Income ($)	Mean New Registrations (per 1,000 people)	Standard Error
1,063	30.07	1.35
1,210	33.57	1.51
1,375	38.97	1.19
1,445	42.38	3.34
1,551	42.27	1.25
1,667	46.27	1.72
1,836	46.40	5.36
2,064	49.12	2.35
	$R^2 = .53$	

Source: Data of Table 5.11.

5.3.4   Housing Status in Relation to Age, Marital Status, and Children

In this function the dependent variable, "housing status," is categorical and has three different values: "owns home," "rents," "other." (Spending units in the latter categories are mostly individuals living rent-free with parents.) The value of this dependent variable is to be related to three independent variables—age, marital status, and children. These independent variables define cells, and the function is obtained simply by calculating, cell by cell, the proportion of spending units in each category of housing arrangement. The calculations are straightforward and no underlying data are given in the example. Standard errors of the proportions are calculated with the usual formulas and the results tabulated as shown in Table 5.13. The influence of age, other things

Figure 5.4 New Car Registrations Per 1,000 Plotted as a Function of Per Capita Disposable Income
(Width of bar represents one standard error.)

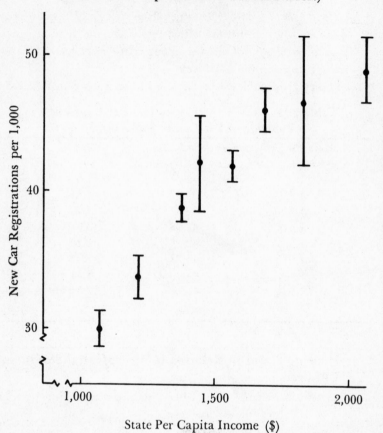

State Per Capita Income ($)

Source: Data of Table 5.11.

equal, can be seen by comparing corresponding cells in the two age classes: Younger people are less likely to own a home, more often live with relatives or rent. In both age groups, marriage is strongly associated with increasing independence: a rise in home ownership and rental, a sharp drop in the proportion living with relatives. In the younger group the arrival of children is associated with further increase in home ownership and decline in renting. The older sample without children consists

**Table 5.13 Housing Status of Spending Units Related to Age,
Marital Status, and Children**
(Tabulated figures are proportions in each housing status;
figures in parentheses are standard errors.)

	Total Number of Spending Units (N)	Proportion of Spending Units that:		
		Own	Rent	Other[a]
Under age 45				
Single	150	.18	.58	.24
		(.03)	(.04)	(.04)
Married:				
No children	150	.35	.62	.03
		(.04)	(.04)	(.01)
Children	930	.61	.37	.02
		(.02)	(.02)	(.004)
45 or over				
Single	390	.48	.38	.14
		(.03)	(.02)	(.02)
Married:				
No children	390	.73	.23	.04
		(.02)	(.02)	(.01)
Children	390	.72	.24	.04
		(.02)	(.02)	(.01)
Total sample	2,550	.59	.35	.06
		(.008)	(.009)	(.004)

[a] Living rent-free with relatives or renting part of another family's dwelling.
Source: Data adapted from *1960 Survey of Consumer Finances* (Ann Arbor: Survey
Research Center, The University of Michigan, 1961).

largely of people whose children are grown, and their housing pattern
is the same as the older group whose children are still at home. Size of the
standard errors indicates that these comparisons can be made with
considerable accuracy.

When, as in this case, a categorical dependent variable has more
than two values, the usual definition of R^2 cannot be applied, and no
calculation has been made.

5.4 RESEARCH DESIGN

In actual research, design is logically prior to data-processing. But data
requirements and general design problems can best be appreciated

against a background of real examples. Throughout the following, we will concentrate our attention on the analysis of wife's labor force participation.

5.4.1 Research and Theory

Research is rooted in theory, and the first step in research is to pose the question the research is supposed to answer. What do we really want to know? The answer to this question is usually much broader than the scope of the function that will result, but without it, it is impossible to proceed.

Behind the study of the relation of husband's income to wife's labor force status lies a much broader, but very specific question. In this case let us suppose the question to be the following: If the United States government reduces the income tax by $1 billion, what will be the effect on unemployment? The tax reduction will stimulate spending. This, in turn, will create jobs, increase employment, and reduce unemployment. But it will also increase the income of breadwinners already employed. If this induces some working wives to leave the labor force, a further reduction in unemployment will result. It is in this specific context, then, that we want to study the relationship between husband's income and wife's working habits.

5.4.2 Specifying the Dependent Variable

The next step is to specify the dependent variable whose behavior is to be studied. How should the wife's status be measured? The most obvious first thought is to use a categorical variable: wife employed, wife not employed. There are many advantages to this variable. It is simple; the question, "Are you now working at a job of any kind?" can be understood and answered by almost everybody.

The disadvantage to this variable is that a wife can herself be unemployed: a person without a job who is actively seeking work. What we want to measure is the extent to which low income leads the wife to *seek* work, rather than her success in finding it. For this purpose we should measure the wife's labor force status. If she is a member of the labor force she either has a job or is actively seeking to find a job. But the disadvantage of this variable is immediately obvious. To get the information, we must ask all wives who answer "No" to the job question a series of additional questions in which we try to determine whether they are "actively" seeking work. These questions are much more difficult to formulate, understand, or answer. They involve much more time and trouble for interviewers, and particularly so when the respondent is a housewife who sometimes works, but who is now taking care of the house. She may not be exactly active in seeking work, but if a good job were offered she might take it—and then again she might not. The difficulty here should not be exaggerated. Any case of serious unemployment will be discovered this way. Moreover, whatever information we get is additional to what we learn about the wife's employment status from the simple question alone.

It might be argued, however, that even labor force status is not an adequate dependent variable, and that account should be taken of the degree of attachment of the wife to the labor force. The vice president of a cosmetics firm, a newspaper or magazine editor, actress, or other established career woman is unlikely to move out of the labor force when her husband's income rises, but a waitress, door-to-door saleswoman, stenographer, or clerk might, and if she is employed only part time it is even more likely. In addition to her employment status an interview might elicit information on why she was working or seeking work. An answer like "We need the money" indicates a lesser attachment to the labor force than "I find my work interesting," "I like to meet people," or "It's my career." In other words, it may be possible to measure wife's labor force status in more than two categories, or even as a numerical variable on some kind of scale.

The final choice of dependent variable is usually a compromise between what would be best for the purpose and what we can afford. A third choice variable that is already available has much to commend it over superior data that have not been collected. We would at least want to use what was at hand as a pilot study before embarking on an expensive project.

5.4.3 Specifying the Independent Variable

Since the basic problem has to do with the relationship of employment and unemployment to income and income taxes, a wife's labor force status is to be related to some measure of family income. It is at once apparent that total family income will not do for this purpose. Any gap in the family income that induced the wife to go to work is at least partly filled up by her own earnings, and the evidence of the original incentive is gone. By the same token, however, it is not adequate to use husband's income as the independent variable. There may be other adult wage earners in the family besides the husband and wife. Moreover, the wife herself may have property income independently of whether she works or not, and this will influence her decision. For these reasons, total income less wife's earnings from employment is superior to husband's income as the independent variable.

Because the basic question deals with the effect of a tax cut, taxes should be deducted to get family *disposable* income net of wife's earnings. This poses another difficulty. Husband and wife probably file a joint income tax return and pay one tax on their combined incomes. This means that family disposable income net of wife's earnings should be measured by first deducting wife's earnings from family income, then recomputing the tax, deducting only the amount that would have been paid had the wife not been employed. The difficulty of getting useful survey responses to such a question is obvious, but given data on the incomes and on the composition of the individual family it is possible for the researcher to estimate such a disposable income at least approximately.

This still leaves the question of how to treat income in kind. The most important form of this is imputed rent on owner-occupied dwellings. Given two families with identical composition and money incomes, one owning its home and the other not, it is quite possible that the necessity to pay rent creates a greater gap in the income of the renting family. Imputing a rental income to the owning family will partially allow for this. On the other hand, wives in home-owning families may be more strongly motivated to work to help furnish the home or to pay off the mortgage. In this case it would be useful to specify home ownership as a separate independent variable in the analysis (see below) rather than to allow for it indirectly by imputation.

Like the dependent variable, the choice of independent variable is usually a compromise between what we would like and what we can afford.

5.4.4 Specification of the Statistical Unit and the Population

Our statistical function is to be derived from a frequency distribution of a sample of *items* for each of which information is available on wife's labor force status and income net of wife's earnings. Up to now we have designated these items loosely as "families," but before data can be collected the nature of the individual items must be explicitly defined.

The term *household* as defined by the Bureau of the Census consists of "all those persons who occupy a house, an apartment, or other group of rooms . . . that constitutes a dwelling unit." Everybody in the house is counted whether related or not. Thus a maid or a boarder living in the house would be counted as part of the household. Such a unit is unsuitable for our purpose.

A *family* refers to a group of persons, related by blood, marriage, or adoption, and residing together. This comes nearer what we want but is still too inclusive, since a single family, in this definition, can include two or more married couples, as when a younger couple lives with the husband's parents.

Probably the best unit for the purpose is the *spending unit*. This is defined by the Survey Research Center at The University of Michigan as a group of people, related by blood, marriage, or adoption, living in the same dwelling, who pool together more than half their combined incomes for expenditure purposes. A household or family can contain one or more spending units, but a spending unit is limited to members of a single family and household.

But it is clear that a spending unit can still contain two husbands and two wives, and that the questions of the relationship of wives' labor force status to net disposable spending unit income is a different one from that in a spending unit with only one couple. Indeed, the two are so different that we would be well advised to treat them separately.

5.4.5 Specification of Other Variables

There are several reasons for including variables in the research design in addition to the dependent variable and the principal independent variable. In the first place, other variables are often of interest in their own right, and their effects can be studied in one research design. Contrast and comparison of impacts of different variables is often useful in

Table 5.14 Wife's Employment Status as a Function of Net Factor Income[a] of Spending Unit and Ages of Children (Figures in parentheses are standard errors.)

Net Factor Income	No Children Under 17	Children 6–17 Only	One or More Children Under 6	Total
Under $500	.281 (.056)	.333 (.020)	.495 (.138)	.35
$500–999	.247 (.054)	.448 (.020)	.506 (.121)	.31
$1,000–1,999	.341 (.050)	.475 (.014)	.496 (.067)	.41
$2,000–2,999	.403 (.070)	.436 (.014)	.435 (.056)	.43
$3,000–4,999	.524 (.040)	.457 (.010)	.375 (.037)	.45
$5,000–7,499	.474 (.040)	.457 (.004)	.316 (.031)	.41
$7,500–9,999	.447 (.058)	.397 (.007)	.281 (.042)	.36
$10,000–14,999	.344 (.062)	.351 (.008)	.197 (.057)	.30
$15,000 and over	.283 (.067)	.229 (.011)	.026 (.038)	.19

Header spanning: "Proportion of S.U.'s with Wife Employed Where There Are:"

[a] Net Factor Income includes husband's wages and salaries plus husband's income from business or farm, plus home production plus total spending unit capital income, including imputations.
Source: Calculated from data supplied by the Survey Research Center, The University of Michigan.

bringing out the meaning of results.

Secondly, taking account of other variables removes them from the unspecified category. This reduces the variance of u_{ij} and improves the accuracy with which the effects of all variables can be observed.

But more important than either of these is the fact that *the apparent influence of any one independent variable depends on what other variables have been allowed for.* Failure to take account of variables in addition to those of immediate interest can result in biased and otherwise misleading results. There are two important kinds of problem: hidden interaction and hidden correlation.

5.4.5.1 HIDDEN INTERACTIONS No factor has a unique effect isolated from others. Economic variables interact, and the impact of any one depends on the values of the others. A given price rise discourages demand more or less depending on income; the marginal productivity of labor depends on the quantity of capital available to work with; the response of a family to a sudden decline in income depends on the amount of money in the bank; the earnings differential between two occupations is different for men and women and depends on the age and experience of the worker. Research results are vastly richer when these interactions can be examined, and there is merit in specifying variables for this reason alone. But in addition, failure to take explicit account of interactions can lead to misleading results.

Both these points are well illustrated by Table 5.14. In this table, wife's employment status is shown as a function of spending unit net factor income and the ages of her children. Note the powerful interaction between children's ages and income in influencing whether the wife works. If there are no very young children, wife's employment tends to *rise* with income up to about $5,000 and to decline thereafter. But if there are children under six, the low-income family badly needs the wife's income to supplement the other sources, and the proportion of such wives employed (50 per cent) is much greater than in the other classes. At the same time, the young children provide a powerful motive for the wife to leave the labor force if the spending unit can afford it. The proportion of working wives declines steadily as income rises and at the upper end of the scale falls far below the other groups.

If the children are not recognized as a variable in the analysis, the functions would appear as in the "total" column. Not only would we miss the insight contributed by the additional variable, but because of the hidden interaction, wife's employment would show only a minor response to spending unit net factor income.

The distortion produced by a hidden interaction depends on sample composition. This can be illustrated in terms of the example of Table 5.8. Suppose the income differential between clerical and sales workers is measured by comparing two samples, each consisting of 300 men and 200 women. If the members of the samples are like those of Table 5.8, the mean incomes of the respective occupations will be practically equal!

111

$$\text{Clerical workers: } \frac{300 \times \$4{,}870 + 200 \times \$3{,}009}{500} = \$4{,}125$$

$$\text{Sales workers: } \frac{300 \times \$5{,}675 + 200 \times \$1{,}788}{500} = \$4{,}120$$

Increasing the proportion of men raises the mean income of sales workers above that of clerical workers. Increasing the proportion of women has the opposite effect. Thus, even though there is no correlation between two interacting variables, failure to take account of both produces a result that depends on the sample proportions and the magnitude of the interaction. It is, of course, impossible to take full account of all interacting variables, but it is essential to specify the most important ones. The prerequisite to successful statistical research is an intimate knowledge of the subject under investigation.

5.4.5.2 HIDDEN CORRELATION The most important source of bias lies in the failure to take specific account of variables that are correlated both with the dependent variable and with one or more of the independent variables. In order to illustrate this kind of bias most clearly, let us leave the problem of wife's labor force status and consider the more extreme example of Table 5.15 and Figure 5.5. The table shows the number of new cars bought and their retail price during each of a period of years (for example, the first column of the table shows the volume of purchases during each of the eight years when the retail automobile price index was between 110 and 130). The "demand" function estimated from this data is so badly biased that it appears to be upward sloped!

One important cause of this bias is the fact that the observations lie on a demand curve that, like Figure 5.1, shifts with income. Years of high income tend to be years of high demand and high prices, but since income is not specified in the function, its correlation with both price and demand is hidden, producing a worthless result.

The relationship of income to sex of receiver charted in Figure 5.2 involved a large number of hidden correlations. No account was taken in the analysis of the fact that the proportion of women working only a part-time week is higher than the proportion of part-time workers among

Table 5.15 Number of New Cars Sold During Years of Specified Car Prices
(Tabulated figures are millions of new cars.)

| | Price Index | | |
	110–129.9	130–149.9	180–200
	3.91	1.96	4.78
	2.65	2.72	6.37
	1.90	3.46	5.09
	1.10	3.76	4.19
	1.53		5.78
	1.93		5.47
	3.53		7.20
	3.51		5.90
$N =$	8	4	8
$\Sigma Y =$	20.06	11.90	44.78
$\Sigma Y^2 =$	57.9774	37.3492	256.8688
$\bar{Y} =$	2.51	2.98	5.60
Sum of squares within cells =	7.677	1.947	6.213
$\hat{\sigma}_p^2 =$	1.097	.649	.888
$\sigma_{\bar{Y}}^2 =$	.137	.162	.111
$\sigma_{\bar{Y}} =$	.37	.40	.33

Source: Data from D. B. Suits, "The Demand for New Automobiles in the United States, 1929–1956," *Review of Economics and Statistics*, XL (August 1958), 273–80.

men. Moreover, the proportion of women working full time who are in low-paid temporary jobs is higher than among men. Women in permanent jobs tend to have lower seniority than men due to absence during the child-raising period, and related to that fact, the proportion of employed women in the low-paid younger age groups and in the older worker groups is higher than for men.

Including these additional variables as an explicit part of the analysis would add to our interest in and understanding of the phenomenon, but more important is the fact that their omission creates a distortion in the results.

Figure 5.5 Automobile "Demand" as Estimated from Table 5.15 (Width of bar represents one standard error.)[a]

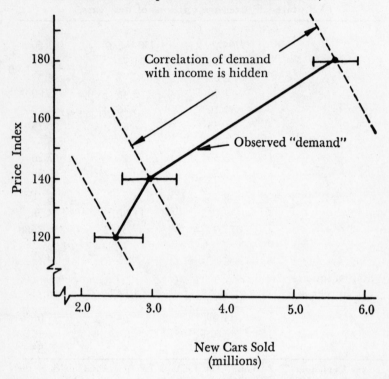

[a] Note that, since, in this case, the dependent variable is plotted on the horizontal axis, the bars indicating the size of the standard error must also lie horizontally.

In general, if Y is a statistical function of X_1, the means of the cells corresponding to $X_1 = A$ and $Y_1 = B$ are

$$\bar{Y}_A = f(A) + \bar{u}_A; \ \bar{Y}_B = f(B) + \bar{u}_B.$$

If X_1 and u are uncorrelated, the values of $\bar{u}$ will tend to be the same in all cells and the difference between $\bar{Y}_A$ and $\bar{Y}_B$ will fairly reflect the effect of X_1. But if u is correlated with X, the values of $\bar{u}$ will tend to vary systematically from cell to cell. Comparing $\bar{Y}_A$ with $\bar{Y}_B$ unfairly imputes to X_1 a difference due in part to some hidden variable, X_2.

The bias is avoided by specifying this variable as X_2, a second variable in the function. The means of two cells with differing values for X_1, but equal values for X_2, will then be

$$\bar{Y}_A = (A, X_2) + \bar{u}_A; \ \bar{Y}_B = (B, X_2) + \bar{u}_B.$$

If X_2 was the only part of u correlated with X_1, $\bar{u}_A$ will now tend to equal $\bar{u}_B$ and comparison of $\bar{Y}_A$ with $\bar{Y}_B$ fairly reflects the effect of X_1 only.

More generally, to measure the effect of a particular variable X_1 on Y requires that the function

$$Y = f(X_1, X_2, \ldots X_k) + u$$

explicitly include every variable X_2, X_3, $\ldots X_k$ *that is correlated with both* X_1 *and* Y. Failure to take account of one of these variables produces a bias whose magnitude varies with the size of the hidden correlation.

The number of intercorrelated variables in the economy is very large. They can never be fully specified, and a statistical result is never entirely free of bias rooted in hidden correlation. But it is quite possible to minimize it and to make sure that all known large correlations are taken into account. Ability to do this grows with the experience of the researcher, and it cannot be emphasized too strongly that the first and most important requirement for statistical research is specialized familiarity with the subject under investigation.

5.4.6 Correlation and Sample Composition

Each combination of values of the independent variables specified for analysis defines an empty cell or bin in our warehouse. Corresponding to each there is a subpopulation of items meeting the description of the cell. Ideally, the task of data-gathering would be to obtain a random sample of each subpopulation, of a size adequate to give the desired accuracy. In practice, however, we are rarely able to do this, since we cannot determine, say, husband's income or children's ages until an item has been drawn.

Instead, we draw a random sample of dwelling units, interview the people living in each and find out in the interview how many children there are and their ages, the family income, and whether the wife works or not. Thus, the contents of our bins will reflect the distribution of incomes and children found in the community at large rather than the distribution we would prefer for greatest accuracy of measurement. Although this is a disadvantage from the standpoint of measurement, it produces an estimated R^2 applicable to the whole population.

A tabulated demand function shows how much price will affect consumption *if* price changes by a given amount, other things equal. The relation of wife's labor force status to husband's income shows the effect of a rise in husband's income *if* it should occur. The tabulated relationship of income to occupation and sex shows how much income varies from one occupation to another *if* a shift in employment should occur and what a shift in employment between men and women would do to community income *if* it came about.

Correlation, on the other hand, depends not only on how much influence a variable would have *if* it varied, but also on how much it is, *in fact*, observed to vary. Even a powerful factor will exhibit a low correlation if it is highly stable, while a rather weak variable can produce a high correlation merely because it varies a lot. A demand schedule estimated during a period of relatively stable prices will show a low correlation of quantity with price—not because price is an unimportant factor in demand, but because price contributes to observed fluctuations only when it changes. Whether the correlation between husband's income and wife's labor force status is high or low depends in part on whether the sample of husbands studied has a high or a low variance in income.

In Table 5.16 are two separate samples of data showing the relationship of a numerical variable to a categorical variable X that takes on the values A, B, C, and D. The corresponding cell means are identical in the two samples and the corresponding variances $\hat{\sigma}_p^2$ vary only slightly because of the differing cell sizes in the two samples. In other words, the two samples reveal identical underlying relationships. Yet the difference in cell proportions in the two samples creates greatly disparate values of R^2.

In short, correlation is seriously influenced by the circumstances under which the observations are made. Even if the observations are a random sample of the entire community, R^2 must be interpreted with caution. In a community in which hardly anybody goes to the doctor, there can be little correlation between medical care and health; in a

Table 5.16 Illustration of Relationship of R^2 to Sample Composition

| | | SAMPLE I: $R^2 = .61$ | | | | | SAMPLE II: $R^2 = .24$ | | | | |
| | | *X category* | | | | | *X category* | | | | |
m	m^2	A	B	C	D	Total	A	B	C	D	Total
1	1	100	–	–	–	100	10	–	–	–	10
2	4	200	10	–	–	210	20	100	–	–	120
3	9	300	20	10	–	330	30	200	100	–	330
4	16	200	30	20	100	350	20	300	200	10	530
5	25	100	20	30	200	350	10	200	300	20	530
6	36	–	10	20	300	330	–	100	200	30	330
7	49	–	–	10	200	210	–	–	100	20	120
8	64	–	–	–	100	100	–	–	–	10	10
f		900	90	90	900	1,980	90	900	900	90	1,980
mf		2,700	360	450	5,400	8,910	270	3,600	4,500	540	8,910
m^2f		9,300	1,560	2,370	33,600	46,830	930	15,600	23,700	3,360	43,590
$\bar{Y}$		3.0	4.0	5.0	6.0	4.5	3.0	4.0	5.0	6.0	4.5

—All corresponding cell means equal—

Sum of squares within cells

$$1,200 + 120 + 120 + 1,200 = 2,640$$
$$120 + 1,200 + 1,200 + 120 = 2,640$$

Accumulated sum of squares within cells equal

Sum of squares among cells

$$900(-1.5)^2+90(-.5)^2+90(.5)^2+900(1.5)^2=4,095$$
$$90(-1.5)^2+900(-.5)^2+900(.5)^2+90(1.5)^2=855$$

Difference in sample proportions
causes difference in sum of squares among cells
hence in total sum of squares
and in R^2

$$R^2 = \frac{\text{S.S. among cells}}{\text{total S.S.}} = \frac{4,095}{6,735} = .61 \qquad R^2 = \frac{\text{S.S. among cells}}{\text{total S.S.}} = \frac{855}{3,495} = .24$$

community in which nearly everybody goes to college there can be little correlation between education and economic status—these things are intimately associated, but there is insufficient sample variance to demonstrate it.

5.4.7 Correlation and Causation

Whenever the direction of causation is known, causes should be treated as independent and the effects as dependent variables, but it must be emphasized that there is nothing about the statistical process to distinguish cause from effect. The direction of causation must be determined by other information.

A chemist or a biologist can use laboratory controls to vary one factor—temperature, say, or diet—and observe its influence on another—reaction time or growth; there is no ambiguity about cause and effect. Although laboratory experiments are impossible in economics, there are economic phenomena in which the direction of causation is perfectly clear. Vegetables are planted, cultivated, and harvested before they are sold on the market for whatever price they will bring. Thus the quantity grown is the cause of short-run price variation and not the other way around. In all these cases familiarity with the subject is used to identify causation.

Since economic variables are interconnected in a complex system of relationships, economic causation is, in general, multilateral. In some circumstances, or for some people, X causes Y; in other circumstances, or for other people, Y caus s X. In still other situations, X and Y are mutually caused by a third variable, Z. The relationship of wife's participation in the labor force to income can again serve as an example. For some families, the need for income stimulates the wife to find a job. Among these families, wives of low-income husbands will work more often than wives of high-income husbands. Husband's income is cause, wife's job is the result. But there are other families in which the wife's job enables the husband to pursue an occupation of low immediate income. A struggling writer or artist, a medical student or a candidate for the Ph.D., a businessman just starting out, or a schoolteacher, is often able to continue by virtue of his wife's earnings. If the wife could not provide the needed income, the husband would have to seek employment with higher immediate return. Among these families, causation runs from wife's employment to husband's income. For still other families, the two variables are mutually caused. Some wives want to work if they can find an interesting or well-paid job, but not otherwise. Since a wife's education is correlated with her husband's, and these are both highly correlated with economic status, the same factors making the husband eligible for interesting or high-income employment are also at work in the case of the wife. Among these families, the proportion of working wives tends to rise with husband's income. The direction of causation in a social system should always be treated as a complex matter, and the researcher will do well to avoid the question, "Does X cause Y?" in favor of the question, "Under what circumstances does X cause Y?"

It follows emphatically that an observed correlation cannot be accepted as proof of either the direction of causation or even that the variables are causally related. The study of variables that are correlated only by virtue of their association with one or more hidden variables often yields amusing results, as in the high positive correlation between per capita consumption of alcoholic beverages in the United States and the level of salaries paid to the clergy. The same kind of fallacy in a more subtle guise can be the source of serious error.

There is, however, one important situation in which the question of causation can be given a categorical answer. If X is observed to have ample variance, and no correlation between X and Y is detected, this is pretty good evidence that X and Y are not causally connected. Thus, although the presence of correlation says nothing about the operation of cause and effect, its absence where it could be expected is valuable evidence against causation. In marginal cases, the question of whether two variables are correlated or not therefore takes on a special importance to be explored in the next chapter.

5.5 SUMMARY

Measurement of economic relationships requires that variables be so specified and measured that their observed behavior will represent a valid approximation to the underlying theoretical structure of the economy. This requires not only that the dependent variable and the principle independent variables be carefully chosen and measured, it also often requires that other variables be included in the analysis to avoid the distortion otherwise produced by hidden interaction and hidden correlation.

The response of the dependent variable to an independent variable can be summarized under two headings: correlation and interaction. To say that two variables are correlated means that in the sample at hand the value of one variable varies with the value of the other. To say that

3.

Class A Accounting Clerks in Selected U.S. Cities, Distributed by Straight-Time Weekly Earnings, by Sex, by Industry

Straight Weekly Earnings ($)	Dayton, Ohio Mfg. men	Dayton, Ohio Mfg. women	Dayton Nonmfg. men	Dayton Nonmfg. women	Memphis, Tenn. Mfg. men	Memphis Mfg. women	Memphis Nonmfg. men	Memphis Nonmfg. women	Des Moines, Iowa Mfg. men	Des Moines Mfg. women	Des Moines Nonmfg. men	Des Moines Nonmfg. women	Salt Lake City, Utah Mfg. men	Salt Lake Mfg. women	Salt Lake Nonmfg. men	Salt Lake Nonmfg. women	Philadelphia, Pa. Mfg. men	Philadelphia Mfg. women	Philadelphia Nonmfg. men	Philadelphia Nonmfg. women	Total
60–64.99	7	–	–	–	–	–	4	27	–	–	6	24	–	–	–	–	–	19	8	32	127
65–69.99	–	6	1	–	–	2	5	5	–	–	6	18	4	–	–	3	2	46	4	44	140
70–74.99	5	6	3	–	7	1	2	6	4	1	6	16	5	–	–	4	32	70	10	67	244
75–79.99	–	8	4	–	6	1	5	13	2	2	6	16	6	–	–	3	13	29	22	103	238
80–84.99	4	26	1	8	6	1	4	21	4	4	2	19	2	2	3	9	13	52	44	113	338
85–89.99	1	6	6	–	6	13	9	14	4	–	1	4	5	2	2	8	13	86	32	124	336
90–94.99	5	12	11	3	4	6	1	5	–	8	–	5	7	5	7	–	10	57	43	74	259
95–99.99	9	5	–	–	8	3	4	–	1	–	–	–	14	8	3	8	17	40	39	20	185
100–104.99	12	7	8	–	11	5	3	1	1	–	4	–	13	8	7	–	14	14	6	37	151
105–109.99	11	9	6	2	12	9	5	14	–	–	2	–	6	2	5	–	36	15	14	34	182
110–114.99	7	8	3	–	7	2	–	–	1	–	1	–	7	–	4	–	22	11	11	11	88
115–119.99	12	9	2	–	9	3	7	–	1	–	–	–	3	–	5	–	3	11	21	25	111
120–124.99	11	2	2	–	7	2	2	2	2	–	2	–	3	–	5	–	22	4	18	–	84
125–129.99	18	3	13	–	13	1	5	–	3	–	–	–	6	–	6	–	1	4	1	6	80
130–134.99	7	1	–	–	9	1	4	–	–	–	–	–	3	–	2	–	–	2	9	–	44
135–139.99	5	6	–	–	6	–	3	–	1	–	–	–	–	–	2	–	–	–	–	2	25
140–144.99	–	1	–	–	–	–	–	–	1	–	–	–	–	–	–	–	–	–	–	–	2
145–150.00	3	–	–	–	–	–	–	–	2	–	–	–	–	–	–	–	–	–	–	–	5

Source: Data compiled from *Occupational Wage Survey*, BLS Bulletin Nos. 1303-39, 1303-40, 1303-42, 1303-32, and 1303-25 (Washington, D.C.: U.S. Department of Labor, Bureau of Labor Statistics, February and March 1962).

two variables interact means that the influence of each of them on a third variable depends on the value of the other.

Once the variables are specified and measured, analysis of the function is relatively simple. It can be done many ways, but where adequate data are available, tabulation is at once the easiest, most complete, and most sophisticated. All other statistical techniques are designed for the special cases where data are inadequate or where a mathematical expression of the function is needed.

Essentially, a table consists of an array of cells defined by values of the independent variables. The response of the dependent variable to any particular independent variable can be seen by comparing cells alike in all other respects. In best practice, the cell means are accompanied by standard errors to indicate the confidence to be placed in them, and by a determination ratio to characterize the closeness of the relationship. A systematic calculating procedure permits accurate calculation of cell means, standard errors, and R^2.

Questions and Problems

1. Look in a beginning economics textbook and list a number of functional relationships described there. See if you can find examples that imply positive correlation, negative correlation, and functions containing categorical variables. Can you find one containing an important interaction?

2. (a) The term *ceteris paribus* or "other things equal" often appears in theoretical discussions. Explain why this expression is used.

(b) How can a theory that holds when "other things are equal" account for behavior of a social system in which "other things" are continually varying?

(c) Perhaps the phrase "effects of other things allowed for" would be more exact and less misleading than "other things equal." Explain.

3. Use the data shown opposite to tabulate straight-time weekly earnings as a function of city, industry, and sex of employee. (The burden of calculation is greatly reduced if several students work on the project

as a team, each taking responsibility for the calculations in a few cells. The computations can then be compiled, checked, and R^2 calculated.) Write a short paragraph describing the relationship: Are earnings correlated with place? With industry? With sex? Are any interesting interactions suggested by the table? What proportion of the total variance in earnings can be associated with the three variables?

4.

Unemployment, 1958, by Region, Type of Industry, and Color: Males with Work Experience, Age 14 and Over

	Agriculture		Nonagricultural Industries	
	Sample Size	Number with Some Unemployment, 1958	Sample Size	Number with Some Unemployment, 1958
North East				
White	479	49	11,581	1,984
Nonwhite	12	8	751	235
North Central				
White	2,022	140	11,461	2,219
Nonwhite	18	8	787	248
South				
White	1,645	183	9,686	1,689
Nonwhite	817	110	1,853	579
West				
White	676	100	6,129	1,136
Nonwhite	70	32	394	147

Source: Data adapted from *Current Population Reports: Labor Force*, Series P-50, No. 91 (Washington, D.C.: U.S. Department of Commerce, Bureau of the Census, June 30, 1959).

Use the data shown to tabulate the relationship of unemployment to industry, region, and race. Write a short paragraph summarizing your findings.

5. Data are available for a cross-section of spending units, giving the income and the amount of vacation expenditure made by each. In a study of the relationship of the two, what other variables should be specified to avoid hidden interaction and hidden correlation?

6. Much of modern economic theory rests on the assumption that consumer expenditure is effect and consumer income is cause. In what cases is the reverse true? Cite cases in which the desire or need for

higher consumption expenditure leads to higher family income. In what cases does higher consumption expenditure actually make possible higher income?

References

1. Mordecai Ezekiel and Karl A. Fox. *Methods of Correlation and Regression Analysis.* 3rd Ed. New York: John Wiley & Sons, 1959. Chapter 3, "The Relation Between Two Variables and the Idea of Function," and Chapter 4, "Determining the Way One Variable Changes When Another Changes by the Use of Averages," provide a short treatment of simple functions and their tabulation. Chapter 26, "Steps in Research Work," although oriented toward regression techniques, is also useful at this point.

2. Paul F. Lazarsfeld and Morris Rosenberg. *The Language of Social Research.* Glencoe, Ill.: The Free Press, 1955. Section II, "Multivariate Analysis," contains many good studies drawn from social science at large in which the analysis consists mainly of tabulating multivariate functions.

3. Martin H. David. *Family Composition and Consumption.* Amsterdam: North-Holland Publishing Co., 1962. This short study contains a large number of tables with two independent variables.

4. Lawrence R. Klein, ed. *Contributions of Survey Methods to Economics.* New York: Columbia University Press, 1954. A useful collection of essays on various topics ranging from research design to results obtained from studies using survey data.

CHAPTER VI

Significance Tests

6.1 INTRODUCTION

When—as in the examples of the last chapter—all the cell means in a large table differ by several standard errors, there is overwhelming evidence of some kind of relationship among the variables. But when cells are few, or the means not well separated, it is often unclear whether the variables are really correlated or not. A *significance* test is a method of evaluating the evidence in these cases. The test to be used in a given situation depends on the kind of relationship to be tested, its form, the kind of variables used, the amount and kind of data, and sometimes the convenience of the researcher. But the basic rationale underlying all tests is the same.

Essentially, a significance test consists of calculating the risk that an observed correlation might be a purely accidental result, generated by the random behavior of uncorrelated variables. Any indication of correlation is based on observed sample evidence, but chance variation can produce the same kind of "evidence," even when the variables are uncorrelated. The heart of all significance tests is thus the calculation of the probability of observing the same evidence in a hypothetical case of no correlation. The lower this risk, the greater is the significance of the evidence, and it is natural to refer to the calculated risk as the *significance level* of the result.

6.2 DIFFERENCE BETWEEN TWO SAMPLE MEANS

The study of the difference between two sample means provides a basic introduction to significance tests. Table 6.1 contains information on the

Table 6.1 Work Sheet for Calculating Outstanding Automobile Debt as a Function of Income

Automobile Installment Debt ($)	m	m^2	Number of Installment Buyers with Income: Under $5,000	$5,000–10,000	Total
1– 499	.250	.0625	55	64	119
500– 999	.750	.5625	46	58	104
1,000–2,000	1.500	2.25	36	83	119
Σf			137	205	342
Σmf			102.25	184.00	286.25
$\Sigma m^2 f$			110.3125	223.3750	333.6875
$\bar{Y}$			.74635	.89756	.83699
(Weighted mean = .83699)					
Σy^2			33.998	58.224	94.0996
(Sum of squares among cells = 1.87762)					
$\hat{\sigma}_p^2$			.24999	.28541	
$\sigma_{\bar{Y}}^2$			.00182	.00139	
$\sigma_{\bar{Y}}$			.042	.037	

$$R^2 = \frac{1.878}{94.100} = .02$$

Source: Illustrative example roughly based on magnitudes given in *1960 Survey of Consumer Finances* (Ann Arbor: Survey Research Center, The University of Michigan, 1961).

incomes and installment debt of a sample of families who bought new cars on credit during 1955. In the summary Table 6.2, the means of the two cells appear to show that, among credit buyers, those with higher incomes used more credit. This may be because they bought larger cars or because they were better risks. On the other hand, the observed $152 difference between the mean debt in the two samples might be nothing more than an accident. To determine the probability of such an accident we explore the distribution of differences between means of random samples.

6.2.1 Distribution of Differences Between Two Means

Consider any two populations, p_1 and p_2, with means, $\bar{Y}_{p_1}$, $\bar{Y}_{p_2}$, and variances, $\sigma_{p_1}^2$, $\sigma_{p_2}^2$. (In our example, one is the population of all credit

Table 6.2 Relationship of Outstanding Automobile Installment Debt to Income

	Income	
	Under $5,000	$5,000–10,000
Mean debt	$746	$898
Standard error	(42)	(37)
Sample size	137	205
	$R^2 = .02$	

Source: Data of Table 6.1.

car buyers with incomes below $5,000, the other is all those with incomes of $5,000 or more.) A sample of N_1 families is drawn from p_1, and N_2 from p_2, the sample means $\bar{Y}_{s_1}$ and $\bar{Y}_{s_2}$ and their difference, $d_s = \bar{Y}_{s_2} - \bar{Y}_{s_1}$, are calculated. Imagine all possible pairs of samples to be drawn and the difference in means of each pair recorded in a warehouse, compiled into a table, plotted, and the mean and variance calculated. This distribution has the following properties.

1. *The mean difference is the difference between population means.* This follows directly from the fact (discussed in Chapter III) that the mean of the sum of two variables is the sum of their means. Here each sample difference, d_s, is the sum of $\bar{Y}_{s_2}$ and $-\bar{Y}_{s_1}$. Hence

$$\bar{d} = \bar{Y}_{s_2} - \bar{Y}_{s_1} = \bar{Y}_{p_2} - \bar{Y}_{p_1}.$$

2. σ_d^2, *the variance of the difference, is the sum of* $\sigma_{\bar{Y}_2}^2$ *and* $\sigma_{\bar{Y}_1}^2$. This follows from the fact that the variance of the sum of two uncorrelated variables is the sum of their variances. $\bar{Y}_{s_2}$ and $-\bar{Y}_{s_1}$ come from independently drawn random samples and are uncorrelated. The variance of $\bar{Y}_{s_2}$ is $\sigma_{\bar{Y}_2}^2$; $-\bar{Y}_{s_1}$ is a product, $(-1) \times \bar{Y}_{s_1}$, so its variance is $(-1)^2 \sigma_{\bar{Y}_1}^2 = \sigma_{\bar{Y}_1}^2$. Therefore

$$\sigma_d^2 = \sigma_{\bar{Y}_1}^2 + \sigma_{\bar{Y}_2}^2.$$

3. *Finally, for large* N_1 *and* N_2, *the distribution of differences is normal.*

In short, d_s, the difference in means of random samples, is normally distributed around a mean equal to the true difference in population means, $\bar{Y}_{p_2} - \bar{Y}_{p_1}$, with a standard error, σ_d, that can be estimated from sample data.

6.2.2 The Null Hypothesis and the Significance Test

We are now in a position to calculate the probability of any given difference arising by accident in a hypothetical case of equal population means. Since this hypothetical case supposes a true difference of zero, it is called a *null hypothesis*.

Under this hypothesis the observed sample difference d_s is simply a random deviation. The probability of a deviation this large is determined from a normal curve in the usual way. For example, calculating from Table 6.1:

$$\sigma_d^2 = \sigma_{\bar{Y}_2}^2 + \sigma_{\bar{Y}_1}^2 = .0014 + .0018 = .0032$$

$$\sigma_d = \sqrt{.0032} = .057 \text{ (thousands of dollars)}$$

or $\qquad \sigma_d = \$57.$

The observed difference was \$152. Under the null hypothesis that $d_p = 0$, the proportion of samples with d_s as large as \$152 is found by entering the normal table at $t = \dfrac{d_s}{\sigma_d} = \dfrac{\$152}{\$57} = 2.6$. We find that .495 of the area of the normal curve is included between the mean and an ordinate erected 2.6σ above the mean. This leaves .005 of the area beyond 2.6σ in one direction, and $2 \times .005 = .01$ beyond $t = 2.6\sigma$ either way.[1]

The figure .01 is the *significance level* of the result. It measures the chance that a difference as great as \$152 could occur by accident in a situation where debt and income were uncorrelated. With such a slight chance of accident, it is safe to conclude that the evidence really indicates correlation. The evidence, in short, is *significant* of correlation.

6.2.3 Significance Level and Its Interpretation

Significance level is interpreted as follows. The assertion that the two populations have different means is based on an observed difference in sample means. But sample evidence is subject to the risk that the observed difference might be merely an accident. To evaluate the evidence

---

1. The normal table applies to the *algebraic* difference, $d_s = \bar{Y}_{s_2} - \bar{Y}_{s_1}$. When $\bar{Y}_{s_2}$ is the larger mean the difference is positive; if $\bar{Y}_{s_2}$ is the smaller mean the difference is negative. But our test is applied to an *absolute* difference of \$152 which can lie in either tail of the normal curve, and both must be taken into account.

we calculate the risk of such an accident. In the example above it was found to be only .01.

A significance test involves weighing evidence. The higher the significance level, that is, the lower the chance of accidental occurrence, the more convincing the evidence; if the significance level is too low, we are unconvinced. Of course, there is no firm dividing point between what convinces and what does not. A significance level is a calculated risk and must be evaluated in terms of the gains and losses at stake in the particular case. In practical economic research, however, the .05 level is generally referred to as "significant," while the .01 level is called "highly significant."

6.2.4 Interpreting Nonsignificant Results

It is important to stress that a low significance level, for example a risk higher than .05, means only that the evidence of correlation is unconvincing. It does *not* provide convincing evidence to the contrary. In fact, nonsignificant evidence quite literally fails to signify *anything;* it leaves us in our original state of ignorance.

The point is clarified by examination of a nonsignificant difference. In Table 6.3 are two random samples of unemployed persons, with the number of weeks each person had been unemployed at the time of the interview. The mean duration in unemployment of former manufacturing employees was 13.54 weeks, while former trade employees showed a mean of 10.74 weeks. Does this evidence signify that the mean duration of unemployment differed between the two populations of unemployed?

From the table we have

$$\sigma_d^2 = \sigma_{\bar{Y}_1}^2 + \sigma_{\bar{Y}_2}^2 = 2.84 + 2.56 = 5.40$$

$$\sigma_d = \sqrt{5.40} = 2.32 \text{ weeks}$$

$$d_s = 15.36 - 12.66 = 2.70 \text{ weeks.}$$

Entering the normal table at $t = \dfrac{2.70}{2.32} = 1.17$, we find .379, that is,

under the null hypothesis, the probability of an absolute deviation as large as 2.70 is $2 \times (.5 - .379) = 2(.121) = .242$.

Table 6.3   Work Sheet for Calculating Duration of Unemployment as a Function of Industry

Number of Weeks Unemployed	m	m^2	Number of Unemployed, by Industry: Manufacturing	Trade	Total
1–5	3	9	16	21	37
6–14	10	100	15	15	30
15 or more[a]	30	900	19	14	33
	Σf		50	50	100
	Σmf		768	633	1,401
	$\Sigma m^2 f$		18,744	14,289	33,033
	$\bar{Y}$		15.36	12.66	14.01
			(Weighted mean = 14.01)		
Sum of squares within cells					
	Σy^2		6,947.52	6,275.22	13,404.99
			(Sum of squares among cells = 182.25)		
	$\hat{\sigma}_p^2$		141.786	128.066	135.40393
	$\sigma_{\bar{Y}}^2$		2.84	2.56	1.354
	$\sigma_{\bar{Y}}$		1.69	1.62	1.17
		$R^2 = \dfrac{182.3}{13,405.0} = .014$			

[a] The mean in this class is approximately 30 weeks.

This high risk constitutes too low a significance level to be dependable; the evidence fails to signify a difference in mean duration of unemployment between the two occupations. But this is *not* evidence that the two means are the same. The lack of significance may be due to the fact that σ_d is large because of small sample size, or because $\hat{\sigma}_p^2$ is exaggerated by failure to control skill, education, region, seniority, or other factors. It may even be that we happened by chance on a pair of samples whose difference was unusually small. Finally, of course, it may be that the two population means are really equal. There is nothing in the evidence to indicate the truth of one of these rather than another.

6.2.5   Summary of Test of Difference in Means

To test the significance of a sample difference $d_s = \bar{Y}_{s_2} - \bar{Y}_{s_1}$, calculate its standard error: $\sigma_d = \sqrt{\sigma_{\bar{Y}_1}^2 + \sigma_{\bar{Y}_2}^2}$. From the normal table find the probability of a chance difference falling beyond $t = \dfrac{d_s}{\sigma_d}$ on either side of the mean. This probability is the significance level. Note that the *lower* the probability, the *higher* the significance of the difference. If the probability of a chance occurrence under the null hypothesis is sufficiently small, say, below .05, we consider the chance of accident too remote and accept the evidence as signifying a difference. If the probability is too high, we hesitate to rely on the evidence.

6.3 ANALYSIS OF VARIANCE

When the independent variable has several values, or when more than one independent variable is specified in the function, the evidence of correlation is the variance among several sample means. The technique of evaluating this evidence is the *analysis of variance*.

Table 6.4 Small Samples of Hourly Wages Paid to Drivers of Light Trucks (under 1-1/2 tons), 4 U.S. Cities, 1961

	Indianapolis	Salt Lake City	Scranton	Buffalo	
	$1.75	$2.15	$1.85	$2.50	
	$1.25	$2.65	$1.55	$2.75	
	$2.05	$1.35	$2.90	$2.65	
	$1.60	$1.65	$1.90	$2.60	
	$2.40	$2.20	$2.50	$2.35	
		$1.90	$1.90	$2.55	
		$2.70	$3.00	$2.65	
				$2.45	
					Total
N	5	7	7	8	27
ΣY	9.05	14.60	15.60	20.50	59.75
ΣY^2	17.1475	31.9300	36.7050	52.6450	138.4275
$\bar{Y}$	1.810	2.086	2.229	2.563	2.213
		(Weighted mean = 2.213)			
Σy^2	.767	1.479	1.939	.114	6.203

$$[\text{Among cities} = 5(1.810-2.213)^2+7(2.086-2.213)^2+7(2.229-2.213)^2$$
$$+8(2.563-2.213)^2 = 1.907]$$

$\hat{\sigma}^2_p$	.1918	.2465	.3232	.0161	
$\sigma^2_{\bar{Y}}$	.0384	.0352	.0462	.0020	
$\sigma_{\bar{Y}}$	.196	.187	.216	.045	

$$R^2 = \frac{1.907}{6.203} = .31$$

Source: The data are random subsamples drawn by the Research Seminar in Quantitative Economics from tabulations of the *Occupational Wage Survey*, BLS Bulletin Nos. 1303-27, 1303-32, 1303-8, 1303-29 (Washington, D.C.: U.S. Department of Labor, Bureau of Labor Statistics, August and December, 1961).

6.3.1 Illustration of the Problem

Table 6.4 shows the hourly wages received by drivers of light trucks in each of 4 cities. The information consists of the wages reported by a random sample of 5 drivers in Indianapolis, 7 in Salt Lake City, 7 in Scranton, and 8 in Buffalo. Since the samples are small and show considerable variance within cities, it is not surprising to find that when tabulated in the usual way in Table 6.5, no clear correlation emerges.

Table 6.5 Average Wages of Drivers of Light Trucks by Cities, 1961

City	Mean Hourly Wage ($)	Standard Error	Sample Size
Indianapolis	1.81	.20	5
Salt Lake City	2.09	.19	7
Scranton	2.23	.22	7
Buffalo	2.56	.05	8
	$R^2 = .31$		

Source: Data of Table 6.4.

The means vary from city to city, but if we compare the differences in successive means to their standard errors we find no pair of neighboring means to be significantly different.

Of course, the difference between the highest average (Buffalo) and the lowest (Indianapolis) looks highly "significant," but a moment's reflection reveals the fallacy of such a comparison. These are not two randomly chosen means but, as the largest and smallest, have the maximum difference of all the pairs in the set. There is a surprisingly good chance that this maximum will exceed two standard errors of the difference, even when the samples come from the same normal population. In fact it can be shown that there is a .90 probability that the maximum difference in a set of 20 sample means exceeds 2 standard errors. For a set as small as 4 sample means the probability is still about 15 per cent.

To test whether the observed variation among sample means signifies a functional relationship or merely reflects an accident of sampling, we need a method that will take account of the variance among *all* the sample means rather than just the differences between particular

131

pairs. The analysis of variance, used for this purpose, derives directly from what we already know about the variance of random samples and its relationship to population variance.

6.3.2 Variance Within Samples

Given one random sample, we can estimate the variance of the population from which it was drawn by the formula

$$\hat{\sigma}_p^2 = \sigma_s^2 \frac{N}{N-1} = \frac{\Sigma y^2}{N-1}.$$

If we are given several such estimates, one from each of several samples of the same population, they will, in general, differ, and they should be averaged together to provide the best point estimate of population variance. For this purpose the weighted mean of the individual estimates is used, the weights being the number of degrees of freedom in the respective samples. Given k samples containing $N_1, N_2, \ldots, N_k$ items with the respective $\hat{\sigma}_p^2$ equal to $(\hat{\sigma}_p^2)_1, (\hat{\sigma}_p^2)_2, \ldots, (\hat{\sigma}_p^2)_k$, the best point estimate of $\hat{\sigma}_p^2$ is given by the weighted mean:

$$\hat{\sigma}_p^2 = \frac{(N_1 - 1)(\hat{\sigma}_p^2)_1 + (N_2 - 1)(\hat{\sigma}_p^2)_2 + \ldots + (N_k - 1)(\hat{\sigma}_p^2)}{(N_1 - 1) + (N_2 - 1) + \ldots + (N_k - 1)}.$$

This average is easily calculated from data already provided when the function is tabulated. Since

$$(N - 1)(\hat{\sigma}_p^2) = (N - 1)\frac{\Sigma y^2}{N - 1} = \Sigma y^2,$$

the numerator of the weighted mean is seen to be the accumulated sum of squares within samples, already familiar as part of the check used in our calculating procedure. The denominator is the total number of degrees of freedom within samples. For the truck drivers' analysis, the population variance estimated within samples is

$$\hat{\sigma}_p^2 = \frac{.767 + 1.479 + 1.939 + .113}{4 + 6 + 6 + 7} = \frac{4.2980}{23} = .1869.$$

That is, *if* the four samples of truck drivers are random samples from the same population, the variance of that population can be estimated to be $\hat{\sigma}_p^2 = .1869$, using only data on the variances within the several samples.

6.3.3 Variances Among Samples

Given a number of samples from the same population, the variance of that population can also be estimated from the behavior of the sample means, without reference to the variance within samples. We already know that the variance in the means of N-item samples obeys the law

$$\sigma_{\bar{Y}}^2 = \frac{\hat{\sigma}_p^2}{N}.$$

Up to now we have used this formula to estimate $\sigma_{\bar{Y}}^2$ from information about $\hat{\sigma}_p^2$, but when we have several samples, we can turn the formula around and use the known means to estimate an unknown $\hat{\sigma}_p^2$. Given k samples containing, respectively $N_1, N_2 \ldots, N_k$ items, with means $\bar{Y}_1, \bar{Y}_2, \ldots, \bar{Y}_k$, the population variance can be estimated by the formula

$$\hat{\sigma}_p^2 = \frac{N_1(\bar{Y}_1 - \bar{\bar{Y}})^2 + N_2(\bar{Y}_2 - \bar{\bar{Y}})^2 + \ldots + N_k(\bar{Y}_k - \bar{\bar{Y}})^2}{k - 1}.$$

In this formula, $\bar{\bar{Y}}$ is, as usual, the grand mean of the k samples combined. The squared deviation of each sample mean from the grand mean is weighted by the number of items in the sample; their sum is divided by the number of degrees of freedom to give the estimated $\hat{\sigma}_p^2$.

In the example of the truck drivers' wages, the grand mean, as shown in Table 6.4, is $\bar{\bar{Y}} = 2.213$. Hence the numerator of the expression above is $5(1.810 - 2.213)^2 + 7(2.086 - 2.213)^2 + 7(2.229 - 2.213)^2 + 8(2.563 - 2.213)^2 = 1.907$. It is immediately seen that this is the accumulated sum of squares among city means, already given in Table 6.4, and familiar as the numerator of R^2.

The number of degrees of freedom is fixed at $k - 1$ by the fact that the weighted sum of the k deviations of sample means from the grand mean must equal 0. If all but one are known, the last can be calculated from the others. In the problem of the truck drivers' wages, the four sample means have $4 - 1 = 3$ degrees of freedom. Dividing the degrees of freedom into the sum of squares among means gives an estimate of $\hat{\sigma}_p^2$:

$$\frac{1.907}{3} = .636 = \hat{\sigma}_p^2.$$

In other words, *if* the four samples of truck drivers were really drawn from the same population—that is, if average pay scales are really the same in the four cities—the variance of the wages of the population of truck drivers ought to be approximately .636.

6.3.4 Comparison of the Two Estimates of Variance: the F Ratio

If the pay scales in the four cities are equal, the four samples should behave like random samples from the same population. In particular the two estimates of population variance ought to be approximately equal. Suppose, however, the pay scales are *not* the same, but vary from city to city. This variation will not affect the variance estimated within cities, for all drivers in the same city are subject to the same scale. But it will cause the city means to exhibit greater variance than is consistent with their being random samples from the same population. The variance estimated among samples will tend to exceed that estimated within samples. Indeed, this is the case with the truck drivers' wages. As just calculated, the two variances are:

$$\text{estimated among samples: } \frac{1.907}{3} = .636$$

$$\text{estimated within samples: } \frac{4.2980}{23} = .1869.$$

The ratio of the two variances, universally designated F, is used to compare the estimates. If the samples actually behave like random samples from the same population, we expect the ratio

$$F = \frac{\text{variance among samples}}{\text{variance within samples}}$$

to be approximately 1.0. When F exceeds 1.0, it constitutes evidence that the samples are drawn, not from the same population, but from populations with different means.

In the case of the truck drivers' wages, $F = \frac{.636}{.1869} = 3.40$. The fact that the variance among samples is 3.4 times that within samples constitutes evidence of variation in wage scales among cities, that is, that city and drivers' pay are correlated variables.

6.3.5 The F Distribution

When the ratio F exceeds 1.0 we have evidence of correlation. But such "evidence" can also occur purely by accident. In other words, before we can accept the value $F = 3.4$ as signifying the existence of variation in pay scales, we must evaluate the probability that such a ratio could occur by accident, even when the samples actually constitute random drawings from the same population.

The F table is a tabulation of the proportion of times that sets of random samples, drawn from the same normal population, give rise to an F ratio exceeding specified values. We can imagine this table to be the result of an experiment in which a set of samples is drawn from the same normal population and the value of F is calculated. A second set is drawn, and the process continued until the results of several billion sets have been accumulated. When the resulting figures are examined we would find that the proportion of sets for which F exceeds any specified value depends on n_1, the number of degrees of freedom of the variance in the numerator, and n_2, the number of degrees of freedom of the variance in the denominator of the ratio.

The F table is given in Appendix C. Corresponding to each n_1 and n_2, the F table gives two values: a smaller one, $F_{.05}$, that is exceeded by accident by .05 and a larger one, $F_{.01}$, that is exceeded by only .01 of all sets of random samples from an uncorrelated population. To test the significance of an observed F, we enter the F table at the proper values of n_1 and n_2 and find the values of $F_{.05}$ and $F_{.01}$. If our observed F exceeds $F_{.01}$, that is, if the chance of accidental observation of so large an F is less than .01, the observed correlation is significant at the .01 level. If the observed value falls between $F_{.05}$ and $F_{.01}$ it is significant at the .05 level, but not at the .01 level. If the observed F is smaller than $F_{.05}$ the analysis fails to show a significant correlation at the .05 level.

To test the significance of the correlation of drivers' wages with city, enter the F table at $n_1 = 3$ and $n_2 = 23$ to find $F_{.05} = 3.03$ and $F_{.01} = 4.76$. The observed value, $F = 3.40$ is significant at the .05 level but not at the .01 level.

6.3.6 The Analysis of Variance Table

The analysis of variance is facilitated if the relevant sums of squares, degrees of freedom and variances are arranged in an analysis table like

Table 6.6 Analysis of Variance: Drivers' Wages

Source	Sum of Squares	d.f.	Variance
Total	6.203	26	.2386
Among cities	1.907	3	.636
Within cities	4.298	23	.1869

$$F = \frac{\text{variance among cities}}{\text{variance within cities}} = \frac{.636}{.1869} = 3.40$$

$$(n_1 = 3, \ n_2 = 23; \ F_{.05} = 3.03, \ F_{.01} = 4.76)$$

$$(\bar{R}^2 = 1 - \frac{.1869}{.2386} = .22)^a$$

[a] See below, section 6.3.8.
Source: Data of Table 6.4.

Table 6.6. This forms a compact summary of all the data used in the test and is often published as part of the final research report. All the necessary figures are produced in the process of tabulating the function and need only be copied from the work sheet. For example, the sum of squares among cities is given explicitly in Table 6.5, and the sum of squares within cities is accumulated from the Σy^2 of the individual cities. There are 27 items in the 4 samples. Thus the number of degrees of freedom among cities is $4 - 1 = 3$ and within cities is $27 - 4 = 23$. Note that, just as the sum of squares among cities plus the sum of squares within cities equals the total sum of squares, so the degrees of freedom among cities plus the degrees of freedom within cities equals the total degrees of freedom. Including the total sum of squares and total degrees of freedom in the table thus provides a useful check on the analysis. It is also useful for calculating the value of R^2 and, as we shall see below, in calculating the adjusted value, $\bar{R}^2$.

6.3.7 Analysis of Variance with Multivariate Functions

When the analysis of variance is used, it is immaterial whether the cells are defined by one or by several variables. The test can be applied to the relationship of a dependent variable to an entire set of independent variables taken together. A highly significant value for F implies the existence of a relationship between the dependent variable and one or more of the independent variables.

For example, the data of Table 6.7 might be used in a study to determine whether the duration of periods of unemployment vary with the age and the sex of the unemployed person. The tabulation in Table 6.8 suggests that duration lengthened with age and was longer for women than men. But the determination ratio, $R^2 = .012$, is quite low, and when the 6 cell means are arrayed in order of magnitude, few pairs of neighboring means differ significantly. It is not obvious that duration of unemployment is really correlated with age and sex. The analysis of variance is applied as a significance test. As shown in the analysis of Table 6.9, the variance among the six cells is highly significantly greater than the variance within cells. We conclude that, while age and sex together account for only about 1.2 per cent of the observed variance in unemployment duration, there is no question that this small correlation exists.

It should be carefully noted, however, that this analysis does not tell us whether the correlation is due to age alone, sex alone, or both together. To make distinctions of this kind requires an extension of the analysis of variance that is beyond the scope of this book.

6.3.8 Adjustment of R^2 for Sample Size, a Digression

The formula

$$R^2 = \frac{\text{sum of squares among cells}}{\text{total sum of squares}}$$

is satisfactory so long as both R^2 and the number of degrees of freedom within cells is large, but it entails a bias that becomes serious for low R^2 or few degrees of freedom. An unbiased estimate, usually designated $\bar{R}^2$, can be calculated directly from the analysis of variance table:

$$\bar{R}^2 = 1 - \frac{\text{variance within cells}}{\text{total variance}}.$$

The effect of this adjustment for degrees of freedom is always to lower the determination ratio. Table 6.5 above gives unadjusted $R^2 = .31$; the adjusted value in Table 6.6 is $\bar{R}^2 = .22$. The unadjusted R^2 of Table 6.8 is .012. The adjusted value in Table 6.9 is $\bar{R}^2 = .008$.

Table 6.7 Distribution of a Sample of Unemployed by Number of Weeks Duration of Unemployment, by Age and Sex

Weeks Unemployed	m	m^2	Age 14–24 men	14–24 women	25–44 men	25–44 women	45 and Older men	45 and Older women	Total
1– 5	3	9	52	44	154	24	116	16	406
6–14	10	100	38	74	130	54	104	52	452
15 and up	30	900	30	62	148	48	146	46	480
Σf			120	180	432	126	366	114	1,338
Σmf			1,436	2,732	6,202	2,052	5,768	1,948	20,138
$\Sigma m^2 f$			31,268	63,596	147,586	48,816	142,844	46,744	480,854
$\bar{r}$			11.97	15.18	14.36	16.29	15.76	17.09	15.05

(Weighted mean = 15.05)

Sum of squares within cells

	14–24 men	14–24 women	25–44 men	25–44 women	45 and Older men	45 and Older women	Total
Σy^2	14,083.9	22,130.3	58,547.1	15,397.7	51,942.8	13,457.1	177,760.5

(Sum of squares among cells = 2,199.7)

	14–24 men	14–24 women	25–44 men	25–44 women	45 and Older men	45 and Older women
$\hat{\sigma}^2_p$	118.35	123.63	135.84	123.18	142.31	119.09
$\dfrac{\sigma_p}{\bar{Y}}$	.986	.687	.314	.978	.389	1.045
$\sigma_{\bar{Y}}$	.99	.83	.55	.99	.63	1.03

$$R^2 = \frac{2,199.7}{177,760.5} = .012$$

Table 6.8 Duration of Unemployment in Relation to Age and Sex (Tabulated figures are mean weeks duration unemployment; figures in parentheses are standard errors.)

	Sex	
Age	Men	Women
14–24 years	11.97	15.18
	(.99)	(.83)
25–44 years	14.36	16.29
	(.55)	(.99)
45 and older	15.76	17.09
	(.63)	(1.03)

$$R^2 = .012$$

Source: Data of Table 6.7.

The difference between R^2 and $\bar{R}^2$ depends on the degrees of freedom n_1 and n_2. It is easily shown that[2]

$$1 - \bar{R}^2 = (1 - R^2) \frac{n_1 + n_2}{n_2}.$$

$\bar{R}^2$ is interpreted the same way as the unadjusted value, but, being unbiased, it is a superior measure of the proportion of variance actually associated with the independent variables.[3]

2. Mathematical proof:

$$(1 - R^2) \frac{n_1 + n_2}{n_2} = \left(1 - \frac{\text{sum of squares among cells}}{\text{total sum of squares}}\right) \frac{n_1 + n_2}{n_2}$$

$$= \left(\frac{\text{total sum of squares} - \text{sum of squares among cells}}{\text{total sum of squares}}\right) \frac{n_1 + n_2}{n_2}$$

$$= \left(\frac{\text{sum of squares within cells}}{\text{total sum of squares}}\right) \frac{n_1 + n_2}{n_2}$$

$$= \frac{\dfrac{\text{sum of squares within cells}}{n_2}}{\dfrac{\text{total sum of squares}}{n_1 + n_2}}$$

$$= \frac{\text{variance within cells}}{\text{total variance}}$$

$$= 1 - \bar{R}^2.$$

3. A slight difference lies in the fact that, unlike R^2 which mathematically cannot be negative, $\bar{R}^2$ can fall below zero. It can be shown, however, that this occurs only when F is less than 1, that is, when there is no evidence of correlation anyhow.

Table 6.9   Analysis of Variance: Duration of Unemployment
in Relation to Age and Sex

Source	Sum of Squares	d.f.	Variance
Total	177,760.5	1,337	132.9
Among cells	2,199.7	5	439.9
Within cells	175,558.9	1,332	131.8

$$F = \frac{439.9}{131.8} = 3.34$$

$$(n_1 = 5, n_2 = 1,000; F_{.05} = 2.22, F_{.01} = 3.04)$$

$$(\bar{R}^2 = 1 - \frac{131.8}{132.9} = .008)^a$$

[a] See below, section 6.3.8.
Source: Data of Table 6.7.

6.3.9   Summary of Analysis of Variance

The purpose of the analysis of variance is to test whether observed variation in cell means signifies a correlation between the dependent and the independent variables under discussion, or whether its magnitude is only such as would be expected from random samples from the same normally distributed population. Under the null hypothesis that the samples come from the same normal population, there are two independent ways to estimate the variance of that population:

1. We can use the sum of squares among cells to calculate the variance among cells.

2. We can use the sum of squares within cells to calculate the variance within cells.

According to the null hypothesis, these two estimates would be the same. If the variance among cells exceeds that within cells, it constitutes evidence that some additional factor is varying among cells. The F table is used to evaluate this evidence. The procedure is as follows:

Given N items divided into k samples with N_j items in the jth sample,

1. Array the sums of squares and degrees of freedom in an analysis of variance table.

2. Calculate total variance, variance among cells, and variance within cells. The general form of the analysis table is then:

Source	Sum of Squares	d.f.	Variance
Total	$\Sigma\Sigma(Y_{ij} - \bar{\bar{Y}})^2$	$N - 1$	$\dfrac{\Sigma\Sigma(Y_{ij} - \bar{\bar{Y}})^2}{N - 1}$
Among cells	$\Sigma N_j(\bar{Y}_j - \bar{\bar{Y}})^2$	$k - 1$	$\dfrac{\Sigma N_j(\bar{Y}_j - \bar{\bar{Y}})^2}{k - 1}$
Within cells	$\Sigma\Sigma(Y_{ij} - \bar{Y}_j)^2$	$N - k$	$\dfrac{\Sigma\Sigma(Y_{ij} - \bar{Y}_j)^2}{N - k}$

3. $F = \dfrac{\text{variance among cells}}{\text{variance within cells}}$.

4. If F exceeds 1, enter the F table at $n_1 = k - 1$, $n_2 = N - k$ to find $F_{.05}$ and $F_{.01}$. If the calculated F exceeds $F_{.05}$, it is significant at the .05 level; if it exceeds $F_{.01}$, it is significant at the .01 level.

5. Calculate $\bar{R}^2 = 1 - \dfrac{\text{variance within cells}}{\text{total variance}}$.

Of course, F can be calculated and tested without preparing an analysis table, but the table forms a compact summary of all information relevant to the test and is often published as part of the research report.

6.3.10 Limitations to the Analysis of Variance

In the discussion above we passed lightly over the fact that the F test is based on sets of samples drawn at random from the *same normal population*. Samples drawn from a normal population will themselves be normally distributed. Moreover, samples drawn from the same population will tend to have equal variances. A variable whose variance tends to be the same in all cells is called *homoskedastic*; when variance in some cells is substantially higher than in others, the variable is *heteroskedastic*.[4] Thus, the analysis of variance is strictly applicable only to data that are both normally distributed within cells and homoskedastic. Fortunately, however, the analysis of variance is a "rugged" technique that provides a useful approximation even for wide departures from both normality and homoskedasticity.

4. The word homoskedastic is derived from the Greek roots *homo* ("same") *skedastikos* ("scatter"). *Skedastikos* is probably also the root of the word "skedaddle."

The most notable case to which the analysis of variance is *not* appropriate is the categorical dependent variable. The distribution of a variable with only two values, 0 and 1, is about as far as possible from a normal distribution. Moreover, within the *j*th cell the variance $\hat{\sigma}_p^2$ of a categorical variable is given by

$$\hat{\sigma}_p^2 = P_j(1 - P_j)\frac{N_j}{N_j - 1}.$$

P_j is the proportion of items in the category, and variation of P_j from cell to cell generates the most blatant heteroskedasticity: If the proportion of responses among 100 items in one cell is .5, we have

$$\hat{\sigma}_p^2 = .5 \times (1 - .5) \times \frac{100}{99} = .253.$$

Among 100 items in another cell a rate of response of .05 would give

$$\hat{\sigma}_p^2 = .05 \times (1 - .05) \times \frac{100}{99} = .480.$$

Fortunately, a simple alternative to the analysis of variance is available for use with categorical variables.

6.4 THE CHI SQUARE (χ^2) TEST OF A CATEGORICAL DEPENDENT VARIABLE

As part of a study of the demand for bus transportation, a sample of 600 people were asked whether they had taken a round trip by bus during the preceding 12 months to a point 100 or more miles from home. The individuals were also asked about their marital status and children, and were separated into three "life cycle" classes: single, married (no children), married (with children). The data of Table 6.10 show the responses tabulated by respondent's life cycle status: of the 160 single respondents, 16 had taken a bus trip, 144 had not; of the 270 married with children, 11 had taken a bus trip, and so on.

The function is tabulated in Table 6.11. We see that the percentage of single people reporting bus trips was somewhat higher than either married group. The latter are much alike. Notice, however, that the differences among these percentages are not large relative to their

Table 6.10   Frequency of Bus Trip by Life Cycle Status

Life Cycle	Number Who: Took Bus Trip	Took no Bus Trip	Total
Single	16	144	160
Married:			
No children	9	161	170
Children	11	259	270
Total	36	564	600

Source: Data are scaled down from Ernest Oksanen, "An Analysis of the Demand for Non-Business Bus Travel" (Ann Arbor: Research Seminar in Quantitative Economics, The University of Michigan, 1959, mimeographed), Table 7, p. 12.

standard errors, and it is not clear that the data reflect anything more than random variation.

6.4.1   Observed and Expected Frequencies

The null hypothesis is that the population proportion of bus trips is equal in all classes, that is, the proportion of trips in each life cycle class is expected to equal the proportion of trips in the table as a whole. A total of 36 out of the 600 people sampled reported a trip, so the proportion of trips in the table as a whole is $36/600 = .06$. Under the null hypothesis, then, we would expect, on the average, $.06 \times 160 = 9.6$ trips to be reported by a sample of 160 single people, with $.94 \times 160 = 150.4$ reporting no trip. Similarly, the values expected for a sample of 170 married with no children are $.06 \times 170 = 10.2$ with trips, and $.94 \times 170 = 159.8$ with no trips; and among 270 married with children, $.06 \times 270 = 16.2$ with trips, and $.94 \times 270 = 253.8$ with no trips.

Table 6.11   Bus Trip as a Function of Life Cycle Status

	Single	Married No Children	Children
Proportion with bus trip	.100	.053	.041
Standard error	(.024)	(.017)	(.012)
Cell size	160	170	270

Source: Data of Table 6.10.

Table 6.12 Calculation of χ^2 from Data of Table 6.10

	Number with Bus Trip					Number with No Bus Trip					Total
	Observed O	Expected E	$O-E$	$(O-E)^2$	$\dfrac{(O-E)^2}{E}$	Observed O	Expected E	$O-E$	$(O-E)^2$	$\dfrac{(O-E)^2}{E}$	
Single	16	$160\times.06=9.6$	6.4	40.96	4.267	144	$160\times.94=150.4$	−6.4	40.96	.272	160
Married:											
No children	9	$170\times.06=10.2$	−1.2	1.44	.141	161	$170\times.94=159.8$	1.2	1.44	.009	170
Children	11	$270\times.06=16.2$	−5.2	27.04	1.669	259	$270\times.94=253.8$	5.2	27.04	.107	270
Total observed	36					564					600
Proportion	.0600					.9400					

$$\chi^2 = 4.267 + .141 + 1.699 + .272 + .009 + .107 = 6.465$$
$$(2 \text{ d.f.; } \chi^2_{.05} = 5.991, \chi^2_{.02} = 7.824)$$

Table 6.12 contains the original data from Table 6.10 and the expected values as just calculated.

6.4.2 Calculation of χ^2

The evidence of correlation is the deviation of the observed frequencies, O, from their expected values, E. To evaluate this evidence, calculate, for each cell, the squared deviation of observed from expected frequencies, and divide by the expected cell frequency, that is, in each cell, j, calculate

$$\frac{(O_j - E_j)^2}{E_j} .$$

The sum of these, over all cells, is the statistic χ^2 (chi square):

$$\chi^2 = \Sigma \frac{(O_j - E_j)^2}{E_j} .$$

In Table 6.12 we have $\chi^2 = 6.465$. This χ^2 has 2 degrees of freedom: Since the deviations in each row and column total zero, once any two deviations in the "Bus Trip" column are specified, the entire table can be calculated. In general, in a table of R rows and C columns there are $(R - 1) \times (C - 1)$ degrees of freedom. Thus in this case, $R = 3$ and $C = 2$, and d.f. $= (3 - 1) \times (2 - 1) = 2$.

6.4.3 The χ^2 Distribution

Even under the null hypothesis that the proportion of people taking bus trips is independent of their life cycle status, the value of χ^2 would rarely be 0, but would vary from sample to sample in a fashion depending on the number of degrees of freedom.

The χ^2 distribution is given in Appendix D. Each figure in the body of the table is the value of χ^2 corresponding to the degrees of freedom, n, at the left, that is exceeded by the proportion of samples shown at the top. The number 23.209, found in row 10 under the proportion .01 means that, with 10 degrees of freedom, only 1 per cent of the time will a χ^2 exceeding 23.209 be found among sets of random samples from the same population.

To determine the significance of $\chi^2 = 6.465$ observed in Table 6.12, enter the χ^2 table at $n = 2$ to find $\chi^2_{.05} = 5.991$; $\chi^2_{.02} = 7.824$. The observed χ^2 lies between these two values and is therefore significant at the .05 level, but not at .02.

6.4.4 Multivalued Categorical Dependent Variable

Application of the χ^2 test to a dependent variable with more than 2 categorical values follows the same procedure as above. Table 6.13 contains

Table 6.13   Attitude of Families Toward Installment Debt

Family Income	Number of Families Who Think Installment Buying Is:			
	Good Idea	Pro-Con	Bad Idea	Total
Under $2,000	107	36	92	235
$2,000–3,999	172	47	118	337
$4,000–7,499	275	71	158	504
$7,500–9,999	64	18	29	111
$10,000 or more	42	18	35	95
Total	660	190	432	1,282

Source: Adapted from George Katona, "Attitudes Toward Saving and Borrowing," in *Consumer Installment Credit*, Part II, Vol. 1, *Conference on Regulation* (Washington, D.C.: U.S. Government Printing Office, 1957), pp. 450–86.

family income and the responses of 1,282 people to the question, "Do you think it's a good idea or a bad idea to buy things on the installment plan?" Since many people had something to say on both sides, respondents were put in three categories: "Good Idea," "Pro-Con," "Bad Idea."

The function, tabulated in Table 6.14, reveals a plausible relationship between response and income. At low incomes where installment payments are a burden and repossessions a constant threat, relatively fewer people think installment buying a good idea; relatively more tend to question it or think of it as a bad idea. Up the income scale we find that the more secure groups, for whom payments are a smaller burden, look upon installment buying with increasing favor. In the very highest incomes, however, people infrequently need to employ installment buying and relatively fewer approve of it; relatively more are doubtful or view it with outright disapproval. However, inspection of the standard

Table 6.14   Attitude Toward Installment Buying
as a Function of Income
(Figures in parentheses are standard errors.)

Family Income	Total Number of Families	Per cent of Families Who Think Installment Buying Is:		
		Good Idea	Pro-Con	Bad Idea
Under $2,000	235	45.5	15.3	39.2
		(3.2)	(2.4)	(3.2)
$2,000–3,999	337	51.0	14.0	35.0
		(2.7)	(1.9)	(2.6)
$4,000–7,499	504	54.6	14.1	31.3
		(2.2)	(1.5)	(2.1)
$7,500–9,999	111	57.7	16.2	26.1
		(4.7)	(3.5)	(4.2)
$10,000 or more	95	44.2	18.9	36.9
		(5.1)	(4.1)	(5.0)

Source: Data of Table 6 13.

errors warns us that the relationship is not measured with great precision.

A χ^2 test of the correlation of attitude and income is made in Table 6.15. As shown by the column totals at the foot of the table, of the 1,282 people questioned, a total of 660 or 51.482 per cent said installment buying was a good idea, a total of 190 or 14.821 per cent expressed opinions on both sides, while 432 or 33.697 per cent said it was a bad idea. Under the null hypothesis, we expect these same percentages to hold regardless of income: Of the 235 with incomes under $2,000 we would expect .51482 $\times$ 235 = 120.983 to say "good idea," .14821 $\times$ 235 = 34.829 to fall in the pro-con group, and the remainder, .33697 $\times$ 235 = 79.188 to say "bad idea." The expected frequencies in the other rows are calculated similarly. As before, the deviation of observed from expected frequency is squared, divided by expected frequency, and accumulated over all cells to give χ^2 = 11.23. Since there are 5 rows and 3 columns, this χ^2 has (5 − 1) $\times$ (3 − 1) = 8 degrees of freedom. Entering the χ^2 table at n = 8 we find $\chi^2_{.05}$ = 15.51. The calculated value fails to attain significance at the .05 level.

Table 6.15   Calculation of χ^2 from Data of Table 6.13

Income Class		Attitude Toward Installment Buying			Total
		Good Idea	Pro-Con	Bad Idea	
Under $2,000	observed (O)	107	36	92	235
	expected (E)	(120.983)	(34.829)	(79.188)	
	$O - E$	−13.983	1.171	12.812	
	$(O - E)^2$	195.524	1.371	164.147	
	$(O - E)^2/E$	1.616	.039	2.073	
$2,000–3,999	O	172	47	118	337
	E	(173.494)	(49.947)	(113.559)	
	$O - E$	−1.494	−2.947	4.441	
	$(O - E)^2$	2.232	8.685	19.722	
	$(O - E)^2/E$	.013	.174	.174	
$4,000–7,499	O	275	71	158	504
	E	(259.469)	(74.698)	(169.833)	
	$O - E$	15.531	−3.698	−11.833	
	$(O - E)^2$	241.212	13.675	140.020	
	$(O - E)^2/E$	.930	.183	.824	
$7,500–9,999	O	64	18	29	111
	E	(57.145)	(16.451)	(37.404)	
	$O - E$	6.855	1.549	−8.404	
	$(O - E)^2$	46.991	2.400	70.627	
	$(O - E)^2/E$	.822	.146	1.888	
$10,000 or over	O	42	18	35	95
	E	(48.908)	(14.080)	(32.012)	
	$O - E$	−6.908	3.920	2.988	
	$(O - E)^2$	47.720	15.366	8.928	
	$(O - E)^2/E$	.976	1.091	.279	
Column total		660	190	432	1,282
Proportion of grand total		.51482	.14821	.33697	

$$\chi^2 = 11.23 \ (n = 8; \ \chi^2_{.05} = 15.51)$$

In this case, the tabulated evidence, however plausible, fails to be convincing, and we cannot be sure whether attitude toward installment buying is really related to income or not. It is worth reminding ourselves once more that low significance does not necessarily imply absence of relationship. In this instance, as a matter of fact, responses of another sample of 3,000 people in another survey showed nearly the identical relationship. When the two samples are taken together, the evidence is overwhelmingly significant.[5] The initial failure of the data to produce a highly significant χ^2 resulted merely from small sample size.

6.4.5 Limitation to χ^2

For large N, it is unnecessary to take the total sample size into direct account in making a χ^2 test. Given the proportions in which the sample is distributed, χ^2 is proportional to N, that is, proportions equal, a larger sample has a larger value of χ^2 than a smaller one, and the larger the sample the better the chance to detect a relationship if one exists.

For small samples, however, the marginal proportions themselves become unstable, and the results of the χ^2 test are unreliable, even when they appear to be highly significant. Although there is no firm rule in the matter, it is usually considered inadvisable to trust a value of χ^2 when the expected frequency in the smallest cell is fewer than 5.

6.4.6 Use of χ^2 with Numerical Variables

In Chapter V, we saw that any numerical variable can be treated as a categorical variable by using it to define classes whose numerical properties are ignored. It follows that χ^2 can be used with numerical dependent variables treated in this fashion.

It is sometimes desirable to do this, particularly when the numerical scale itself is of questionable validity. For example, in a study of the factors affecting the amount of individual education, we might measure education by number of years of schooling. This is a straightforward procedure and has obvious merit, and if it yields significant results is unexceptionable. At the same time, the educational "distances" between finishing the eighth grade and a high school diploma on the one hand, and between finishing high school and a college degree on the other, are probably not nearly as equal as the equal four-year intervals would

5. See George Katona, "Attitudes Toward Saving and Borrowing," in *Consumer Installment Credit*, Part II, Vol. 1, *Conference on Regulation* (Washington, D.C.: U.S. Government Printing Office, 1957), pp. 450–86.

imply. The scale is ordinally valid: A college degree is *more* education than a high school diploma. It is not clear that the difference in number of years really indicates *how much* more education is involved. It some-times happens that tests using a numerical variable fail to show a significant relationship merely because the variable is improperly scaled. In such cases, a χ^2 test can be used to explore the matter further, in-dependently of the numerical scale.

6.4.7 Summary of χ^2

The purpose of χ^2 is to test whether the category to which an item be-longs is correlated with specified independent variables. The independent variables define classes, and the data consist of the number of items in each class observed in each category. The data can be arrayed in a table like the following where A, B, C represent classes defined by inde-pendent variables, and a, b, c, d represent categories of the dependent variable. The observed cell frequencies are represented by O_{Aa}, O_{Ab}, and so on, the class totals by O_A, O_B, O_C; the category totals by O_a, O_b, and so on, and the grand total by O_T.

	Category				
Class	a	b	c	d	Total
A	O_{Aa}	O_{Ab}	O_{Ac}	O_{Ad}	O_A
B	O_{Ba}	O_{Bb}	O_{Bc}	O_{Bd}	O_B
C	O_{Ca}	O_{Cb}	O_{Cc}	O_{Cd}	O_C
Total	O_a	O_b	O_c	O_d	O_T

The null hypothesis is that the proportional distribution of cate-gories a, b, c, d, is the same in all classes A, B, C, that is, that the pro-portions of O_A, O_B, O_C to be expected in a, b, c, d are the same as the proportions of O_T that fall in a, b, c, d. Thus, the total O_A should be distributed among a, b, c, and d in the proportions O_a/O_T, O_b/O_T, O_c/O_T, and O_d/O_T, and similarly for the other rows. From this we can calculate the number of items expected to fall in each of the cells of the table:

$$E_{Aa} = O_A \times O_a/O_T; \qquad E_{Ba} = O_B \times O_a/O_T; \qquad \text{and so on.}$$

In each cell the difference between observed frequency and expected frequency, squared and divided by expected frequency, measures the departure of that cell observation from expectation. Summed over all cells, this becomes χ^2, the total departure of observation from the null hypothesis.

If there are R rows and C columns in the table, this value of χ^2 is associated with $(R - 1)(C - 1)$ degrees of freedom, and its significance can be determined from a χ^2 table.

χ^2 can be used with one or several independent variables, but it does not distinguish among the variables; a significant χ^2 does not tell us whether the dependent variable is correlated with one, or with several of the independent variables.

6.5 SUMMARY OF SIGNIFICANCE TESTS

A significance test is a more precise evaluation of evidence, to be used where the existence of a relationship is not clearly apparent in a table. In this chapter we have examined the three most commonly used tests. Many others are used in more advanced work for special purposes, but all have the same logical structure and, once this is understood, the differences among the tests become largely a matter of detail. All significance tests contain the same basic elements:

1. Evidence of the relationship is presented (a difference between means, an F ratio, χ^2, and so on).

2. A null hypothesis is formulated that the evidence was observed by accident.

3. The risk of such an accident is calculated. This risk is the significance level of the test.

4. The significance level is used to evaluate the evidence. The lower the risk, the higher the significance of the evidence. Highly significant evidence is taken to show the existence of the relationship. Nonsignificant evidence shows nothing one way or the other.

Significance tests are not ends in themselves, but are auxiliary tools to be used when needed. They are not needed when the existence of correlation is apparent to the unaided eye, and their application in such cases is wasted time and effort. Moreover, even when they are required, they do not occupy the center of the research design.

The significance test is a statisticians' way of cross-examining a witness whose veracity is open to doubt. A high significance level carries with it the conviction that what the witness says is true, but it is not necessarily the whole truth, nor is it necessarily relevant to the matter at hand. Properly understanding, interpreting, and applying the evidence still remains the central task.

Questions and Problems

1. **Distributions of Samples of Mortgaged and Nonmortgaged Houses by Value, 1959**

Value (thousands of $)	Nonmortgaged Houses	Mortgaged Houses
Under 2.5	1	1
2.5–4.99	4	1
5.0–7.49	6	3
7.5–9.99	5	7
10.0–12.49	7	5
12.5–14.99	1	4
15.0–19.99	4	4
20.0 and over[a]	2	5

[a] Mean in this class is approximately $30.0 (thousand).
Source: Data are a random subsample from material tabulated in *1960 Survey of Consumer Finances* (Ann Arbor: Survey Research Center, The University of Michigan, 1961).

Tabulate the relationship between house value and mortgage status, and test its significance. Write a short paragraph summarizing your findings.

2. **A Sample of Families by Income and by Years of School Completed by Head of Family, Detroit, 1952**

Family Income	Years of School Completed by Head				
	6 or less	7–8	9–11	12	Some College
Under $3,000	63	47	38	24	8
$3,000–4,999	65	100	106	77	53
$5,000–6,999	41	58	91	88	53
$7,000–7,999	8	11	18	32	24
$8,000 or more[a]	16	45	32	35	47

[a] Mean of this class is about $11,000.
Source: Data are from *A Social Profile of Detroit, 1952* (Ann Arbor: Detroit Area Study, Survey Research Center, The University of Michigan, 1953).

Tabulate the relationship of income to education and test its significance. Write a short paragraph summarizing your findings.

3. Test the significance of the relationship of state income to new car registrations, using the data of Table 5.11.

4. In 1952 a sample of people were interviewed and asked whether they intended to buy a new car or not. One year later the people were reinterviewed to find out whether they had or had not bought a new car. The results were:

Expressed	Performance	
Intentions:	Bought	Did not Buy
To buy	50	50
Not to buy	4	96

Test the significance of purchase intentions as a predictor of performance.

5. In a later year, the study of purchase intentions was repeated, and an effort was made to determine whether, intention given, performance was related to income. The 71 people who expressed intentions to buy had incomes and performance as follows:

Income	Bought	Did not Buy
Under $4,000	7	12
$4,000–5,999	10	10
$6,000–9,999	10	7
$10,000 or more	8	7

Test the significance of the relationship of income to performance.

6. The relationships used as examples in Chapter V are all so highly significant by inspection that a formal test is unnecessary, but going through the procedure is a useful exercise. Test each of them.

References

1. Frank L. Wolf. *Elements of Probability and Statistics*. New York: McGraw-Hill Book Co., 1962. The important test statistics are mathematically dealt with in three chapters: χ^2 in Chapter 11, F in Chapter 12, and Student's t in Chapter 13.

2. George P. Wentworth and Joseph G. Bryan. *Introduction to Probability and Random Variables*. New York: McGraw-Hill Book Co., 1960. The concluding chapter, "Some Statistical Uses of Probability," is a good treatment of significance tests with emphasis on logic and underlying reasoning rather than formal mathematics.

3. Wilfred J. Dixon and Frank J. Massey, Jr. *Introduction to Statistical Analysis*. New York: McGraw-Hill Book Co., 1957. Chapter 9 deals with the means of two populations, Chapter 10 with the analysis of variance. Chapter 14, "Probability of Accepting a False Hypothesis," deals with the problems of risk in connection with significance tests.

CHAPTER VII

The Function as an Equation I: Simple Linear Regression

7.1 INTRODUCTION

Tabulation has two serious limitations. In the first place, even when data have been tabulated, it is often necessary to represent the relationship, at least approximately, by an equation. A table is poorly adapted for the study of elasticities, marginal productivities, multipliers, and other quantitative aspects of economic functions. Much modern research, for example the construction of econometric models, requires that relationships be expressed by simple mathematical formulas. Secondly, tabulation requires a substantial amount of data. A small sample puts a severe limit to the number of cells that can be explored, even when the function is restricted to a single independent variable.

Linear regression is a method of approximating a statistical function by a simple linear equation. Moreover, because of its relative simplicity, it can be usefully applied even to samples too small to tabulate. These two points are illustrated by Tables 7.1 and 7.2 and the accompanying charts.

Table 7.1 contains family beef consumption tabulated as a function of income. The small standard errors indicate that the function is measured with considerable precision, and when plotted in Figure 7.1, the cell means fit tightly to a smooth curve. Although the equation of this curve is complicated, it can be usefully approximated by a straight line. What the linear approximation loses in ability to describe detail is made up, in part at least, by the simplicity of its equation.

Table 7.2 contains the total annual production and the farm price of onions for each of 11 years. Detailed tabulation of onion demand is

Figure 7.1 Beef Consumption as a Function of Family Income, U.S., 1955

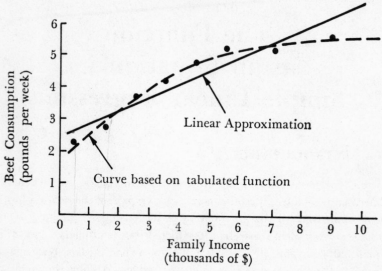

Source: Data of Table 7.1.

Table 7.1 Family Beef Consumption as a Function of Family Income, U.S., 1955

Family Income	Mean Weekly Beef Consumption (pounds)	Standard Error[a]	Number of Families
Under $1,000	2.13	.11	532
$1,000–1,999	2.82	.09	647
$2,000–2,999	3.70	.09	692
$3,000–3,999	4.25	.08	867
$4,000–4,999	4.86	.08	865
$5,000–5,999	5.16	.11	513
$6,000–7,999	5.23	.10	530
$8,000–10,000	5.67	.17	181

[a] Standard errors are approximate and are not supplied in the original.
Source: Adapted from *Food Consumption of Households in the United States,* Household Food Consumption Survey 1955, Report No. 1 (Washington, D.C.: U.S. Department of Agriculture, 1956).

Table 7.2 Total Production and Farm Prices of Onions,
U.S., 1944–55

Year	Production (millions of cwt.)	Price ($ per cwt.)
1944	24.0	2.40
1945	18.8	3.38
1946	25.2	1.78
1947	18.4	4.16
1948	21.2	2.64
1949	19.6	2.94
1950	23.0	1.75
1951	20.0	3.34
1952	20.2	4.62
1953	25.2	1.37
1954	22.2	2.14
1955	21.4	2.37

Source: *Agricultural Statistics 1960* (Washington, D.C.: U.S. Department of Agriculture, 1961).

clearly impossible. There are hardly as many individual items in Table 7.2 as there were large samples in Table 7.1! When the data are plotted in Figure 7.2, the points appear to spread around a central tendency, but are too scattered to locate it accurately. The dashed line looks plausible, but wide departures from it would look equally plausible. With accurate measurement out of the question, a straight line is used to approximate the relationship.

Not all linear regressions are such poor approximations. In fact, many economic functions are actually linear, or nearly so. At any rate, as we shall see in the next chapter, it is easy to measure departures from linearity, and where these are significantly large, a simple transformation of variables often results in substantial improvement in the approximation.

7.2 THE EQUATION OF A STRAIGHT LINE

Any straight line can be represented by an equation in the form

$$Y = a + bX.$$

Figure 7.2   Scatter of Onion Prices on Total Production, U.S., 1944–55

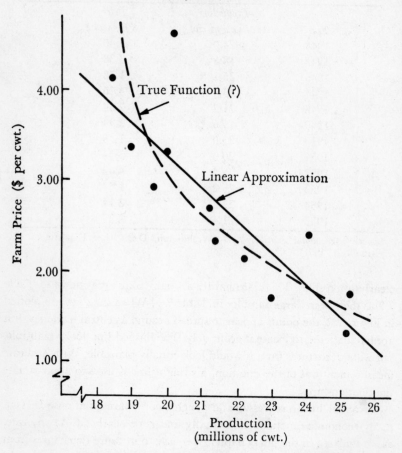

Source: Data of Table 7.2.

In this equation, a is the value of Y corresponding to $X = 0$, that is, it is the height at which the line strikes the Y axis, and is often called the *Y-intercept*. The *slope* of the line, b, is the amount by which Y changes for a unit increase in X; it is positive or negative as the line slopes upward or downward, and the steeper the slope, the greater the absolute value of b. The line of Figure 7.3 has the intercept $a = 1$, and the slope $b = \frac{1}{2}$. Its equation is, thus, $Y = 1 + \frac{1}{2} X$.

158

Figure 7.3   The Straight Line Corresponding to the
Equation $Y = 1 + \frac{1}{2}X$.

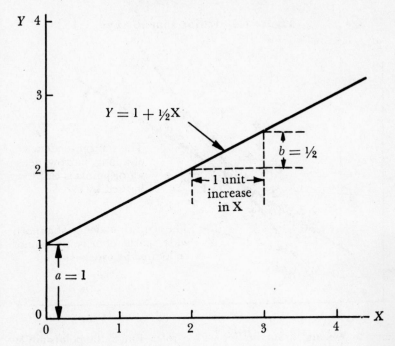

A straight line is determined by any two points, or by any one point and the slope. Thus, the values of a and b identify a unique line. Conversely, given any line, unique values of a and b can be determined. Therefore, the problem of representing the function by a simple linear equation is equivalent to representing it by a straight line.

The statistical process used to fit a straight line to a set of observed points is called *linear regression*, and the equation of the line that results is called a *regression equation*. The slope b in the regression equation is known as the *regression coefficient*.

7.3   LINE FITTED BY EYE

The problem of linear regression is to find the line that follows the central tendency through the scatter of points formed when correspond-

159

ing values of X and Y are plotted. If the scatter is dense, long, and narrow, like the dots in Figure 7.4, it is easy to locate this central tend-

Figure 7.4   Fitting Lines by Eye

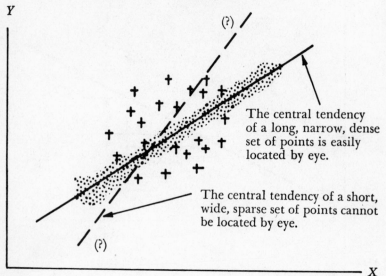

The central tendency of a long, narrow, dense set of points is easily located by eye.

The central tendency of a short, wide, sparse set of points cannot be located by eye.

ency by eye and draw the line with a ruler. But if the points are few, or—like the crosses in Figure 7.4—scattered in a fat cloud, the best line is difficult to locate. A more objective criterion is required.

7.4   THE LEAST SQUARES CRITERION

The logic underlying linear regression can be seen in terms of Figure 7.5. Figure 7.5A is a representation of a statistical function as we have treated it up to now. The values of X define cells. The function is estimated by the cell means, $\bar{Y}_j$. The individual items Y_{ij} vary around the mean under the impact of other factors.

In Figure 7.5B, almost all the data have been removed, leaving only one item per cell. The objective of regression is to use these few points to determine the properties of the function. For this purpose we

Figure 7.5 Relation of Tabulated Function to Linear Regression

A. Tabulated Function

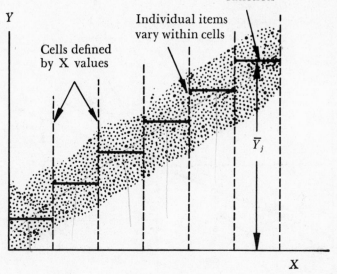

Cell means locate the function

Individual items vary within cells

Cells defined by X values

$\overline{Y}_j$

Y

X

B. Linear Regression

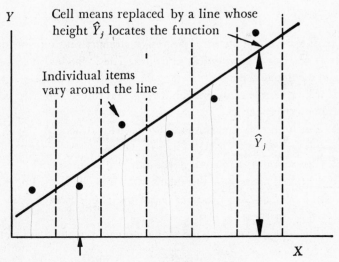

Cell means replaced by a line whose height $\hat{Y}_j$ locates the function

Individual items vary around the line

$\hat{Y}_j$

Y

X

Individual X values replace classes

Figure 7.6 The Least Squares Regression Line Has the Properties of a Mean

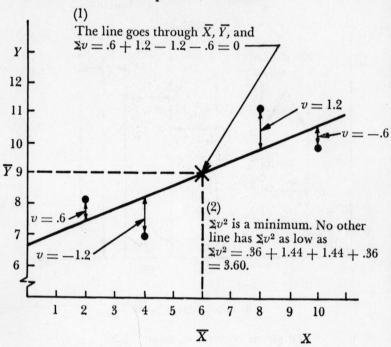

(1)
The line goes through $\overline{X}$, $\overline{Y}$, and
$\Sigma v = .6 + 1.2 - 1.2 - .6 = 0$

$v = 1.2$

$v = -.6$

$v = .6$

$v = -1.2$

(2)
Σv^2 is a minimum. No other
line has Σv^2 as low as
$\Sigma v^2 = .36 + 1.44 + 1.44 + .36$
$= 3.60.$

replace the means of Figure 7.5A by a straight line representing as nearly as possible the *locus* of these means. The individual points are to relate to the line in the same way they formerly related to the cell means.

It will be recalled from section 3.1.3.5 that this relationship involves two important properties:

1. The sum of the deviations of the individual items from the mean is zero.

2. The sum of the squared deviations is a minimum.

If the points are to bear this relationship to the line, the line must be so constructed that the deviations, v_j, of the points from the line have these same properties:

1. The deviations of the individual points from the line must total zero:

$$\Sigma v_j = 0.$$

2. The sum of the squared deviations must be smaller than from any other line:

$$\Sigma v_j^2 = \text{minimum}.$$

Because of this property the line that best approximates the locus of means is called a *least squares* line. The properties of a least squares line are shown in Figure 7.6.

7.5 THE NORMAL EQUATIONS

If we represent the line by the equation $Y = a + bX$, the deviations become $v_j = Y_j - a - bX_j$. The criteria above require that a and b be so chosen that

(1) $\Sigma v_j = \Sigma (Y_j - a - bX_j) = 0$

(2) $\Sigma v_j^2 = \Sigma (Y_j - a - bX_j)^2 = \text{minimum}.$

These two criteria reduce to two *normal equations* whose solutions yield the values of a and b corresponding to the least squares regression:[1]

(1) $a = \bar{Y} - b\bar{X}$

(2) $b = \dfrac{\Sigma (X_j - \bar{X})(Y_j - \bar{Y})}{\Sigma (X_j - \bar{X})^2} = \dfrac{\Sigma x_j y_j}{\Sigma x_j^2}.$

1. Derivation of the normal equations is as follows. Let $\hat{Y}_j$ be the height of the line corresponding to X_j. Then:

(1) $\qquad\qquad v_j = Y_j - \hat{Y}_j = Y_j - (a + bX_j)$

so $\qquad\qquad \Sigma v_j = \Sigma Y_j - Na - b \Sigma X_j = 0.$

Dividing by N:

$$\bar{Y} - a - b\bar{X} = 0$$

and $\qquad\qquad a = \bar{Y} - b\bar{X}.$

(2) Substituting this value of a into $\hat{Y}_j = a + bX_j$:

$$\hat{Y}_j = (\bar{Y} - b\bar{X}) + bX_j$$

and $\qquad v_j = Y_j - \hat{Y}_j = Y_j - (\bar{Y} - b\bar{X}) - bX_j = y_j - bx_j$

So $\qquad \Sigma v_j^2 = \Sigma y_j^2 - 2b\Sigma x_j y_j + b^2 \Sigma x_j^2.$

Set the derivative of this expression (with respect to b) equal to 0 to obtain a minimum:

163

The lower-case letters, as usual, represent deviations from means.

Equation (1) says that the least squares line must pass through the means $\bar{X}$, $\bar{Y}$. This determines a point on the line. Equation (2) defines the slope of the line. Together they define one point and the slope and hence determine the line uniquely.

7.6 CALCULATION OF LEAST SQUARES REGRESSION

One way to calculate a least squares regression is to find $\bar{X}$, $\bar{Y}$ and the deviations $x_j = X_j - \bar{X}$; $y_j = Y_j - \bar{Y}$, and substitute them into the normal equations. The calculations would appear as in Table 7.3, but

Table 7.3 Calculation of Linear Regression, $Y = a + bX$, "Direct" Method

X	$(X-\bar{X})$ x	Y	$(Y-\bar{Y})$ y
2	−4	8	−1
4	−2	7	−2
6	0	9	0
8	2	11	2
10	4	10	1

$$\bar{X} = 6 \qquad\qquad \bar{Y} = 9$$

$$\Sigma x^2 = 16 + 4 + 0 + 4 + 16 = 40$$
$$\Sigma xy = 4 + 4 + 0 + 4 + 4 = 16$$
$$\Sigma y^2 = 1 + 4 + 0 + 4 + 1 = 10$$

$$b = \frac{\Sigma xy}{\Sigma x^2} = \frac{16}{40} = .4$$

$$a = 9 - .4(6) = 6.6$$

this uses none of the familiar short cuts, nor is there any built-in check on the calculations. As standard practice, it is faster and more accurate to follow the steps shown in Table 7.4:

$$\frac{d\Sigma v_i^2}{db} = -2\Sigma x_i y_i + 2b\Sigma x_i^2 = 0.$$

So
$$b = \frac{\Sigma x_i y_i}{\Sigma x_i^2}.$$

Table 7.4 Standard Work Sheet for Linear Regression

Step		X	Y	Check C
(1)	Copy data and check	2 16 8 64		10
		4 28 7 49		11
(2)	Add corresponding X and	6 54 9 81		15
	Y to get check total:	8 88 11 121		19
	$X_j + Y_j = C_j$.	10 100 10 100		20
(3)	Sum columns	30 286 45 415		75
	(Check: 30 + 45 = 75)			

Handwritten in column: 4, 16, 36, 64, 100, 220 (X²); 100, 220–400, 200

(4) Matrix for sums of squares and cross-products

	X	Y	C
X	220	286	506 √
	(ΣX^2)	(ΣXY)	(ΣXC)
Y		415	701 √
		Σy^2	ΣyC

(Check: 220 + 286 = 506
286 + 415 = 701)

(5) Matrix of deviations

$$\frac{N\Sigma X^2 - (\Sigma X)^2}{N} = \Sigma x^2$$

$$\frac{N\Sigma XY - (\Sigma X)(\Sigma Y)}{N} = \Sigma xy$$

and so on.

	x	y	c
x	40	16	56 √
y		10	26 √

Handwritten: $5 \cdot 220 - 400$; $\frac{5(415)}{30 \; 45}$

(Check: 40 + 16 = 56
16 + 10 = 26)

(6) $$b = \frac{\Sigma xy}{\Sigma x^2} = \frac{16}{40} = .4$$

(7) $$a = \frac{\Sigma Y - b\Sigma X}{N} \qquad a = \frac{45 - .4(30)}{5} = 6.6$$

(8) $$Y = 6.6 + .4X$$

1. Arrange the corresponding values of X and Y in columns. Check for copying mistakes.

2. Add the corresponding values of X_j and Y_j and record the totals, C_j, in a third column to serve as check total:

$$X_j + Y_j = C_j.$$

3. Calculate ΣX_j, ΣY_j, ΣC_j. (Check: $\Sigma X_j + \Sigma Y_j = \Sigma C_j$)

4. A matrix, laid out as shown, provides a compact format to receive the sums of squares and cross-products as they are calculated. Calculate ΣX_j^2 and enter it in the row and column labeled X. Calculate $\Sigma X_j Y_j$ and enter in row X, column Y. Calculate $\Sigma X_j C_j$ and enter in row X, column C. (Check: $\Sigma X_j^2 + \Sigma X_j Y_j = \Sigma X_j C_j$)

Calculate ΣY_j^2 and enter in row Y, column Y. Calculate $\Sigma Y_j C_j$ and enter in row Y, column C. (Check: $\Sigma X_j Y_j + \Sigma Y_j^2 = \Sigma Y_j C_j$)

5. Prepare a similar matrix, labeling rows and columns with lower-case letters, to receive squares and products of deviations: Σx_j^2, $\Sigma x_j y_j$, and so on.

Sums of squared deviations are calculated by the usual short-cut formula, for example,

$$\Sigma x_j^2 = \frac{N\Sigma X_j^2 - (\Sigma X_j)^2}{N}.$$

Sums of products of deviations are calculated by an extension of the short-cut formula, for example,

$$\Sigma x_j y_j = \frac{N\Sigma X_j Y_j - (\Sigma X_j)(\Sigma Y_j)}{N}.$$

These are calculated and entered in the appropriate place in the matrix. (Check: $\Sigma x_j^2 + \Sigma x_j y_j = \Sigma x_j c_j$; $\Sigma x_j y_j + \Sigma y_j^2 = \Sigma y_j c_j$)

6. Calculate $b = \dfrac{\Sigma x_j y_j}{\Sigma x_j^2}$.

7. Calculate $a = \dfrac{\Sigma Y_j - b\Sigma X_j}{N}$.

8. Write the complete equation in the form
$$Y = a + bX.$$

To plot the line on the scatter diagram, select two well-spaced values X_0 and X_1 and calculate $\hat{Y}_0 = a + bX_0$, $\hat{Y}_1 = a + bX_1$. The least squares regression line is then ruled through the points $(X_0, \hat{Y}_0)$ and $(X_1, \hat{Y}_1)$.

7.7 EXAMPLES

The following examples illustrate the application of linear regression to different functions and give some interpretations of the results.

7.7.1 Demand for Onions

The calculations of Table 7.5 give the demand equation for onions as a linear regression of price (Y) on quantity (X):

$$Y = 10.258 - .348X.$$

Table 7.5 Calculation of Regression of Farm Price on Total Production of Onions

Year	X Production (million cwt.)	Y Price ($ per cwt.)	C Check
1944	24.0	2.40	26.40
1945	18.8	3.38	22.18
1946	25.2	1.78	26.98
1947	18.4	4.16	22.56
1948	21.2	2.64	23.84
1949	19.6	2.94	22.54
1950	23.0	1.75	24.75
1951	20.0	3.34	23.34
1952	20.2	4.62	24.82
1953	25.2	1.37	26.57
1954	22.2	2.14	24.34
1955	21.4	2.37	23.77
Totals	259.2	32.89	292.09 √

_100.91_ (margin note near 1946 row)

	X	Y	C
X	5,659.52	689.260	6,348.780 √
Y		100.9075	790.1675 √
	x	y	c
x	60.80000	−21.16400	39.63600 √
y		10.76149	−10.40251 √

$$b = \frac{-21.164}{60.800} = -.348$$

$$a = \frac{32.89 + (.348)(259.2)}{12} = 10.258$$

$$Y = 10.258 - .348X$$

$$R^2 = \frac{b\Sigma xy}{\Sigma y^2} = \frac{-.348 \times -21.164}{10.76149} = .68$$

Source: Data of Table 7.2.

Table 7.6 Actual and Calculated Onion Prices and Calculated Residuals

Year	Production (X)	Actual Price (Y)	Calculated Price ($\hat{Y} = 10.258 - .348X$)	Residual ($v = Y - \hat{Y}$)
1944	24.0	$2.40	$1.90	.50
1945	18.8	3.38	3.71	−.33
1946	25.2	1.78	1.49	.29
1947	18.4	4.16	3.85	.31
1948	21.2	2.64	2.88	−.24
1949	19.6	2.94	3.44	−.50
1950	23.0	1.75	2.25	−.50
1951	20.0	3.34	3.30	.04
1952	20.2	4.62	3.23	1.39
1953	25.2	1.37	1.49	−.12
1954	22.2	2.14	2.53	−.39
1955	21.4	2.37	2.81	−.44
Total	259.2	32.89	32.89[a]	.00[a]

Residual sum of squares = $\Sigma v_j^2 = 3.3905$

[a] Individual items do not add to total because of rounding.
Source: Data of Table 7.5.

The negative value of b indicates that larger quantities must be sold at lower prices; an increase in production of 1 million cwt. is associated with a fall in price of $.348 per cwt. The value of a ($10.258 per cwt.) locates the general level of the demand curve. Mathematically, a is the price that would correspond to "zero production," but this interpretation has no economic meaning and should be avoided.

The plotted regression line is shown in Figure 7.2. The individual points deviate from the regression line partly because of curvature in the true function, and partly as a result of u, the influence of unspecified variables. The comparison of actual and calculated prices is given in Table 7.6.

7.7.2 Weekly Beef Consumption as a Function of Family Income

Since class means have already been calculated for beef consumption, the linear regression can be fitted directly to these rather than to the

**Table 7.7   Calculation of Weekly Beef Consumption
as a Function of Family Income**

	X Income (thousands of $)	Y Beef Consumption (pounds per week)	C check	
	.5	2.13	2.63	
	1.5	2.82	4.32	
	2.5	3.70	6.20	
	3.5	4.25	7.75	
	4.5	4.86	9.36	
	5.5	5.16	10.66	
	7.0	5.23	12.23	
	9.0	5.67	14.67	
Totals	34.0	33.82	67.82	√

	X	Y	C	
X	201.5000	167.3100	368.81	√
Y		153.9888	321.2988	√

	x	y	c	
x	57.000	23.57500	80.575	√
y		11.01475	34.58975	√

$$b = \frac{23.575}{57.0} = .41359$$

$$a = \frac{33.82 - .41359 \times 34}{8} = 2.46974$$

$$Y = 2.470 + .414 X$$

$$R^2 = \frac{b\Sigma xy}{\Sigma y^2} = \frac{.414 \times 23.575}{11.01475} = .89$$

Source: Data of Table 7.1.

underlying data. The calculations, shown in Table 7.7, give

$$Y = 2.470 + .414X.$$

The value of b indicates that, as an average approximation over all families, a difference in family income of $1,000 was associated with a difference in weekly beef consumption of .414 pounds. The linear approximation is plotted in Figure 7.1. The pattern of deviations of the

169

cell means from the regression is associated with curvature of the true function, the influence of unspecified variables already having been averaged out.

7.8 THE COEFFICIENTS OF DETERMINATION AND CORRELATION

In regression, the statistics R^2 and R are usually referred to as the *coefficients* of determination and correlation, but the concepts are exactly analogous to the determination and correlation ratios. The calculated value $\hat{Y}_j = a + bX_j$ replaces the cell mean $\bar{Y}_j$, and the residual $v_j = Y_j - \hat{Y}_j$ replaces the deviation of individual items from cell means. In place of the sum of squares among cells we have:

$$\text{regression sum of squares} = \Sigma(\hat{Y}_j - \bar{Y})^2 .$$

In place of the sum of squares within cells we have:

$$\text{residual sum of squares} = \Sigma(\hat{Y}_j - Y_j)^2 = \Sigma v_j^2 .$$

These are related to the total sum of squares by the identity:[2]

$$\Sigma(Y_j - \bar{Y})^2 = \Sigma(\hat{Y}_j - \bar{Y})^2 + \Sigma(v_j^2) .$$

The unadjusted coefficient of determination is then defined as

$$R^2 = \frac{\text{regression sum of squares}}{\text{total sum of squares}} = \frac{\Sigma(\hat{Y}_j - \bar{Y})^2}{\Sigma y_j^2} .$$

2. Mathematical proof:

$$Y_j = \hat{Y}_j + v_j$$
$$y_j = Y_j - \bar{Y} = (\hat{Y}_j - \bar{Y}) + v_j$$
$$\Sigma y_j^2 = \Sigma(\hat{Y}_j - \bar{Y})^2 + \Sigma v_j^2 + 2\Sigma v_j(\hat{Y}_j - \bar{Y}) .$$

To prove the identity, we must establish that the last term on the right is zero. Substituting

$$v_j = y_j - bx_j, \text{ and } \hat{Y}_j - \bar{Y} = bx_j,$$

we have
$$2\Sigma(y_j - bx_j)(bx_j) = 2b(\Sigma x_j y_j - b\Sigma x_j^2) .$$

But $b = \frac{\Sigma x_j y_j}{\Sigma x_j^2}$, so the term in parentheses becomes

$$(\Sigma x_j y_j - \Sigma x_j y_j) = 0.$$

170

The higher the correlation, the better the observed points are represented by a straight line. A short, wide scatter of points like the crosses of Figure 7.4 will give a low R^2; a long, narrow scatter, like the dots in Figure 7.4, will give a high R^2. The square root of R^2 is R, the unadjusted coefficient of correlation. By convention, the sign of b is attached to R; the correlation is positive or negative as the line slopes upward or downward.

As with tabulated functions, the R^2 of a linear regression depends on the impact of the specified variable compared to unspecified stochastic factors, and is also affected by sample composition. In addition, the R^2 of a linear regression depends on how much curvature there is in the scatter of points. The more curvature, the lower R^2. In other words, a low value of R^2 indicates that the points in the scatter do not cling closely to the linear regression. This may be due to the random impact of unspecified variables, or it may be due to the fact that the true relationship is a sharply curved one and poorly approximated by the straight line.

7.8.1 Calculation of R^2

The total sum of squares Σy_i^2 already appears in the matrix of deviations. The regression sum of squares could, if desired, be calculated from the values of $\hat{Y}$ given in Table 7.6, but is more conveniently calculated by a short-cut formula:[3]

$$\text{regression sum of squares} = \Sigma(\hat{Y} - \bar{Y})^2 = b\Sigma x_j y_j.$$

The figures required for this calculation are readily located in the matrix of deviations. As shown in Table 7.8 below, the regression sum of squares can be recorded in an analysis of variance table and R^2 calculated as an adjunct to the F test. This also makes it easy to calculate the adjusted value, $\bar{R}^2$, if desired.

3. Mathematical proof of this formula is as follows:

$$\hat{Y}_j - \bar{Y} = bx_j$$

so

$$\Sigma(\hat{Y}_j - \bar{Y})^2 = b^2\Sigma x_j^2.$$

Replace one of the b's by

$$b = \frac{\Sigma x_j y_j}{\Sigma x_j^2}$$

and get

$$\Sigma(\hat{Y}_j - \bar{Y})^2 = b\frac{\Sigma x_j y_j}{\Sigma x_j^2} \cdot \Sigma x_j^2 = b\Sigma x_j y_j.$$

As computed in Table 7.5, we have $R^2 = .68$ for the regression of onion price on production, that is, 68 per cent of the total observed variance in onion prices is (linearly) associated with variation in production. Since the demand is downward sloped, the correlation of prices with production is $R = -\sqrt{.68} = -.83$.

For beef consumption (Table 7.7), $R^2 = .89$. This high R^2 is characteristic of regressions fitted to means. It is due primarily to the fact that all of the within-cell variance has been eliminated by using cell means as the data in the regression. If most of the variance to be explained is already averaged out, the R^2 will naturally be large. In fact, the primary reason that this R^2 is not even higher is that the line is a rather poor approximation to what is obviously a curvilinear function.

7.9 ANALYSIS OF VARIANCE AND LINEAR REGRESSION

As is true of tabulated functions, it is sometimes not obvious whether the variables in a regression are really related or not, and a significance test is needed. The analysis of variance can be applied for this purpose.

The significance of a tabulated function is tested by comparing the variance among cell means with the variance within cells. In the regression, as we have seen, the role of the cell mean is replaced by the calculated value $\hat{Y} = a + bX$. Thus, in place of the sum of squares among cells we have

$$\Sigma(\hat{Y} - \bar{Y})^2 = \text{regression sum of squares,}$$

while in place of the sum of squares within cells we have

$$\Sigma(Y_j - \hat{Y}_j)^2 = \text{residual sum of squares.}$$

The regression sum of squares has already been calculated by the short-cut formula of the preceding section. The residual sum of squares can be obtained directly by squaring the calculated residuals as shown in Table 7.6, but it is more conveniently obtained by subtracting the regression sum of squares from the total:

$$\text{residual sum of squares} = \Sigma y^2 - b\Sigma x_j y_j.$$

In the case of the onion demand problem this gives

$$\text{residual sum of squares} = 10.76149 - 7.36507 = 3.39642.$$

This agrees with the direct calculation in Table 7.6 as near as rounding errors permit.

The sums of squares are recorded in an analysis of variance table together with the appropriate degrees of freedom:

1. The total sum of squares is, as usual, associated with $N - 1$ degrees of freedom.

2. The regression sum of squares is associated with only 1 degree of freedom. This follows from the fact that one point on the regression line is already determined by the means $\bar{X}$, $\bar{Y}$. If only one other point is specified, the line is determined and all remaining values of $\hat{Y} - \bar{Y}$ can be computed.

3. The residual sum of squares is associated with $N - 2$ degrees of freedom. The residuals must satisfy the two least squares conditions, hence if all but two v's are known, the missing two can be calculated.

The table is completed in the usual way by dividing each sum of squares by its degrees of freedom to get three variances. The F ratio,

$$F = \frac{\text{regression variance}}{\text{residual variance}},$$

is employed as a significance test of correlation just as with a tabulated function. The analysis table can be shown symbolically as below.

Analysis of Variance

Source	Sum of Squares	d.f.	Variance
Total	$\Sigma y_j^2 = (Y - \bar{Y})^2$	$N - 1$	$\dfrac{\Sigma y_j^2}{N - 1}$
Regression	$b\Sigma x_j y_j$	1	$b\Sigma x_j y_j$
Residual	$\Sigma y_j^2 - b\Sigma x_j y_j$	$N - 2$	$\dfrac{\Sigma y_j^2 - b\Sigma x_j y_j}{N - 2}$

$$F = \frac{\text{regression variance}}{\text{residual variance}}$$

Once the regression has been worked out, the analysis of variance takes little additional effort. $\bar{X}$, b, N, and the matrix of deviations contain all the information required, not only for the analysis of variance, but also for calculating R^2, $\bar{R}^2$, and three important standard errors to

Table 7.8 Analysis of Variance, R^2, $\bar{R}^2$, and Standard Errors for Regression of Onion Prices on Production

Carried forward from Table 7.5

	x	y
x	60.80000	−21.16400
y		10.76149

$$\bar{X} = 21.6, \quad b = -.348, \quad N = 12$$

Analysis of variance:

Source		Sum of squares		d.f.	Variance
Total	Σy^2	$= 10.76149$		$N - 1 = 11$	.97831
Regression	$b\Sigma xy = (-.348)(-21.164) =$	7.36507		1	7.36507
Residual	$\Sigma y^2 - b\Sigma xy$	$= 3.39642$		$N - 2 = 10$	.33964

$$F = \frac{\text{regression variance}}{\text{residual variance}} = \frac{7.36507}{.33964} = 21.68$$

$$(n_1 = 1, \ n_2 = 10; \ F_{.01} = 10.4)$$

$$R^2 = \frac{7.36507}{10.76149} = .68 \qquad\qquad R = -\sqrt{.68} = -.83$$

$$\bar{R}^2 = 1 - \frac{.33964}{.97831} = .65 \qquad\qquad \bar{R} = -\sqrt{.65} = -.81$$

Standard errors:

(1) Standard error of Y, given X

$$\sigma_{y.x} = \sqrt{\sigma_v^2} = \sqrt{.33964} = .582$$

(2) Standard error of b

$$\sigma_b^2 = \frac{\sigma_v^2}{\Sigma x^2} = \frac{.33964}{60.8} = .00558$$

$$\sigma_b = \sqrt{.00558} = .075$$

(3) Standard error of a

$$\sigma_a^2 = \frac{\sigma_v^2}{N} + \bar{X}^2\sigma_b^2 = \frac{.33964}{12} + (21.6)^2(.00558) = 2.63171$$

$$\sigma_a = \sqrt{2.63171} = 1.62$$

Final statement of regression:

$$Y = 10.26 - .348 X$$
$$(1.62) \quad (.075)$$

Source: Data of Table 7.5.

be discussed below. The required values are carried over from Table 7.5 to Table 7.8, and the analysis is shown.

The value of F shown is highly significant of a correlation of onion prices with production.

7.10 CURVATURE AND THE *F* RATIO

One aspect of the application of the analysis of variance to regression requires special attention. When a regression is a linear approximation to a curvilinear relationship, the residual variance involves, in addition to the random impact of unspecified variables, the systematic deviation of the curve from a straight line. The greater the curvature of the function, the greater the apparent residual variance and the smaller *F*. Thus, an *F* too small to show significance may arise from substantial curvature rather than from absence of correlation.

7.11 THE ADJUSTED COEFFICIENT OF DETERMINATION, $\bar{R}^2$

Like the determination ratio, the coefficient of determination tends to overstate the closeness of relationship unless it is adjusted for the size of the sample. The adjustment is exactly analogous to that used earlier. The adjusted coefficient of determination is given by

$$\bar{R}^2 = 1 - \frac{\text{residual variance}}{\text{total variance}} .$$

This adjustment is conveniently made at the foot of the analysis of variance table before the standard errors are calculated, as shown in Table 7.8.

7.12 STANDARD ERRORS

Three important standard errors are associated with a least squares linear regression: (1) $\sigma_{y \cdot x}$, the standard error of estimate, (2) σ_b, the standard error of the slope, and (3) σ_a, the standard error of the intercept.

7.12.1 The Standard Error of Estimate

One important application of a linear regression is to estimate the value of Y, given X. Suppose the onion crop this year is expected to be 20.0 million cwt., and we are required to estimate the price it will bring. Setting $X = 20.0$, calculate the point estimate

$$\hat{Y} = 10.258 - .348 \times 20 = \$3.30 .$$

175

The standard error of this estimate is required to establish a confidence interval. The deviation of an observed from an estimated price is v, and σ_v^2, the residual variance, has already been calculated. Its square root, written $\sigma_{y\cdot x}$, is the standard error of estimate of Y, given X. In Table 7.8 the standard error of estimate of onion prices is $\sigma_{y\cdot x} = .58$.

In general, the shape of the distribution of v is unknown, and an exact confidence level cannot be assigned. It will be recalled, however, that about 60 per cent of all items in a peaked distribution are within 1σ, and about 90 per cent within 2σ of the mean. Therefore, in estimating Y, given $X = 20$, about 90 per cent confidence is associated with the interval

$$Y = \$3.30 \pm 2 \times (.58) = \$3.30 \pm 1.16 .$$

The force of this statement can be seen by looking back at the residuals of Table 7.6. Eleven out of the twelve calculated values fall well within \$1.16 of the actual value. One of the residuals exceeds \$1.16, but only slightly.

The standard error of estimate is only meaningful when the deviations, v, are predominantly the effect of unspecified variables. When v is a manifestation of curvature, its behavior is not described by σ_v^2. For example, beef consumption, calculated at family income of \$5.0 thousand, is

$$\hat{Y} = 2.470 + .414 \times 5.0 = 4.54 .$$

Inspection of Figure 7.1 quickly shows that the actual mean consumption of families with this income is about 5.9 pounds. The difference, $5.9 - 4.54 = .46$ pounds, is mostly due to the deviation of the curvilinear function itself from the linear approximation and will *always* occur when consumption is "estimated" from the linear regression. In this circumstance a "confidence interval" based on $\sigma_{y\cdot x}$ would be meaningless.

7.12.2 Standard Error of b

The slope of the regression is estimated from a sample. If another sample were drawn, even with the same X's, variation from unspecified causes would make the second estimate of b differ from the first. Repeating this experiment over and over would generate a distribution of b's, each estimated from the same set of N specified values of X. This distribution has the variance

$$\sigma_b^2 = \frac{\sigma_v^2}{\Sigma x_j^2}.$$

The standard error of b is given by

$$\sigma_b = \sqrt{\frac{\sigma_v^2}{\Sigma x_j^2}}.$$

While this formula can be mathematically demonstrated, it is readily understood from Figure 7.7.[4] Think of the sample figuratively, as contained in a pipe or tube whose length is σ_X^2 and whose width is σ_v^2. The regression line is like a rod inside the pipe. When the pipe is long and slender (σ_v^2/σ_X^2 is small), σ_b^2 is small, for there is little room for the regression line to vary from sample to sample. If the pipe is short and fat, the position of the rod can vary greatly from sample to sample, so b has high variance. But the pipe is not empty. The more points are "stuffed inside" (that is, the larger N), the less freedom for the regression line to rattle around, and the smaller σ_b^2. Combining these factors we have

$$\sigma_b^2 = \frac{\sigma_v^2}{N\sigma_X^2} = \frac{\sigma_v^2}{\Sigma x_j^2}.$$

The standard error of b is used like any other standard error. The exact effect of an increase of 1 million cwt. on onion prices is unknown. The point estimate, $b = -.348$, is associated with a standard error:

4. Mathematical proof:

$$b = \frac{\Sigma x_j y_j}{\Sigma x_j^2} = \frac{1}{N\sigma_X^2} [x_1 y_1 + x_2 y_2 + \ldots + x_N y_N].$$

When the X's are held constant, b is seen to be the product of a constant, $1/N\sigma_X^2$, and a sum, each of whose items is a constant, x, times a variable, y. Applying the properties of the variance, we have

$$\sigma_b^2 = \frac{1}{N^2\sigma_X^4} (\Sigma x_j)^2 \sigma_y^2 = \frac{N\sigma_X^2}{N^2\sigma_X^4} \sigma_y^2.$$

But when X is fixed, Y varies only from other factors. Under these circumstances, $\sigma_y^2 = \sigma_v^2$ and the formula immediately becomes

$$\sigma_b^2 = \frac{\sigma_v^2}{N\sigma_X^2} = \frac{\sigma_v^2}{\Sigma x_j^2}.$$

Figure 7.7 Illustration of the Formula $\sigma_b^2 = \dfrac{\sigma_v^2}{\Sigma x_j^2}$

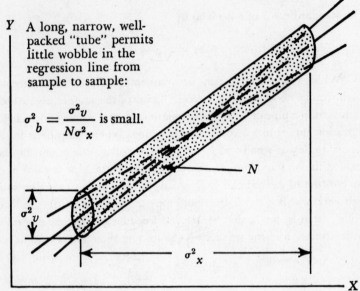

Y A long, narrow, well-packed "tube" permits little wobble in the regression line from sample to sample:

$\sigma^2_b = \dfrac{\sigma^2_v}{N\sigma^2_x}$ is small.

σ^2_v

N

σ^2_x

X

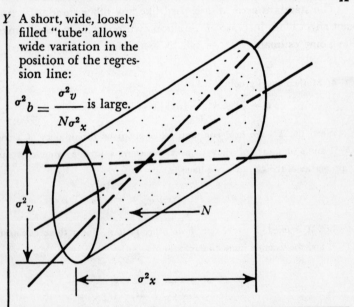

Y A short, wide, loosely filled "tube" allows wide variation in the position of the regression line:

$\sigma^2_b = \dfrac{\sigma^2_v}{N\sigma^2_x}$ is large.

σ^2_v

N

σ^2_x

X

$\sigma_b = .075$. A 95 per cent confidence interval for b would therefore be approximately

$$b = -.348 \pm 2(.075) = -.348 \pm .15\,.$$

7.12.3 σ_b as a Significance Test

The standard error of b also provides an alternative significance test for the linear regression. Under the null hypothesis of no correlation, the true value of b is zero, and the observed value is a chance accident. The significance of b can be calculated by a t test similar to that used for the difference between two means. The significance level is found by entering the normal table (or, for few residual degrees of freedom, the Student distribution) at $t = \dfrac{b}{\sigma_b}$. For onion demand, $t = \dfrac{.348}{.075} = 4.64$; since n is small, enter the Student distribution at $n = 10$ to find that the .01 level of significance is $t = 3.17$. The regression is significant at better than the .01 level, in agreement with the F test made earlier.

In modern research reporting, it is customary to record σ_b in parentheses below b in any statement of the regression equation.

7.12.4 The Standard Error of a

Since a merely serves to set the general level of the linear approximation, its standard error, σ_a, is less interesting than σ_b, but it is sometimes needed. For example, if a demand curve appeared to shift between two periods, that is, to show different values of a, σ_a would help us evaluate the observed difference. The value of σ_a^2 is given by[5]

5. This formula follows directly from the estimate of a:
$$a = \bar{Y} - b\bar{X}.$$
Once the values of X are fixed, $\bar{Y}$ can vary only because of unspecified variables, hence
$$\sigma_{\bar{Y}}^2 = \frac{\sigma_{y \cdot x}^2}{N} = \frac{\sigma_v^2}{N}.$$
Moreover, $\bar{X}$ is a constant so the variance of $\bar{X}b = \bar{X}^2$ (variance of b) $= \bar{X}^2 \sigma_b^2$. The variance of a is then the sum of the variances of its independent components:
$$\sigma_a^2 = \frac{\sigma_v^2}{N} + \bar{X}^2 \sigma_b^2,$$
and the standard error of a is $\qquad \sigma_a = \sqrt{\dfrac{\sigma_v^2}{N} + \bar{X}^2 \sigma_b^2}\,.$

179

$\sigma_a^2 = \dfrac{\sigma_v^2}{N} + \bar{X}^2 \sigma_b^2$. The standard error of a is $\sigma_a = \sqrt{\dfrac{\sigma_v^2}{N} + \bar{X}^2 \sigma_b^2}$.

7.13 UNITS OF MEASUREMENT AND LINEAR REGRESSION

The values of R^2, R, F, and $t = b/\sigma_b$ are independent of the units in which X and Y are measured. That is, the correlation between onion prices and production is $-.83$ regardless of whether production is measured in tons, hundredweights, pounds, or kilograms, or whether prices are measured in dollars per hundredweight, cents per pound, or thousands of dollars per hundred tons.

The values of a and b, on the other hand, depend directly on the units employed, and any change in units will be reflected in a corresponding change in the values of a or b or both. This means that the values of a and b in two regression equations cannot be compared unless the two equations contain the same variables, measured in identical units. Many economic functions, however, can be compared by calculating *elasticities* which are unit-free expressions.

7.14 MEASUREMENT OF ELASTICITY

By definition, elasticity with respect to X is measured as the percentage increase in Y produced per 1 per cent change in X. Where ΔX and ΔY are increments, the respective percentage increases are $\dfrac{\Delta X}{X}$ and $\dfrac{\Delta Y}{Y}$ and elasticity with respect to X, E_x, is defined by

$$E_x = \frac{\dfrac{\Delta Y}{Y}}{\dfrac{\Delta X}{X}} = \frac{X}{Y} \cdot \frac{\Delta Y}{\Delta X}.$$

On a straight line, $\dfrac{\Delta Y}{\Delta X} = b$, so the formula becomes

$$E_x = \frac{X}{Y} b,$$

and elasticity varies from point to point with the ratio X/Y. However, since b is estimated from *all* the values of X and Y, the elasticity is most appropriately measured at the means and we estimate

$$E_x = \frac{\bar{X}}{\bar{Y}} b.$$

For onion demand we have the elasticity with respect to production:

$$E_x = \frac{\bar{X}}{\bar{Y}} b = \frac{21.6}{2.74} (-.348) = -2.74,$$

that is, a 1.0 per cent increase in output tends, on the average, to generate a 2.74 per cent decline in onion prices. Demand elasticity with respect to production is sometimes called the *price flexibility* of demand.

Analysis of demand more often centers on price *elasticity*. Since price is the dependent Y in our equation, price elasticity is E_y. Clearly

$$E_y = \frac{1}{E_x},$$

and we have price elasticity of onion demand given by

$$E_y = \frac{1}{-2.74} = -.37,$$

that is, an increase of 1 per cent in onion prices tends on the average to reduce consumption slightly more than one-third of 1 per cent.

7.15 ALLOWING FOR OTHER VARIABLES

The problem of hidden correlation can occur in regression just as in the case of tabulated functions. If some factor that influences Y happens to be correlated with the movements of X as observed in the sample, it must be taken into account to avoid bias in the estimate of the effect of X on Y. For example, the price of onions is strongly affected, not only by output, but by the general level of prices as a whole. Other things equal, onion prices rise and fall under the same monetary pressures that influence the price level. Fluctuations in production merely cause onion prices to vary around the level established by other forces. During the period covered by the data of Table 7.2 there happened to be little correlation between movements in the general price level and movements

Table 7.9 Work Sheet for Calculation of Onion Demand Equation in Terms of Relative Prices

Year	Onion Production (X)	Onion Prices ($ per cwt.)	Consumer Price Index (1957–59 = 100)	Relative Price of Onions (Y = Price/C.P.I.)	Check Total (C = X + Y)
1944	24.0	2.40	60.8	3.95	27.95 ✓
1945	18.8	3.38	62.6	5.40	24.20 ✓
1946	25.2	1.78	69.4	2.56	27.76
1947	18.4	4.16	85.1	4.89	23.29
1948	21.2	2.64	89.4	2.95	24.15
1949	19.6	2.94	87.1	3.38	22.98
1950	23.0	1.75	87.6	2.00	25.00
1951	20.0	3.34	95.5	3.50	23.50
1952	20.2	4.62	96.7	4.78	24.98 ✓
1953	25.2	1.37	96.4	1.42	26.62 ✓
1954	22.2	2.14	95.4	2.24	24.44 ✓
1955	21.4	2.37	94.4	2.51	23.91 ✓
Total	259.2			39.58	298.78 ✓

$$X \quad 5{,}659.52 \qquad Y \quad 831.378 \qquad C \quad 6{,}490.898$$

$$r \qquad 147.7876 \qquad\qquad 979.1656$$

$$x \quad 60.8 \qquad y \quad -23.55 \qquad c \quad 37.25$$

$$17.2396 \qquad\qquad -6.3104$$

$$b = \frac{-23.55}{60.8} = -.3873$$

$$a = \frac{39.58 - (-.3873)(259.2)}{12} = 11.664$$

$$Y = 11.664 - .387X$$

$$R^2 = \frac{(-.3873)(-23.55)}{17.2396} = .53$$

$$E_x = \frac{\bar{X}}{\bar{Y}} \cdot b = \frac{21.600}{3.2983}(-.3873) = -2.54$$

$$E_y = \frac{1}{E_x} = \frac{1}{2.54} = -.39$$

Sources: Data of Tables 7.2 and 10.7.

in onion production, thus neglect of the price level as a variable affecting onion prices did not result in a biased estimate. Over a somewhat longer period of time, however, when general growth in the level of production happens to coincide with general increase in the price level, failure to allow for the price level can result in serious distortion. In fact, during a period in which the general price level is rising rapidly, the price of onions might rise even in the face of increasing production. If no account were taken of the effect of the price level itself, the value estimated for b would be positive!

Although proper allowance for the effect of other variables often requires the use of multiple regression—a technique beyond the scope of this book—it can sometimes be accomplished within the limitations of simple linear regression. This is done by combining several factors into a single composite variable. For example, to make allowance for the effect of the general level of prices on the onion demand equation, we replace onion prices by a new composite dependent variable composed of the ratio of the price of onions to a suitable measure of the price of goods as a whole. To the extent that onion prices vary merely in proportion to all other prices, the value of this composite dependent variable remains unchanged. The independent variable, production, is thus permitted to account only for the relative movement of onion prices, freeing the estimate of its effect from the bias that would otherwise occur.

The procedure is illustrated in Table 7.9, using the onion production and price data of Table 7.2, and employing the Consumer Price Index as a measure of price level.[6] Relative onion prices, obtained by dividing onion prices by the index, are then used as the composite dependent variable in a linear regression on production. Since the dependent variable of Table 7.9 differs from that of Table 7.5, the two regression equations are not strictly comparable. Their elasticities, however, can be compared and prove to be nearly equal. This fact confirms the absence of bias in the original regression mentioned above.

Many other factors can be allowed for in similar fashion. For example, the price of onions is influenced by the number of people to be fed by the supply. The effect on prices of a rise in population is the opposite of

6. See Chapter X.

Figure 7.8 Actual and Calculated Onion Prices, U.S., 1944–55

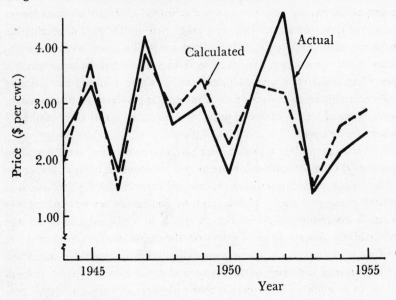

Source: Data of Table 7.2.

that of an increase in output. Both factors can be introduced into the demand equation by employing the composite variable "output per head" as the independent variable. Sometimes several variables are combined in a single composite. Analysis of the consumption function, for example, usually takes account of earnings, transfer payments, personal taxes, population, and the price level in a single composite variable, "real per capita disposable income."

7.16 TIME SERIES AND AUTOCORRELATION OF RESIDUALS

The demand for onions is typical of economic relationships that must be studied by using time series. Among the unspecified factors influencing the demand for onions there are many that change only slowly from year to year: living standards, tastes, customs and habits, and the style and quality of goods in general. In consequence, the deviations of obervations from the regression line likewise tend to move slowly. Thus, if demand is above its calculated value one year, it is likely to remain above it the next. The residuals of Table 7.6 are a good example. Three of the first four are positive; the next three are negative, followed by two positive and then three negative residuals. This behavior stands out when actual and calculated prices are plotted against time in Figure 7.8.

Since the value of the residual at one time is correlated with its own preceding value, this phenomenon is called *autocorrelation* of residuals. Autocorrelated residuals are not independently drawn, but constitute a clustered sample whose variance usually understates the true residual variance. In consequence, the values of F, R^2, standard errors, and so on are distorted, exaggerating the appearance of precision in the regression.

While autocorrelated residuals do not produce bias in the estimates of a and b, they *do* bias their standard errors, and the latter should be evaluated with this in mind.

7.17 SUMMARY OF REGRESSION

Simple linear regression is a method for approximating a stochastic function by a straight line fitted to the data to minimize the sum of squared deviations. It expresses the function as an equation and can be employed to good advantage even with samples too small to tabulate. Using a compact calculating format, the approximation is computed as an equation

$$Y = a + bX.$$

The values $\hat{Y}$ calculated from the equation play a role in analysis analogous to that of $\bar{Y}$ in a tabulated function. Standard errors enable us to assign confidence limits to the estimate of individual values of Y, given a value for X, and to estimate the reliability of the estimates of a and b. R^2 is defined and calculated in a manner analogous to that used with tabulated functions, and the analysis of variance provides a significance test if required.

Curvature in the underlying function will cause overstatement of the residual variance with attendant exaggeration of standard errors and understatement of R^2 and significance. This problem will be pursued further in the next chapter.

Linear regression requires the same careful attention to the problems of hidden correlation and hidden interaction as in the tabulation of functions. The influence of additional variables can often be allowed for by the use of composite expressions that combine several factors into one variable.

Regressions calculated from time series often give rise to understatement of residual variance due to autocorrelation of residuals. Some of the problems of time series will be explored in Chapter IX.

Questions and Problems

1. Fit a linear regression to the data of Table 5.11. Write a paragraph interpreting your result.

2. Fit linear regressions to the data given in Table 5.1, using class marks of household income as values of X and tabulated family bread consumption as Y. Write a paragraph interpreting your result and comparing the relationship in the Northeastern region to that in the South.

3.

Portland Cement, Average Monthly Shipments and Average Finished Stocks, End of Month, 1948–60

Year	Shipments (million bbls.)	Stocks (million bbls.)
1948	17.0	12.7
1949	17.2	17.1
1950	19.0	15.1
1951	20.1	16.2
1952	20.9	17.4
1953	21.7	19.3
1954	22.8	19.5
1955	24.7	18.6
1956	26.0	22.2
1957	24.3	27.5
1958	25.8	30.5
1959	28.2	31.8
1960	26.2	35.5

Source: Data from *Business Statistics, 1961* (Washington, D.C.: U.S. Department of Commerce, Office of Business Economics, 1961).

Explore the relationship of stock of finished cement (Y) to cement shipments (X) by a linear regression. If monthly shipments rise by 1 million barrels, what increase would you expect in the stock of finished cement? This is a simple form of investment accelerator. When cement demand (shipments) rises, production must increase enough to meet both the higher sales rate and the additional inventory requirements. Suppose demand shifts upward by 1 million barrels in June and maintains its new level. What would happen to the rate of production in June? In July? In August? Suppose demand declined by 1 million barrels in June, what would happen to production in June? In July? In August?

4. It is reasonable to suppose that the rate of increase in wages depends on the proportion of unemployment. Test the hypothesis by fitting a regression to the following data and testing it for significance. Write a short paragraph summarizing your results.

Unemployment Rate and Increase in Manufacturing Workers' Average Hourly Earnings, 1950–61

Year	Average Rate of Unemployment (per cent of labor force)	Annual Increase in Average Hourly Earnings (cents per hour)
1950	5.3	7
1951	3.3	12
1952	3.1	9
1953	2.9	9
1954	5.6	4
1955	4.4	8
1956	4.2	9
1957	4.3	10
1958	6.8	6
1959	5.5	8
1960	5.6	7
1961	6.7	6

Source: Data from *Employment and Earnings Statistics*, BLS Bulletin No. 1312 (Washington, D.C: U.S. Department of Labor, Bureau of Labor Statistics, 1961), supplemented by *Survey of Current Business* (Washington, D.C.: U.S. Department of Commerce, Office of Business Economics) various issues.

Reference

1. Mordecai Ezekial and Karl A. Fox. *Methods of Correlation and Regression Analysis*. 3rd Ed. New York: John Wiley & Sons, 1959. Chapter 5 deals with simple linear regression. Linear correlation and standard errors are treated in Chapter 7. Chapter 8 contains calculating procedures.

The Function as an Equation II: Simple Curvilinear Regression by Transformation of Variables

In the preceding chapter we saw how a function can be approximated by a linear regression. For most purposes this is satisfactory, but sometimes the curvature itself is a matter of considerable research interest. The nature of the underlying theory may demand a curvilinear formulation of the equation, or the curvature may be so sharp that the function is not amenable to study by linear approximation. In this chapter we shall measure the apparent curvature in a function and test it for significance. We shall then explore a simple method of curvilinear regression that has wide applicability.

8.1 DEFINITION AND MEASUREMENT OF CURVATURE

Consider a least squares linear regression $Y = a + bX$, fitted to a set of data. The data are said to show curvature if it is possible to partition the X axis into classes forming a categorical variable X^* in such a way that the residuals from the regression are correlated with X^*.[1]

This is illustrated in Figure 8.1, p. 192. When the X axis is divided to define the 6 classes A, B, C, D, E, and F, it is clear that the mean residual $\bar{v}$ varies significantly among classes. The relationship of v to X^* can be tabulated, and the determination ratio R^2 measures the amount of curvature.

---

1. If the function is curved, the points at the extremes of the scatter will tend to lie on one side of the straight line, while the points in the middle lie on the other. Taken as a whole, the regression of v on X will show zero correlation, but if divided into cells by X^* classes, v will show correlation with X^*.

Table 8.1 Deviations of Observed
from Calculated Value $Y = 322.79 +$

Deviation (v)	m	m^2	$250–749	$750–1,249
−$2,000 and under	−2.5[a]	6.25	–	–
−$1,999 to −1,500	−1.750	3.0625	–	–
−$1,499 to −1,000	−1.25	1.5625	–	–
−$ 999 to − 500	− .750	.5625	2	4
−$ 499 to − 250	− .375	.140625	10	18
−$ 249 to − 100	− .175	.030625	30	34
−$ 99 to − 50	− .075	.005625	6	60
−$ 49 to − 0	− .025	.000625	4	40
$ 0 to 49	.025	.000625	4	50
$ 50 to 99	.075	.005625	8	12
$ 100 to 249	.175	.030625	8	12
$ 250 to 499	.375	.140625	–	22
$ 500 to 999	.750	.5625	–	4
$1,000 to 1,499	1.250	1.5625	–	–
$1,500 to 1,999	1.750	3.0625	–	–
$2,000 or more	4.0[a]	16.000	–	–

Σf		72	256
Σmf		−8.950	−5.70
$\Sigma m^2 f$		3.77876	11.99500
Mean deviations $\bar{v}$		−.12431	−.02227
Sum of squared deviations within cells		2.66622	11.86808
δ^2_p		.038088	.04672
$\sigma^2_{\bar{v}}$		.00053	.00018
$\sigma_{\bar{v}}$		.023	.013

$$R^2 = \frac{3.626}{215.733} = .017$$

[a] Class mean.
Source: The linear regression was fitted to data for 908 wage-earner families in small northeastern cities, selected from among the tabulations of *Family Expenditure in Selected Cities 1935–36*, BLS Bulletin No. 648 (Washington, D.C.: U.S. Department of Labor, Bureau of Labor Statistics, 1939). Note the low levels of income characteristic of the period.

8.2 AN EXAMPLE

According to Keynesian consumption theory, the marginal propensity to consume declines with increasing income. This implies that the re-

Family Consumption Expenditure
.689X, by Family Income Classes

Family Income Class				
$1,250– 1,749	$1,750– 2,249	$2,250– 2,999	$3,000 and over	Total
–	–	–	4	4
–	–	–	4	4
–	–	–	8	8
4	8	4	12	34
18	10	20	16	92
18	10	12	2	106
32	20	10	–	128
60	20	8	6	138
20	24	–	6	104
20	8	10	–	58
34	18	12	4	88
30	26	10	2	90
6	16	10	4	40
–	2	–	–	2
–	–	–	8	8
–	–	–	4	4
242	162	96	80	908
6.90	15.10	.550	−7.90	0.00
14.310	22.730	12.94625	149.9725	215.7325
.02851	.09321	.00573	−.09875	0.000
(Weighted mean = 0)				
14.11326	21.32252	12.9431	149.1992	215.7325
(Sum of squares among cells = 3.626)				
.05881	.00116	.13769	1.88860	
.00024	.000007	.00144	.02361	
.016	.0028	.037	.154	

lationship of family consumption expenditure to income is not linear, but a curve whose slope declines with increasing income. To explore this theoretically interesting proposition, a linear regression of consumption expenditure Y on income X was fitted to data derived from a sample of 908 families. The result was

$$Y = 322.79 + .689X \qquad \bar{R}^2 = .70$$
$$(35.44) \quad (.090)$$

191

Figure 8.1 Curvature

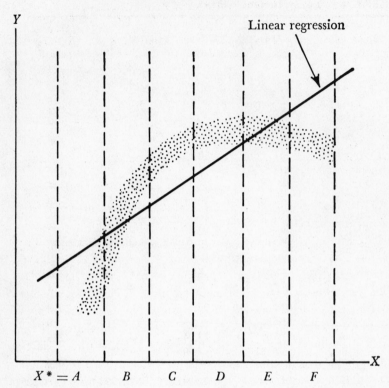

The original data and calculations are not given, but the deviations of individual family consumption expenditures from their calculated values were classified by income as shown in Table 8.1. It is easily seen that the mean deviation is negative in the two lowest and in the highest income classes, and positive for the middle income groups. In other words, consumption of high and low income families lies, on the average, below the regression line, while that in the middle income group lies, on the average, above. This implies that the relationship of consumption to income has a shape similar to that shown in Figure 8.1.

The relationship between the deviation from the linear regression

Table 8.2 Deviations of Observed from Calculated Consumption as a Function of Family Income

Income ($)	Mean Deviation ($)	Standard Error ($)	Number of Families
250–749	−124	23	72
750–1,249	− 22	13	256
1,250–1,749	29	16	242
1,750–2,249	93	3	162
2,250–2,999	6	37	96
3,000 and over	− 99	154	80
	$R^2 = .017$		

Source: Data of Table 8.1.

and X^*, defined by the 6 income classes, is calculated in the usual way and tabulated in Table 8.2. $R^2 = .017$ implies that only slightly more than 1.7 per cent of the deviation from the regression is associated with curvature. This means that curvature is not substantial and the linear regression will serve adequately for most purposes.

But our problem is not whether the curvature is great, but whether it exists *at all*. The significance of the correlation is tested by the analysis of variance in Table 8.3. The only novel aspect of this analysis is the fact that since the dependent variable, v, is the residual from a linear regression fitted to N points, its total degrees of freedom is $N - 2$, the number of degrees of freedom appropriate to residuals from a regression.

Table 8.3 Analysis of Variance Testing the Significance of Curvature in the Consumption Function

Source	Sum of Squares	d.f.	Variance
Total residual	215.7325	906	.2381
Among cells	3.626	5	.7252
Within cells	212.106	901	.2354

$$F = \frac{.7252}{.2354} = 3.08$$

$$(n_1 = 5, \ n_2 = 1,000; \ F_{.01} = 3.04)$$

Source: Data of Table 8.1.

Thus, the sum of squares of the 908 residuals has 906 degrees of freedom. The F ratio shows highly significant variance in v among income classes.

Thus, the test reveals very slight, but highly significant, curvature in the consumption function. To capture this curvature in a mathematical equation we need some way to replace the linear approximation with a curvilinear one.

8.3   TRANSFORMATION OF VARIABLES

A simple procedure that applies to a wide variety of curves is that of transforming variables. The idea is simple. If Y is not a linear function of X, perhaps it can be represented as a linear function of the logarithm of X or of $1/X$, or X^2 or of some other transformation of X. Or perhaps the logarithm, reciprocal, square, or some other function of Y can be used in place of Y. The transformation to be employed depends on the nature of the curve to be fitted. Two common types are often met with.

8.3.1   The Semilogarithmic Curve

Many curves can be approximated by substituting the logarithm of X in place of X. The beef consumption curve of Chapter VII is one of these.

In Figure 7.1, p. 156, it appears that the higher family income, the smaller the rise in beef consumption associated with a fixed dollar income increase. In fact, inspection of the dotted line suggests that at all income levels, a given *percentage* increase in income increases beef consumption by the same number of pounds. For example, reading off the curve, we have roughly:

Income ($)	Beef Consumption (pounds per week)
2,000	3.2
4,000	4.2
8,000	5.3

Source: Figure 7.1.

Each doubling of income is associated with an increase of about 1 pound per week in beef consumption. In other words *geometric* increases

Figure 8.2   Beef Consumption as a Function of Family Income: Comparisons of Linear and Curvilinear Regression

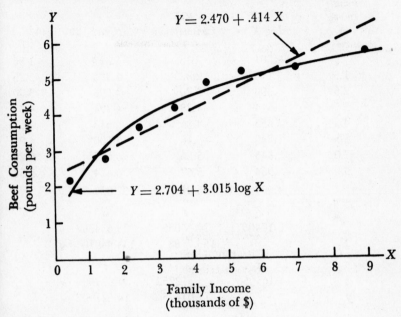

Source: Data of Table 7.1.

in X produce *arithmetic* increases in Y. The general form of such a function is represented by a semilogarithmic equation:

$$Y = a + b \log X.$$

While this equation describes a curvilinear relationship between Y and X, it is easily calculated as a *linear* relationship between Y and the transformed variable $Z = \log X$. The procedure is applied in Table 8.4 and results in the regression

$$Y = 2.704 + 3.015 \log X.$$

To plot this curve, calculate $\hat{Y}$ for appropriately spaced values of X and draw a smooth curve through the points. The improvement in approximation is apparent when the curve is compared with the linear regression in Figure 8.2. A more exact measure of the improvement is

195

Chapter VIII · Simple Curvilinear Regression

Table 8.4 Work Sheet for Calculation of Regression of Weekly Beef Consumption on Log Income

Family Income X (thousands of $)	Log X = Z	Beef Consumption Y	Check C	Ŷ
.5	−.301	2.13	1.829	1.80
1.5	.176	2.82	2.996	3.23
2.5	.398	3.70	4.098	3.90
3.5	.544	4.25	4.794	4.34
4.5	.653	4.86	5.513	4.67
5.5	.740	5.16	5.900	4.94
7.0	.845	5.23	6.075	5.25
9.0	.954	5.67	6.624	5.58
	4.009	33.82	37.829 √	

	Z	Y	C	
Z	3.174067	20.46030	23.634367 √	
Y		153.9888	174.44910 √	

	z	y	c	
z	1.165056	3.512252	4.677309 √	
y		11.01475	14.527002 √	

$$b = \frac{3.512252}{1.165056} = 3.014663$$

$$a = \frac{33.82 - 3.014663\,(4.009)}{8} = 2.716$$

$$Y = 2.716 + 3.015 \log X$$

Source	Sum of squares
Total	11.01475
Regression	10.5883
Residual	.4264

$$R^2 = \frac{10.5883}{11.01475} = .96 \qquad R = +.98$$

Source: Data of Table 7.1.

provided by comparing the coefficients of determination. For the curve, $R^2 = .96$: All but 4 per cent of the observed variance among cell means is captured by the semilogarithmic equation. Compare this with $R^2 = .89$ for the straight line.

8.3.2 The Double Logarithmic Transformation

Another frequently used transformation is illustrated by the demand for cabbage. Data for production and price are given in Table 8.5. A linear regression has $R^2 = .42$, but as seen in Figure 8.3, the function might be

Figure 8.3   Alternative Approximations to the Demand for Cabbage

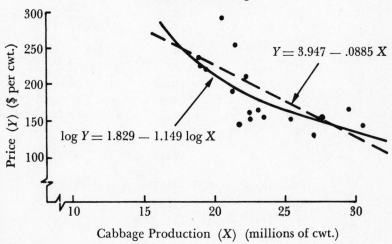

Source: Data of Table 8.5.

better approximated by a curve. The distribution of the points suggests the general hyperbolic shape of a curve of constant elasticity.

The equation of a curve with (constant) elasticity E_x at every point is

$$\log Y = a + E_x \log X .$$

This rather complicated curve is easily estimated as a linear regression

$$W = a + bZ$$

where $W = \log Y$, and $Z = \log X$. Clearly, $b = E_x$.

197

Table 8.5 Demand for Cabbage Approximated by Linear Regression

Cabbage Production X (millions of cwt.)	Price Y ($ per cwt.)	Check C
29.1	1.68	30.78
31.0	1.41	32.41
27.2	1.53	28.73
22.6	2.15	24.75
25.3	1.51	26.81
22.6	1.60	24.20
27.0	1.33	28.33
21.5	2.58	24.08
20.6	2.92	23.52
23.4	1.57	24.97
21.9	1.45	23.35
19.0	2.24	21.24
23.0	1.61	24.61
19.1	2.21	21.31
21.1	1.94	23.04
19.0	2.39	21.39
373.4	30.12	403.52 √

	X	Y	C
X	8,913.06	685.337	9,598.397 √
Y		60.1026	745.4396 √

	x	y	c
x	198.83750	−17.58850	181.24900 √
y		3.40170	−14.18680 √

$$b = \frac{-17.5885}{198.83750} = -.088457$$

$$a = \frac{30.12 + (.088457)(373.4)}{16} = 3.947$$

$$Y = 3.947 - .0885 X$$
$$(.606)^a \quad (.0257)^a$$

Analysis of variance	Sum of squares	d.f.	Variance
Total	3.40170	15	.22678
Regression	1.55587	1	1.55587
Residual	1.84583	14	.13184

$$\bar{R}^2 = 1 - \frac{.13184}{.22678} = .42$$

$$F = \frac{1.556}{.132} = 11.79 \qquad (n_1 = 1,\ n_2 = 14;\ F_{.01} = 8.86)$$

[a] Calculation of standard errors not shown.
Source: Data are from *Agricultural Statistics, 1960* (Washington, D.C.: U.S. Department of Agriculture, 1961).

Calculated as shown in Table 8.6, cabbage demand is approximated by

$$W = 1.829 - 1.149\, Z.$$
$$\quad\ (.405)\quad (.296)$$

This is a curve whose elasticity with respect to X is $E_x = -1.149$; the *price* elasticity of cabbage demand is $E_y = \dfrac{1}{E_x} = \dfrac{1}{-1.149} = -.87$. The significance of the regression of W on Z is determined by the analysis of variance in the usual way. Note, however, that the value of $\bar{R}^2$ is not strictly comparable to that of the linear regression. The reason is that the two regressions have different dependent variables: The linear regression applies to the variable $Y = $ price of cabbage, while the curve of constant elasticity is a linear regression employing the variable $W = $ log price of cabbage.

The curve of Figure 8.3 is plotted by calculating values of $\hat{W}$ and plotting $\hat{Y} = $ antilog $\hat{W}$ against X.

8.4 SUMMARY

A linear regression may be inappropriate for theoretical reasons or because the curvature in the function under study is too great to be approximated by a straight line. The amount of curvature can be measured by tabulating the residuals from the linear regression, and, if necessary, the evidence of curvature can be tested for significance by the analysis of variance.

The theory of fitting curves with transformed variables is simple. If Y is not linearly related to X, we try to find some way of transforming Y into W and X into Z so that W and Z *are* linearly related. The transformation required is discovered by inspecting the properties of the scatter of points. The logarithm is the most common transformation employed, but other curves can be fitted by replacing one or both variables by their square, square root, reciprocal, arc tangent, or other function.

In the next chapter the semilogarithmic transformation will be used to fit a compound interest trend.

Table 8.6 Calculating Demand for Cabbage
as a Curve of Constant Elasticity

Log Production Z	Log Price W	Check Total C	Calculated Log Price $\hat{W}$	Antilog $\hat{W} = \hat{Y}$ ($ per cwt.)
1.464	.225	1.689	.147	1.40
1.491	.149	1.640	.116	1.31
1.435	.185	1.620	.180	1.51
1.354	.332	1.686	.273	1.88
1.403	.179	1.582	.217	1.65
1.354	.204	1.558	.273	1.88
1.431	.124	1.555	.185	1.53
1.332	.412	1.744	.298	1.99
1.314	.465	1.779	.319	2.08
1.369	.196	1.565	.256	1.80
1.340	.161	1.501	.289	1.95
1.279	.350	1.629	.359	2.29
1.362	.207	1.569	.264	1.84
1.281	.344	1.625	.357	2.28
1.324	.288	1.612	.308	2.03
1.279	.378	1.657	.359	· 2.29
21.812	4.199	26.011		

	Z	W	C	
Z	29.799648	5.650239	35.449887	√
W		1.266127	6.916366	√
	z	w	c	
z	.0644390	−.0740477	−.0096087	√
w		.1641519	.0901041	√

$$b = \frac{-.0740477}{.0644390} - 1.149113$$

$$a = \frac{4.199 + (1.149113)(21.812)}{16} = 1.829$$

$$W = 1.829 - 1.149\,Z$$
$$(.405)^{a} \quad (.296)^{a}$$

Analysis of variance	Sum of squares	d.f.	Variance
Total	.1641519	15	.0109434
Regression	.0850892	1	.0850892
Residual	.0790627	14	.0056473

$$\bar{R}^2 = 1 - \frac{.0056473}{.0109434} = .48$$

$$F = \frac{.08509}{.00565} = 15.06 \quad (n_1 = 1, n_2 = 14; F_{.01} = 8.86)$$

[a] Calculation of standard errors not shown.
Source: Data of Table 8.5.

Questions and Problems

1.

Potatoes: Production and Relative Wholesale Price, 1949–59

Year	Production (millions of cwt.)	Relative Wholesale Price, New York[a] ($ per cwt.)
1949	241	2.67
1950	259	1.82
1951	196	3.71
1952	211	3.14
1953	232	1.68
1954	220	2.78
1955	227	2.62
1956	244	2.25
1957	240	2.85
1958	266	1.89
1959	243	2.76

[a] New York wholesale price deflated by Consumer Price Index (see Chapter X).

Source: Data from *Agricultural Statistics, 1960* (Washington, D.C.: U.S. Department of Agriculture, 1961).

Approximate the demand for potatoes as a curve of constant elasticity by regression of log price (W) on log production (Z). A table of logarithms will be found in Appendix A. How large is the price elasticity of demand? Does this magnitude seem plausible? Plot the scatter of points and the calculated demand curve. Does the curve seem to fit better than a simple linear regression, or would a straight line fit just as well? Fit a linear regression. How does the fit compare with that of the curve?

2. The educational ambition of parents for their children depends on a number of factors. After taking several of these into account, the relationship between ambition (measured on a special scale) and parents' income is given by the following table:

Educational Ambition by Parents' Income

Parents' Income	Mean Educational Ambition
Under $2,000	4.44
$2,000–2,999	4.69
$3,000–4,999	5.03
$5,000–7,499	5.21
$7,500–9,999	5.34
$10,000–14,999	5.44
$15,000 and over[a]	5.64

[a] Mean income in this class is approximately $20,000.
Source: Data adapted from Martin David and others, *Educational Achievement, Its Causes and Effects*, Monograph 23 (Ann Arbor: Survey Research Center, The University of Michigan, 1961).

On the educational ambition scale, 4.0 represents a high school diploma, while 6.0 represents a college degree. Plot the relationship of educational ambition to income. Is the curvature in the relationship plausible? Why? What kind of transformation will tend to straighten out the relationship? Apply this transformation and express the relationship of educational ambition to income as a curvilinear regression. Plot the regression curve. How well does it fit? Write a paragraph summarizing your results.

Reference

1. Mordecai Ezekial and Karl A. Fox. *Methods of Correlation and Regression Analysis*. 3rd Ed. New York: John Wiley & Sons, 1959. Chapter 6 deals with the problem of transformation of variables and several useful transformations are studied.

CHAPTER IX

Time Series

A *time series* is a sequence of measurements moving through time. The population of the United States as shown by decennial census, gross national product by year, unemployment by quarters, daily prices on the New York Stock Exchange are all time series. The use of time series data in regressions has been discussed above, but movements over time are themselves often important economic phenomena to be measured and analyzed. Foremost is the problem of measuring long-run economic growth, that is, the secular trend. In addition, when data are available for intervals shorter than a year, economic time series are subject to seasonal variation: More ice cream is sold in July than in January; more farm labor is employed in September than December. Not only is seasonality interesting in its own right, but for many purposes data must be seasonally adjusted before other relationships can be studied.

9.1 THE SECULAR TREND

Table 9.1 shows annual per capita consumption of dried and of frozen fruits in the United States for the period 1944–59. A glance at the table is sufficient to show that, while there is year-to-year variation, the growth of consumption has a strong central tendency. Indeed, the time path of the data can be described as a stochastic relationship between consumption, Y, and time, T, in the form

$$Y = f(T) + u .$$

The systematic part of this function, called the *trend* of the data, is the

Table 9.1 Per Capita Consumption of Dried and Frozen Fruit, U.S., 1944–59

Year	Dried Fruits	Frozen Fruits
	(pounds per capita)	
1944	6.1	2.0
1945	6.0	2.3
1946	4.5	3.1
1947	3.7	3.2
1948	3.9	3.0
1949	4.1	3.5
1950	4.1	4.3
1951	3.8	4.8
1952	3.8	6.6
1953	3.7	7.1
1954	3.9	7.4
1955	3.6	8.7
1956	3.6	8.8
1957	3.6	9.0
1958	3.0	7.9
1959	3.1	8.8

Source: *Agricultural Statistics, 1960* (Washington, D.C.: U.S. Department of Agriculture, 1961), p. 208.

central tendency of the growth path. The data of Table 9.1 show a marked upward—or positive—trend in consumption of frozen fruits and a downward—or negative—trend in consumption of dried fruit.

It is to be emphasized that the time path of the variable is only *described* by the trend. The observed behavior is the consequence of a number of intricately related causes whose net effect can be measured in relation to the passage of time, but the passage of time is not itself a cause of the behavior. For example, the shift of consumption from dried to frozen fruit was a consequence of technological change, of an attendant alteration in price structures, and of shift in consumer tastes.

9.1.1 The Trend as a Linear Regression

While trends can be fitted by eye, more satisfactory results are obtained by fitting the trend as a least squares regression of Y on T. For this purpose we select some convenient year to serve as an origin from which

Figure 9.1   Per Capita Consumption of Frozen Fruit, U.S., 1944–59

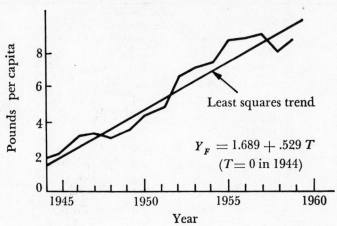

$$Y_F = 1.689 + .529\,T$$
$$(T = 0 \text{ in } 1944)$$

Source: Data of Table 9.1.

to measure T and let $T = 0$ in this year.[1] Corresponding values of T are assigned to all other years, and a least squares regression is fitted in the usual way as shown in Table 9.2.

The value of a in the regression shows the height of the trend in the year $T = 0$. The slope of the regression shows the amount by which the trend level rose per year, that is, b is the average annual increase over the period. The trend for frozen fruit, for example, stood at 1.689 pounds per capita in 1944 and rose .529 pounds per capita each year.

Since the object of fitting the trend is to describe the course of the time series, it is important to compare the trend with the original data. After the equation has been obtained, the trend line should be plotted by drawing a straight line through points calculated for the first and last years. In Figure 9.1, although the actual per capita consumption of

1. It is immaterial which year we choose for the origin. One convenient choice is to set $T = 0$ in the first year. This has the advantage of keeping T positive for all years. Sometimes the center year is chosen as $T = 0$. This makes T negative for years preceding and positive for years following the base year, but the fact that $\Sigma T = 0$ facilitates calculations: $a = \bar{Y}$, moreover $\Sigma ty = \Sigma TY$ and $\Sigma t^2 = \Sigma T^2$, so $b = \dfrac{\Sigma TY}{\Sigma T^2}$. See Table 9.3.

Table 9.2   Least Squares Linear Trend Fitted to Frozen Fruit Consumption

Year	Time (T)	Per Capita Consumption (pounds) (Y_F)	Check (C)
1944	0	2.0	2.0
1945	1	2.3	3.3
1946	2	3.1	5.1
1947	3	3.2	6.2
1948	4	3.0	7.0
1949	5	3.5	8.5
1950	6	4.3	10.3
1951	7	4.8	11.8
1952	8	6.6	14.6
1953	9	7.1	16.1
1954	10	7.4	17.4
1955	11	8.7	19.7
1956	12	8.8	20.8
1957	13	9.0	22.0
1958	14	7.9	21.9
1959	15	8.8	23.8
Total	120	90.5	210.5

	T	Y	C
T	1,240	858.6	2,098.6
Y		614.63	1,473.23

	t	y	c
t	340	179.85	519.85
y		102.74	282.59

$$b = \frac{179.85}{340} = .529$$

$$a = \frac{90.5 - .529\,(120)}{16} = 1.689$$

$$Y_F = 1.689 + .529\,T$$

(T measured in years, 1944 = 0)

Source: Data of Table 9.1.

Figure 9.2 Per Capita Consumption of Dried Fruit, U.S., 1944–59

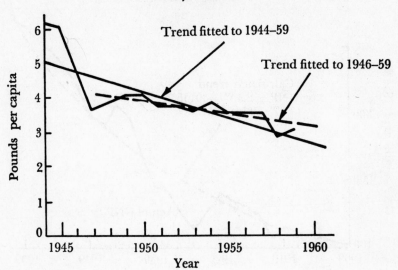

Source: Data of Table 9.1.

frozen fruit fluctuated widely, the linear trend provides a satisfactory description of the general direction of movement over the entire period.

9.1.2 Broken Trends

The forces generating the trend do not always operate smoothly. Time series often have sharp breaks in their general movement, and a *broken* trend may yield more useful results. That is, the series is subdivided into periods each having a smooth trend and a regression fitted to each.

Sometimes the data at the beginning or end of a time series deviate so far from the general trend that they seriously distort the regression. In this case the trend is broken to exclude these points. The trend of Figure 9.2 is heavily influenced by the first two or three years of the period. After an initial decline from 6.1 to 4.5 pounds per capita, dried fruit consumption showed only a slight downward trend for the re-

Figure 9.3   Real Gross National Product of the U.S., 1909–61

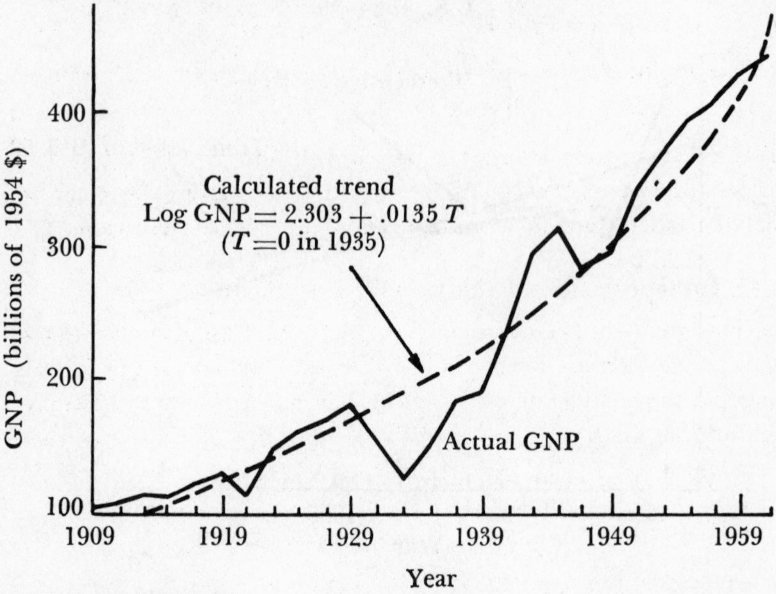

Source: Data of Table 9.3.

mainder of the period. Removing the first two or three years and fitting the trend to the remainder improves the relationship, as shown.

9.1.3   Exponential (Compound Interest) Trends

The slope of a linear trend is a fixed quantity per time period. For example, per capita frozen fruit consumption is represented as increasing .53 pounds per year. Often, particularly over long spans of time, this is an inadequate description. As can be seen in Figure 9.3, the trend of real GNP in the United States since 1909 would be poorly represented by a straight line. Rather than a fixed annual dollar amount, growth has approximated a constant annual *percentage* increase.

A time series increasing by a constant percentage has the growth properties of compound interest. An initial principle of P_o, invested at interest rate r, will at the end of T years have grown to

$$P_t = P_o (1 + r)^T.$$

Since time enters this expression as an exponent, the trend is called *exponential*.

208

Expressed in logarithms, the compound interest formula becomes:

$$\log P_t = \log P_o + T \log (1 + r).$$

But if we set $\log P_o = a$, and $\log (1 + r) = b$, this expression becomes

$$\log P_t = a + bT.$$

This is a linear regression using a transformed variable $Y = \log P_t$ and is calculated and plotted as explained in the preceding chapter. The calculation of GNP growth as an exponential trend is shown in Table 9.3.

9.1.4 Interpretation of the Exponential Trend

An exponential trend describes the time series by a compound interest formula. The steeper the regression line—that is, the larger b—the higher the compound rate of growth r. The magnitude of r is readily obtained from b.

$$b = \log (1 + r)$$

so

$$\text{antilog } b = 1 + r$$

and

$$r = (\text{antilog } b) - 1.$$

The exponential trend of real GNP is

$$Y = 2.303 + .0135 \, T$$

$$\text{antilog } .0135 = 1.0315$$

so

$$r = 1.0315 - 1 = .0315$$

that is, from 1909 to the present, real United States GNP has been increasing at an average rate of 3.2 per cent per year, compounded.

Another useful characteristic of an exponential trend is L, the period of time required for the trend magnitude, Y, to double. This is given by[2]

$$L = \frac{\log 2}{b} = \frac{.30103}{b}.$$

2.
$$\log 2Y_o = a + b(T_o + L) = a + bT_o + bL$$
$$\log 2Y_o = \log 2 + \log Y_o = \log 2 + a + bT_o.$$
Subtracting $a + bT_o$ from both expressions, we get
$$\log 2 = bL$$

whence
$$L = \frac{\log 2}{b} = \frac{.30103}{b}.$$

When the trend is downward, b is negative and so is L. This means that the series doubles when it moves "backward"; moving forward L years cuts the value of the trend in half. Such a period is called a *half-life* of the trend.

209

Table 9.3   Exponential Trend Fitted to U.S. Gross National Product, 1909–61

Year	GNP (billions of 1954 $)	T (1935 = 0)	Y (log GNP)
1909	104	−25	2.017
1911	110	−23	2.041
1913	117	−21	2.068
1915	111	−19	2.045
1917	121	−17	2.083
1919	133	−15	2.124
1921	115	−13	2.060
1923	149	−11	2.173
1925	162	− 9	2.210
1927	171	− 7	2.233
1929	182	− 5	2.260
1931	153	− 3	2.185
1933	127	− 1	2.104
1935	153	0	2.185
1937	183	1	2.265
1939	189	3	2.277
1941	238	5	2.377
1943	297	7	2.473
1945	314	9	2.497
1947	282	11	2.450
1949	293	13	2.467
1951	342	15	2.534
1953	369	17	2.567
1955	393	19	2.594
1957	407	21	2.610
1959	428	23	2.631
1961	441	25	2.644
Total	—	0	62.174

$$\bar{Y} = 2.3027$$

$$\Sigma T^2 = 5,850 \qquad \Sigma TY = 79.059$$

$$b = \frac{79.059}{5,850} = .01351$$

Trend equation: $Y = 2.303 + .01351\,T$

(Y = log of GNP, T in years measured from 1935 = 0)

Source: GNP data 1909–55 from *U.S. Income and Output* (Washington, D.C.: U.S. Department of Commerce, Office of Business Economics, 1958). Later figures from various issues of *Survey of Current Business*.

For growth in real GNP, $L = .30103/.0135 = 22.3$, that is, United States production tended to double every $22\frac{1}{3}$ years.

9.1.5 Applications of Trends

9.1.5.1 THE TREND AS A LONG-RUN FORECAST

Since the trend is a quantitative description of the central tendency of a series of past values, it lends itself directly to a "forecast" of the following sort: "*If* growth continues in the future along its past trend, X years from now the value of Y will be $\hat{Y}$." The forecast is obtained by inserting the appropriate value of T into the trend equation. If the growth of frozen fruit consumption continues along its trend, by 1970 it will reach 15.4 pounds per capita:

$$T = 1970 - 1944 = 26$$
$$\hat{Y} = 1.689 + .529 \, T = 1.689 + .529 \, (26) = 15.4 \, .$$

Such a "forecast" is likely to be wide of the mark. The trend is a rough description of the path of a complex economic system, and extrapolation of the trend is an empty exercise unless this complex system is itself well understood. Indeed, continuation of a trend is often meaningless or physically impossible. For example, according to its trend, dried fruit consumption will be -2 pounds per capita in thirty years!

On the other hand, when wisely used, the trend is a useful guide to the general order of magnitude of long-run movements. As we have seen, the exponential annual trend of United States real GNP represents doubling in the level of output every $22\frac{1}{3}$ years. In planning for the future of the economy, we would do well to allow for continuing increases of this order of magnitude and for the shifts in the size and composition of demand that they imply.

9.1.5.2 TREND REMOVAL AND CYCLICAL ANALYSIS

One of the most common uses of the calculated trend is to remove the secular movement from a time series in order to study its cyclical properties. Economic time series rarely grow smoothly along trends, but proceed by a series of bursts of activity, sometimes growing more rapidly, sometimes less rapidly. As a result, the actual values of a time series form a series of cycles around the trend. Although these cycles can be seen when the trend is drawn through the actual series as in Figure 9.1, they are more easily studied if the trend itself is removed from the series, leaving the cyclical behavior isolated for analysis. This is done by expressing each actual value in the time series as a percentage of the calculated trend for the same date. The resulting time series has no trend, but oscillates around a central value of 100. Table 9.4 shows the removal of the trend

Table 9.4 Removal of Trend from Consumption of Frozen Fruit

Year	Per Capita Consumption Actual	Per Capita Consumption Calculated Trend	Actual as Per Cent of Trend
1944	2.0	1.69	118.3
1945	2.3	2.22	103.6
1946	3.1	2.75	112.7
1947	3.2	3.28	97.6
1948	3.0	3.81	78.7
1949	3.5	4.33	80.8
1950	4.3	4.86	88.5
1951	4.8	5.39	89.1
1952	6.6	5.92	111.5
1953	7.1	6.45	110.0
1954	7.4	6.98	106.0
1955	8.7	7.51	115.8
1956	8.8	8.04	109.5
1957	9.0	8.57	105.0
1958	7.9	9.10	86.8
1959	8.8	9.62	91.5

Source: Actual consumption from Table 9.1; trend values calculated from $Y_F = 1.689 + .529T$.

from frozen fruit consumption. The cyclical movement shows clearly when the resulting series is plotted in Figure 9.4.

9.2 SEASONAL VARIATION

When time series data are available by months, weeks, quarters, or other periods shorter than a year, they show a seasonal behavior that is

Figure 9.4   Per Capita Consumption of Frozen Fruit, Percentage of Trend, U.S., 1944–59

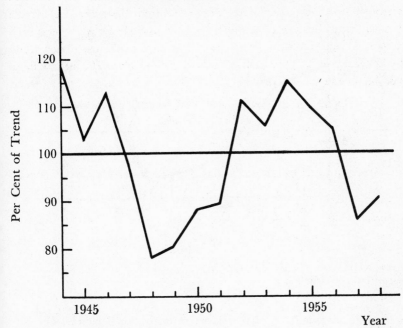

Source: Data of Table 9.4.

especially noticeable when data for several years are plotted on the same chart, as in Figures 9.5 and 9.6. The chart of crude cottonseed oil production shows a seasonal low in June, July, and August, followed by a rapid rise to a seasonal peak in October, declining again to the summer low. Although showing greater variation from year to year, a strong seasonal pattern is also clearly evident in new automobile sales, which reach a seasonal low in September, climb to a flat seasonal peak in late spring, and fall back thereafter to the September level.

The causes of seasonality vary widely from series to series. The timing of cottonseed oil production is closely related to the harvest and ginning of cotton. The seasonal behavior of automobile sales is related partly to the fact that new models are introduced in the fall; in addition, buyers are reluctant to get new cars in winter weather, hence the spring

Figure 9.5   Crude Cottonseed Oil Production, Monthly, 1958–60

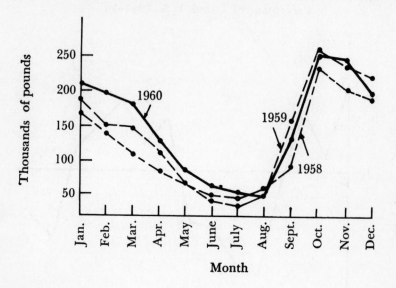

Source: Data of Table 9.5.

sales peak. Seasonality is often related to institutional factors. For example, jewelry sales are characterized by two sharp seasonal peaks, one in December, associated with Christmas, and a secondary peak in June, associated with graduations and weddings.

Regardless of their source, the study of seasonal fluctuations is important for many reasons. Production and sales planning depend on familiarity with the seasonal characteristics of the industry. In addition, seasonal factors must be taken into account in evaluating short-run economic movements. In February 1958, for example, monthly new car sales reached a low point. In March and April, sales began to climb, but whether this upturn indicated real improvement in the demand for new cars could only be determined after allowance for the normal seasonal increase. Data intended to serve as indicators of current economic activity are usually presented on a *seasonally adjusted* basis. Finally, seasonal fluctuations must often be allowed for when monthly or quarterly time series data are used in analysis of functions, particularly in regression.

Figure 9.6 New Passenger Car Registration, Monthly, 1958–60

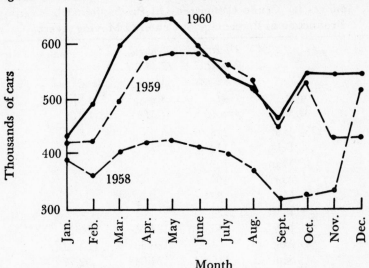

Source: *Survey of Current Business,* various issues.

9.2.1 Seasonal Indexes

The pattern of seasonal variation is described by a set of *seasonal indexes,* one for each period. Each index characterizes the level of activity during the period as a percentage of the annual average. If January sales are typically 75 per cent of annual average monthly sales, the January seasonal index is 75. A seasonal index of 115 for November means November sales are characteristically 15 per cent above the annual monthly rate.

Rough estimates of seasonal indexes can often be made from a chart of the series. In Figure 9.5, the annual average rate of production of crude cottonseed oil is about 150,000 pounds per month. During July, however, the rate is typically about 50,000 pounds per month; the seasonal index for July is roughly 50/150 = .33. At the October peak, production is at the rate of about 260,000 pounds per month, so the October seasonal index is about 260/150 = 1.73.

The practical construction of seasonal indexes is a refinement of this method, both incorporating greater accuracy and designed to avoid the bias that would otherwise result from trends in the data.

Table 9.5 Work Sheet for Calculation of Monthly Seasonal Indexes for Crude Cottonseed Oil Production: Observed Production as Percentage of Centered Moving Average

Year and Month	Observed Production (thousands of pounds)	Centered 12-Month Moving Average (CMA)	Production as % of CMA
1957 Jan.	208		
Feb.	170		
Mar.	139		
Apr.	100		
May	82		
June	54		
July	43	128.96	33.34
Aug.	44	126.38	34.82
Sept.	115	124.04	92.71
Oct.	224	122.38	183.04
Nov.	204	121.00	168.60
Dec.	181	119.71	151.20
1958 Jan.	175	119.33	146.65
Feb.	141	119.58	117.91
Mar.	112	118.96	94.15
Apr.	87	118.79	73.24
May	62	119.33	51.96
June	43	119.42	36.01
July	45	120.13	37.46
Aug.	48	121.17	39.61
Sept.	96	123.21	77.92
Oct.	239	126.00	189.68
Nov.	202	127.38	158.58
Dec.	185	127.46	145.14
1959 Jan.	188	127.00	148.03
Feb.	153	126.67	120.79
Mar.	149	129.58	114.99
Apr.	117	133.38	87.72
May	65	139.25	46.68
June	42	139.25	30.16
July	35	141.75	24.69

TABLE 9.5 (cont.)

	Aug.	50	144.58	34.58
	Sept.	164	147.75	111.00
	Oct.	262	149.67	175.05
	Nov.	243	151.16	160.76
	Dec.	221	152.96	144.48
1960	Jan.	212	154.50	137.22
	Feb.	197	155.13	126.99
	Mar.	181	153.79	117.69
	Apr.	131	152.33	86.00
	May	87	152.42	57.08
	June	63	152.04	41.44
	July	51	151.92	33.57
	Aug.	49	151.67	32.31
	Sept.	133	150.21	88.54
	Oct.	258	149.79	172.24
	Nov.	249	150.67	165.26
	Dec.	206	151.13	136.30
1961	Jan.	224	150.88	148.46
	Feb.	179	150.75	118.74
	Mar.	164	149.75	109.52
	Apr.	138	148.67	92.82
	May	101	149.04	67.77
	June	60	149.67	40.09
	July	48	149.63	32.08
	Aug.	49	150.33	32.59
	Sept.	109		
	Oct.	256		
	Nov.	260		
	Dec.	210		
1962	Jan.	219		
	Feb.	201		

Source: Monthly data of cottonseed oil production from *Survey of Current Business*, various issues.

9.2.2 Constructing Seasonal Indexes

To derive a set of monthly indexes requires monthly data covering a period of several years. The steps are shown applied to crude cottonseed oil production.

217

1. In Table 9.5, production during each month is divided by the mean of the 12-month period of which it is the center. The 12-month period with a given month in the center includes the five and a half preceding and the five and a half following months. For example, the 12-month period centered on April includes the five months preceding with half of the preceding October, and the five following months with half of the following October:

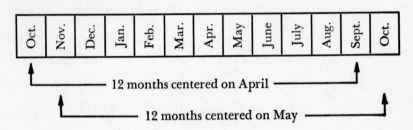

The centered 12-month period is used rather than the calendar year to avoid bias from the trend. With an upward trend, for example, earlier months in the calendar year will tend to be a smaller proportion of the year than those coming later with the benefit of a few months' trend growth. To avoid this bias we put every month at the *center* of the year to which it is compared.

Once the monthly data are arrayed, the centered 12-month averages are easily calculated. For example, the April-centered average is:

$$\frac{\text{Oct.} + 2(\text{Nov.} + \text{Dec.} + \text{Jan.} + \text{Feb.} + \text{Mar.} + \text{Apr.} + \text{May} + \text{June} + \text{July} + \text{Aug.} + \text{Sept.}) + \text{Oct.}}{24}$$

The observed rate of production for each month is recorded in the first column of Table 9.5. The corresponding centered moving average is recorded in the second column. Each observed rate is divided by the corresponding centered moving average and expressed as a percentage in the third column.

2. The observed percentages are arrayed by month and year in Table 9.6 and mean percentages calculated for each month. Before computing the means, the percentages should be inspected for extreme values associated with such phenomena as strikes, breakdowns, and so

Table 9.6 Work Sheet for Calculation of Monthly Seasonal Indexes for Crude Cottonseed Oil Production: Calculation of Monthly Mean Percentage of CMA

Month	1957	1958	1959	1960	1961	Mean
Jan.	–	146.65	148.03	137.22	148.46	145.09
Feb.	–	117.91	120.79	126.99	118.74	121.11
Mar.	–	94.15	114.99	117.69	109.52	109.09
Apr.	–	73.24	87.72	86.00	92.82	84.95
May	–	51.96	46.68	57.08	67.77	55.87
June	–	36.01	30.16	41.44	40.09	36.93
July	33.34	37.46	24.69	33.57	32.08	32.23
Aug.	34.82	39.61	34.58	32.31	32.59	34.78
Sept.	92.71	77.92	111.00	88.54	–	92.54
Oct.	183.04	189.68	175.05	172.24	–	180.00
Nov.	168.60	158.58	160.76	165.26	–	163.30
Dec.	151.20	145.14	144.48	136.30	–	144.28
				Mean		100.01

Source: Data of Table 9.5.

on. Any that can be identified should be eliminated before the mean is calculated.

3. If the 12 resulting means average 100 per cent, they are the final seasonal indexes. Sometimes, especially when extreme values have been eliminated, the means will average slightly more or less than 100, and it is necessary to multiply them by a common adjustment factor. This factor is obtained by dividing the average of the 12 means into 100. For example, if the 12 means average 98, they are raised by multiplying each by 100/98, if they initially average 105, they are lowered by multiplying each by 100/105.

9.2.3 Application of Seasonal Indexes

9.2.3.1 SEASONAL ADJUSTMENT Seasonal adjustment is the basis of all applications of seasonal indexes. It consists of dividing the level of activity observed during a given month by the corresponding seasonal index. For example, a rate of crude cottonseed oil production of 180,000 pounds during March corresponds to a seasonally adjusted rate of

180,000/1.091 = 165,000 pounds per month. This means that in a year during which production varied in the characteristic seasonal pattern, a March production level of 180,000 pounds implies an annual average rate of 165,000 pounds per month.[3]

9.2.3.2 SHORT-RUN COMPARISONS Since they are free of purely seasonal factors, movements in seasonally adjusted data reflect changes in basic economic conditions (combined, of course, with temporary disturbances). For example, the rate of crude cottonseed oil production in August 1961 was 49,000 pounds. In September, largely as a result of seasonal factors, it rose to 109,000 pounds. Comparison of the seasonally adjusted rates gave: August: 49,000/.348 = 141,000 pounds per month; September: 109,000/.925 = 118,000 pounds per month. That is, the observed increase from August to September was considerably less than the normal seasonal gain and represented a decline on a seasonally adjusted basis. The implications of such a decline depend on its causes. In this instance, it was only a delay in the beginning of the big production season, probably associated with slightly delayed cotton harvests.

9.2.3.3 SHORT-RUN FORECASTING Since underlying factors tend to move slowly from month to month, the short-run changes to be expected in observed data are largely the result of seasonality. For example, in September 1961 the level of crude cottonseed oil production was observed to be 109,000 pounds, or 118,000 pounds seasonally adjusted. As a first approximation, it is reasonable to suppose that the seasonally adjusted rate during October will continue at this level. Since the October seasonal index is 180, this implies a forecast of actual October production of 1.80 × 118,000 = 212,000 pounds. Of course, this is only a first approximation and can be improved by bringing to bear more information. For example, we already knew that September production had been abnormally low because of a delay in the harvest, and an upward adjustment would have produced a more accurate forecast.

---

3. When the seasonally adjusted monthly figure is multiplied by 12, the result is *seasonally adjusted at annual rate* and indicates the total that would result if the observed monthly rate were continued for a year, varying only seasonally.

9.2.3.4 SEASONALITY AND THE MEASUREMENT OF ECONOMIC RELATIONSHIPS The proper treatment of seasonal factors in the study of functions depends on the way they enter the relationship. Sometimes the independent variable moves in a characteristic seasonal pattern that is transmitted directly to the dependent variable by a functional relationship that is itself seasonally stable. As demonstrated in Figure 9.7, seasonal variation in X (for example, cement production) generates

Figure 9.7   Schematic Illustration of a Function Without Seasonal Shift

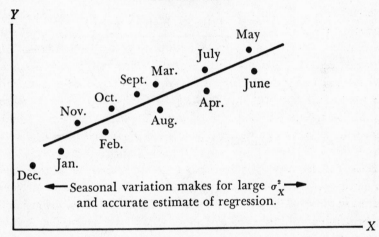

seasonal fluctuations in Y (for example, employment in the cement industry). More workers are employed in July than in February because more cement is produced in July than in February. There are seasonal movements along the same function, but there is no seasonal shift in the function itself. With functions like this, seasonal factors increase the variance in the independent variable and enhance the precision with which the function can be estimated. Seasonal variation is a positive advantage that would be lost if adjusted data were used.

Often, however, seasonal factors are themselves variables in the function. Demand is often characterized by seasonal variation. Given income, price, and other factors, ice cream sales are higher in July than in January. As another example, many manufacturing firms maintain a rate of production steadier than their sales, building up stocks during slack seasons and drawing them down later on. Thus, seasonal factors become an important element in the relationship between sales and inventories. In other cases, production costs vary with outside temperature, weather conditions, and so on.

Using the technique of Chapter V, a function like this is represented by a line that shifts seasonally, as shown in Figure 9.8. We see that unless

Figure 9.8   Schematic Illustration of a Function With Seasonal Shift

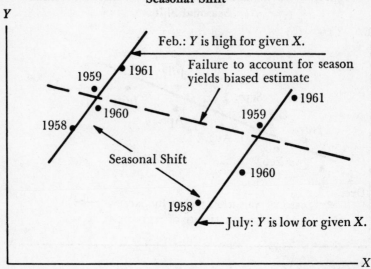

seasonality is taken into account, the hidden correlation of X (for example, sales) with seasonal factors will produce a biased estimate of its influence on Y (for example, inventory stocks). The effect of season is allowed for by using seasonally adjusted variables throughout the analysis. Seasonally adjusted variables are a special case of the composite variable studied in Chapter VII.

9.3   SUMMARY

A time series is generated by the complex interplay of economic forces, but its behavior can be described in terms of two systematic components: a long-run drift, or trend, and an annual pattern of seasonal variation.

222

Trend is usually described by a regression of the variable on time. Often a simple linear regression is adequate, but sometimes an exponential trend, characterizing the movement by a compound interest growth rate, is more useful.

Seasonal fluctuations are described by seasonal indexes expressing the typical ratio of the level of the month, quarter, or other period to the average for the 12-month period of which it is the center.

Trend and seasonal indexes have a number of applications in economic and business planning, analysis, forecasting, and research.

Questions and Problems

1. **Real Net Value of Privately Owned Structures and Equipment, U.S. Manufacturing Firms, End of Year, 1928–61**

Year	Value (billions of 1954 $)[a]	Year	Value (billions of 1954 $)[a]
1928	55.9	1945	55.7
1929	58.7	1946	61.0
1930	59.4	1947	55.6
1931	58.3	1948	69.2
1932	55.9	1949	70.7
1933	54.2	1950	72.5
1934	52.8	1951	75.3
1935	51.7	1952	78.0
1936	51.6	1953	80.6
1937	52.7	1954	82.2
1938	51.9	1955	84.1
1939	51.5	1956	87.5
1940	52.4	1957	91.9
1941	54.8	1958	92.0
1942	54.6	1959	92.5
1943	53.7	1960	93.6
1944	53.6	1961	94.0

[a] See Chapter X.

Source: *U.S. Income and Output* (Washington, D.C.: U.S. Department of Commerce, Office of Business Economics, 1958), supplemented by *Survey of Current Business* (Washington, D.C.: U.S. Department of Commerce, Office of Business Economics, July 1962).

Plot the data and write a short paragraph describing the growth of the value of manufacturing fixed capital since 1928. Would you fit a single trend to the entire period? Why? Fit an exponential trend to the post-World War II period 1946–61. Plot the calculated trend on your chart. How well does it describe the data? What annual compound interest growth rate does the trend represent? If this trend continues, how long would it take for manufacturing fixed capital to double? According to the trend, how much fixed capital would you expect by 1980? How much faith would you put in such a forecast? (Look at the period 1928–45.) Remove the trend from the data of 1946–61 and plot the result. Describe the cyclical behavior shown.

2.

Shipments of Warm-Air Furnaces, Monthly, 1957–61
(thousands per month)

Month	1957	1958	1959	1960	1961
Jan.	80.3	74.0	90.3	78.3	76.6
Feb.	70.8	71.1	87.6	79.9	78.8
Mar.	79.1	75.8	96.4	82.8	80.7
Apr.	78.5	75.0	99.0	86.8	81.1
May	78.3	83.1	102.1	88.5	90.6
June	89.7	102.8	121.1	107.4	107.2
July	90.8	98.0	128.3	99.2	104.2
Aug.	121.6	129.4	153.3	132.0	129.0
Sept.	149.2	159.7	173.2	147.5	149.4
Oct.	133.3	151.5	174.7	139.7	152.4
Nov.	96.8	119.6	121.6	99.9	99.6
Dec.	62.6	94.8	87.9	73.3	85.6

Source: Data from *Survey of Current Business* (Washington, D.C.: U.S. Department of Commerce, Office of Business Economics) various issues.

Plot the data to show the seasonal pattern and write a brief description of it. Use the chart to make a rough estimate of the seasonal indexes for January and for August. Calculate the 12 monthly seasonal indexes. In the first four months of 1962 shipments of warm-air furnaces were: January, 86.8; February, 81.0; March, 86.9; April, 90.4. Put these on a seasonally adjusted basis. Seasonally adjusted, were shipments rising or falling during early 1962? Make a "forecast" of shipments for May 1962.

References

1. Julius Shiskin and Harry Eisenpress. *Seasonal Adjustments by Electronic Computer Methods*. New York: National Bureau of Economic Research, 1958. A thorough discussion of the application of modern computer techniques to seasonal data.

2. Simon Kuznets. *Seasonal Variations in Industry and Trade*. New York: National Bureau of Economic Research, 1933. Part I, "The Economic Problems of Seasonal Variations and their Statistical Measurement," contains a useful discussion of the causes of seasonal variation and methods of measurement. The remainder of the volume is devoted to studies of seasonality in particular industries.

3. Gerhard Tintner. *Econometrics*. New York: John Wiley & Sons, 1952. Chapter 8, "The Trend," contains a short discussion of trends, especially curvilinear trends fitted by various methods.

CHAPTER X

Aggregation
and Index Numbers

The economy is a system for the production, exchange, and consumption of millions of individual commodities. We have neither time nor resources to study the operation of millions of individual markets; some kind of simplifying approximation is needed. Aggregation and index number compilation are part of the process of classifying individual economic variables into groups and measuring their behavior as a whole.

10.1 HOMOGENEITY AND AGGREGATION

Aggregation means adding up the total quantity of a homogeneous commodity. A commodity is *homogeneous* when any one unit of it can be substituted for any other unit. Clearly, the property of homogeneity is not absolute but varies with the use being made of the commodity. Sacks of wheat grown on different soil types are perfect substitutes as food but probably differ in certain chemical properties. Pig iron from different ores may be identical for the manufacture of steel rails but can have different magnetic properties. A Number 10 can of spinach hardly substitutes for a Number 10 can of cherries in making a pie but is a perfect substitute in occupying space on a grocery shelf. The difference in utility and prestige of ownership between a new and a ten-year-old automobile is substantial, but both cars make the same contribution to traffic congestion and parking problems. Kilowatt hours of electricity, tons of coal, cubic feet of natural gas, and barrels of oil are broadly substitutable when measured in B.T.U. or other common energy units. In short, commodities that are widely different from one point of view are often

226

homogeneous from another, provided they are measured in appropriate units.

10.1.1 Values and Units

From an economic standpoint, all goods have a common unit in terms of which they are, in a very real sense, substitutes: the dollar's worth. Tons of coal cannot be added to bushels of oranges, but a million dollars' worth of coal plus 3 million dollars' worth of oranges is an aggregate worth 4 million dollars. Replacing a million dollars' worth of oranges by a million dollars' worth of shirts leaves a 4 million dollar aggregate of goods.

Unlike physical units, however, values change over time. A dollar's worth is more or less in qua tity depending on current prices, and value aggregates vary both with tne physical amounts of goods and with the unit of measure itself.

To make meaningful comparisons, the value unit must be held fixed. For this purpose, a representative price, or *weight*, is selected for each commodity and, once chosen, is held constant. Weighted aggregates are then constructed by evaluating the individual components at their fixed prices and summing the values. Variation in the resulting aggregate necessarily reflects only variation in the amount and composition of the physical quantities.

10.1.2 Selection of Weights

Economically valid weights must be derived from observed prices. The practice often followed is to choose prices as of some representative base year. In the national accounts of the United States at the present time, for example, constant price aggregates are expressed in terms of 1954 prices.

In selecting weights, care must be taken to avoid prices that are unusual: We would not choose prices from a year of crop failure in which agricultural prices are relatively high, or from a year like 1947 when prices were still adjusting from wartime controls. Perhaps the best weights consist of average prices over several years rather than those singled out from any particular year.

10.1.3 Computation of Aggregates in Constant Prices

If we represent the quantity of the ith good in year t by Q_{it} and its fixed weight by P_{io}, then A_t, the constant price aggregate of year t, is

$$A_t = \sum_i P_{io}Q_{it}.$$

The compilation of a constant price aggregate is illustrated by citrus fruit production. Data on the annual production and farm prices of three principle citrus crops are given in Table 10.1. The constant

Table 10.1 Production and Farm Prices of Three Major Citrus Crops, 1949–59

Year	Oranges Production (millions of boxes)	Price ($ per box)	Grapefruit Production (millions of boxes)	Price ($ per box)	Lemons Production (millions of boxes)	Price ($ per box)	Total Value (millions of $)
1949	102.6	2.24	36.5	1.81	11.4	3.59	336.8
1950	116.3	1.97	46.6	1.09	13.5	2.82	318.0
1951	117.4	1.50	37.5	.86	12.8	3.46	252.6
1952	119.7	1.71	38.4	1.08	12.6	3.90	295.3
1953	125.4	1.93	47.1	.85	16.1	2.73	326.0
1954	130.0	1.94	42.2	.99	14.0	2.79	333.1
1955	131.7	2.41	45.4	.95	13.3	3.14	402.3
1956	131.4	2.09	44.8	1.21	16.2	2.27	365.6
1957	108.9	3.06	39.8	1.42	16.9	2.19	426.8
1958	129.1	3.22	43.8	1.44	17.3	2.06	514.4
1959	127.5	n.a.	41.4	n.a.	17.9	n.a.	n.a.

n.a. = data not available.
Source: Data are from *Agricultural Statistics, 1960* (Washington, D.C.: U.S. Department of Agriculture, 1961).

price aggregate is calculated in Table 10.2, using 1954 farm prices as weights.

10.1.4 Quantity Indexes

A quantity *index number* shows the percentage movements of a time series of aggregates. One year is selected as a base year, and each aggregate in the series is expressed as a percentage of the base-year value. If t_o is the base year chosen, I_t, the index for year t, 'has the formula

$$I_t = \frac{\sum\limits_i P_{io}Q_{it}}{\sum\limits_i P_{io}Q_{ito}}.$$

Table 10.2 Work Sheet for Calculation of Aggregate Citrus Fruit Production, 1954 Farm Prices, and Index of Citrus Fruit Production, 1951 = 100

| Year | Oranges | | Grapefruit | | Lemons | | Aggregate, 1954 Prices (millions of $) | Index of Production (1951 = 100) |
	Production (millions of boxes)	Value at $1.94 (millions of $)	Production (millions of boxes)	Value at $.99 (millions of $)	Production (millions of boxes)	Value at $2.79 (millions of $)		
1949	102.6	199.0	36.5	36.1	11.4	31.8	266.9	88.8
1950	116.3	225.6	46.6	46.1	13.5	37.7	309.4	102.9
1951	117.4	227.8	37.5	37.1	12.8	35.7	300.6	100.0
1952	119.7	232.2	38.4	38.0	12.6	35.2	305.4	101.6
1953	125.4	243.3	47.1	46.6	16.1	44.9	334.8	111.4
1954	130.0	252.2	42.2	41.8	14.0	39.1	333.1	110.8
1955	131.7	255.5	45.4	44.9	13.3	37.1	337.5	112.3
1956	131.4	254.9	44.8	44.4	16.2	45.2	344.5	114.6
1957	108.9	211.3	39.8	39.4	16.9	47.2	297.9	99.1
1958	129.1	250.5	43.8	43.4	17.3	48.3	342.2	113.8
1959	127.5	247.4	41.4	41.0	17.9	49.9	338.3	112.5

Source: Data of Table 10.1.

229

There are two reasons for expressing an aggregate as an index number. In the first place, percentage movements are often more informative than quantities. Percentage comparisons are facilitated by expressing the aggregate of each year as a percentage of its value at some base date. Secondly, index numbers are useful when the quantities aggregated constitute only a sample of the items whose behavior is to be studied. The sample aggregate, as such, is meaningless, but its percentage behavior represents the aggregate as a whole.

The best-known quantity index in the United States is the monthly Federal Reserve Board Index of Industrial Production. The F.R.B. index is compiled for total industrial production and also by producing sectors (industry groupings) and by components of final output (market groupings). The present base of the F.R.B. index is 1957 = 100.

10.1.5 Choice of Base Period

The base period of an index number is chosen for convenience and need not correspond to the period used in determining the weights. In Table 10.2, the index number of citrus fruit production is expressed on the base 1951 = 100, although the weights were drawn from production of 1954. The Index of Prices Paid by Farmers (see below) is published by the United States Department of Agriculture with the base period 1910–14 = 100, although the most recent weights were drawn from 1950. The Consumer Price Index, using 1952 weights, was shifted from 1947–49 = 100 to 1957–59 = 100, beginning in January 1962.

Once an index number has been compiled on one base, it can be shifted to any other by dividing the series by the old index for the year desired as the new base. For example, the index of citrus production can be shifted to 1959 = 100 by dividing the series by 112.5, the old 1959 index.

10.2 PRICE INDEXES

10.2.1 Paasche Price Indexes

The problem of averaging prices is similar to that of aggregating physical quantities. Indeed, once a series of aggregate production has been measured in constant prices, a price index is easily obtained by dividing the current value of the series by its value in constant prices:

$$\text{price index} = \frac{\text{current production at current prices}}{\text{current production at constant prices}}.$$

Since exactly the same physical production appears in both numerator and denominator of this expression, variation in the ratio reflects only variation in prices. The price index will have the value 100 for the period from which the weights in the aggregate were chosen. If 1960 prices are used in the aggregate, the price index number has the base 1960 = 100. This index number, called a *Paasche index*, after its inventor, has the formula

$$\text{Paasche price index} = \frac{\sum_i Q_{it} P_{it}}{\sum_i Q_{it} P_{io}}.$$

It can easily be seen that a price index is similar to a quantity index except that the roles of price and quantity are reversed. In a price index, prices are being averaged, using quantities as weights. Since current physical quantities appear as weights in a Paasche index, it is also known as a *current weight* price index. A Paasche index is also an *implicit deflator;* when it is divided into the current value of total output, the result is aggregate output at constant prices.

The construction of a Paasche index of citrus fruit prices is shown in Table 10.3. Current values of output are divided by aggregate production in 1954 prices to give the index on a 1954 base.

The most familiar Paasche index numbers in present use are the implicit deflators of the gross national product and its components. These indexes are published in connection with the United States national accounts.

10.2.2 Laspeyres Price Indexes

Since the weights they employ change every period, the construction of Paasche price indexes is expensive except as a by-product of the compilation of constant price aggregates. The *Laspeyres* price index with fixed quantity weights is not only generally cheaper, but is more meaningful for many purposes. A Laspeyres index measures the variation in cost of a fixed "package" of goods. For example, the operation

Table 10.3 Calculation of a Paasche Index of Citrus Prices, 1949–59

Year	Aggregate Value of Production (millions of $) Current Prices[a]	1954 Prices[b]	Paasche Index[c] (1954 = 100)
1949	336.8	266.9	126.2
1950	318.0	309.4	102.8
1951	252.6	300.6	84.4
1952	295.3	305.4	96.7
1953	326.0	334.8	97.4
1954	333.0	333.1	100.0
1955	402.3	337.5	119.2
1956	365.6	344.5	106.1
1957	426.8	297.9	143.3
1958	514.4	342.2	150.3
1959	n.a.	338.3	n.a.

[a] From Table 10.1.
[b] From Table 10.2.
[c] Aggregate value in current prices divided by aggregate value in 1954 prices.
n.a. = data not available.

of an average farm of a particular type requires a certain number of bags of fertilizer, a number of gallons of gasoline, a number of pounds of spray material, barbed wire, and so on. The current value of this fixed set of inputs is the cost of operating a typical farm. Where Q_{io} is the average amount of the ith commodity used, and P_{it} is its price in year t, the cost of operation is given by

$$\text{Current cost} = \sum_i Q_{io} P_{it}.$$

The composite of goods constitutes a fixed "market basket" of commodities whose total cost to the buyer depends on the prices of its individual items. The movements in cost of this market basket are represented as an index number by expressing the series as a percentage of its value during a convenient base period, t_o.

$$\text{Index of Prices Paid by Farmers} = \frac{\sum_i Q_{io} P_{it}}{\sum_i Q_{io} P_{it_o}}.$$

10.2.3 Selection of Weights

The validity of a price index requires that the weights, that is, the quantities making up the market basket, be properly selected for the purpose of the index. Moreover, since production technique, expenditure habits, and type and availability of goods change, the weights require periodic revision. One of the most carefully compiled price indexes, the Consumer Price Index, published monthly by the United States Bureau of Labor Statistics, uses weights obtained periodically by interviewing a stratified sample of wage-earner families drawn from 97 American cities.

> In each city the Bureau selected a representative sample of families. A Bureau interviewer visited and interviewed each sample family and obtained a complete record of the kinds, qualities and amounts of foods, clothing, furniture and all other goods and services the family bought in 1950; and how much was spent for each item. Then the family records for all wage-earner and clerical-worker families were averaged together for each city.
>
> The Bureau has been calculating the Consumer Price Index for nearly four decades. The first "index market basket" was based on a survey of expenditures by consumers in 1918. Because people's buying habits changed, a new study and a new "market basket" were made for the years 1934–1936. During World War II, when many things were scarce and goods were rationed, the "market basket" was adjusted to reflect these changes; and again in 1950 the Bureau estimated the effect of postwar changes. The 1952 "market basket" represents the latest revision and brings the index up to date in terms of current buying. It includes such items as TV sets and frozen foods that were not a part of our living pattern a few years ago; and it includes changes that have occurred in the amounts, kinds, and qualities of things people buy.[1]

10.2.4 Selecting Prices

A useful price index must ordinarily cover millions of individual commodities. To keep a complete index up to date would be impossible, and we must resort to sampling. By inspecting the past behavior of many price series, a few are selected whose movements are representative of wide classes of commodities. The Consumer Price Index, whose move-

1. *The Consumer Price Index* (Washington, D.C.: U.S. Department of Labor, Bureau of Labor Statistics, January 1953), p. 3.

233

Table 10.4 Calculation of a Laspeyres Index of Citrus Prices Using 1954 Production as Weights

Year	Oranges (weight 130.0) Price ($ per box)	Weighted Price	Grapefruit (weight 42.2) Price ($ per box)	Weighted Price	Lemons (weight 14.0) Price ($ per box)	Weighted Price	Total Weighted Prices	Price Index (1954 = 100)
1949	2.24	291.2	1.81	76.4	3.59	50.3	417.9	125.5
1950	1.97	256.1	1.09	46.0	2.82	39.5	341.6	102.6
1951	1.50	195.0	.86	36.3	3.46	48.4	279.7	84.0
1952	1.71	222.3	1.08	45.6	3.90	54.6	322.5	96.8
1953	1.93	250.9	.85	35.9	2.73	38.2	325.0	97.6
1954	1.94	252.2	.99	41.8	2.79	39.1	333.1	100.0
1955	2.41	313.3	.95	40.1	3.14	44.0	397.4	119.3
1956	2.09	271.7	1.21	51.1	2.27	31.8	354.6	106.5
1957	3.06	397.8	1.42	59.9	2.19	30.7	488.4	146.6
1958	3.22	418.6	1.44	60.8	2.06	28.8	508.2	152.6

Source: Data of Table 10.1.

234

ments represent the average behavior of all commodities bought by wage-earner families, is actually compiled from a representative sample of only about 300 prices. For example, all cereals and bakery products are represented by only nine products: wheat flour, biscuit mix, corn meal, rice, rolled oats, corn flakes, white bread, soda crackers, and vanilla cookies.

10.2.5 Specification of Commodities

The commodities chosen as representative must be described and specified in complete detail as to quality, style, design, grade, size, quantity, and other relevant aspects. If the individual items in the market basket are not rigidly fixed, variation in the things being priced will ruin the index. If the price of beef were represented by Grade B stew meat one month and prime sirloin the next, the price index would exhibit wild and meaningless oscillations.

The detail of specification required is indicated by the following descriptions of three commodities priced in compiling the Bureau of Labor Statistics Wholesale Price Index:

1. "Beans, dry, with pork and tomato sauce, not oven baked, No. 300 can, priced canner to wholesaler or chain store, delivered, per dozen cans."

2. "Polo shirt, boys', cotton, single ply combed yarn, crew neck, short sleeves, 3½–5 lb./dozen, priced manufacturer to retailer, f.o.b. factory, per dozen."

3. "Axminster broadloom (roll price), 21/4 width, all wool, 50 to 70 rows, priced manufacturer to wholesaler, jobber, dealer, or distributor, f.o.b. mill, per square yard."

10.2.6 Calculating a Laspeyres Index

Once data have been compiled, the cost of the specified market basket is easily calculated and expressed as a percentage of base year. A Laspeyres price index for citrus fruit is constructed in Table 10.4, using the 1954 levels of production as weights. Note, incidentally, the comparison with the Paasche index of Table 10.3. Although these two indexes are unusually close, substantial agreement is generally found between the two kinds of indexes when economically meaningful weights are used in their construction. If weights are carefully and properly selected, the question of whether a Paasche or a Laspeyres index should be used is secondary.

10.2.7 Laspeyres Index as a Weighted Mean of Price Relatives

An interesting property of the Laspeyres index is the fact that it can be approached from a different point of view and calculated as a weighted mean of price relatives. This permits derivation of the price index even in circumstances where a fixed market basket of physical commodities cannot be easily defined.

The first step in compiling a weighted mean of price relatives is to express each price series as a series of price relatives. A *price relative* is formed by dividing each price in the series by its price in the base period and expressing the result as a percentage. For example, if the price of apples was $5.69 per box in 1952 and $3.50 in 1958, the 1952 price relative of apples (on the base 1958 = 100) is $5.69/3.50 = 162.6 per cent. Price relatives series for several fruits are shown in Table 10.6.

The next step is to assign each series of relatives a relative weight equal to the outlay on the item in question as a proportion of total expenditure. Relative weights are usually obtained from the total value of the respective commodities marketed during a particular base period, or from surveys of household expenditure. As we saw above, the weights in the Consumer Price Index are obtained by survey of the expenditure patterns of wage-earner families. Let V_i be the relative weight of the ith commodity. Then the formula for the price index becomes:

$$\text{weighted mean of price relatives} = \sum_i V_i \frac{P_{it}}{P_{io}}.$$

The compilation of a price index of fruits and nuts using representative prices is shown in Tables 10.5 and 10.6. The 1958 farm values of the individual crops are shown in Table 10.5 together with the individual prices selected to represent blocks of commodities. In Table 10.6, the price relatives of the representative commodities are assigned their block weights and averaged.

Table 10.5   Assignment of Weights and Representative Prices for an Index of Fruit and Nut Prices

Crop	Value of 1958 Crop (billions of $)	Weight = Crop Value / Total Value	Representative Price
Citrus fruit, total	.526		
Oranges	.415		Florida oranges, Chicago market auction price per box.
Grapefruit	.063	$\frac{.526}{1.417} = .371$	
Lemons	.036		
Limes	.001		
Tangerines	.010		
Tangelos	.001		
Noncitrus tree fruit, total		.490	
Apples	.178		Winesap apples, New York market auction price per box.
Peaches	.132	$\frac{.490}{1.417} = .346$	
Pears	.054		
Cherries	.043		
Apricots	.016		
Plums and Prunes	.057		
Others	.010		
Other fruit, total		.302	California Thompson seedless grapes, average price Eastern and Midwest auction.
Grapes	.203	$\frac{.302}{1.417} = .213$	
Cranberries	.014		
Strawberries	.085		
Tree nuts, total		.099	
Pecans	.048		Pecans, season average price per pound received by farmers.
Walnuts	.033	$\frac{.099}{1.417} = .070$	
Almonds	.015		
Filberts	.003		
All Crops	1.417	1.000	

Source: Data are from *Agricultural Statistics, 1960* (Washington, D.C.: U.S. Department of Agriculture, 1961).

10.2.8   Advantages to Weighted Mean of Price Relatives

Although, when calculated from the same data the results are identical with the Laspeyres index, there are two great advantages in using the weighted mean of price relatives to calculate a price index.

1. The use of price relatives facilitates combining the prices of specific individual representative commodities into the index, giving them weight in proportion to the larger blocks of commodities they are supposed to represent.

Table 10.6   Compilation of a Farm Price Index
of Fruits and Nuts as a Weighted Mean of Price Relatives

Year	Florida Oranges (citrus weight = .371)			Winesap Apples (noncitrus weight = .346)		
	Price ($ per box)	Price Relative (1958 = 100)	Weighted Relative	Price ($ per box)	Price Relative (1958 = 100)	Weighted Relative
1952	3.95	88.6	32.9	5.69	162.6	56.3
1953	4.08	91.5	33.9	5.01	143.1	49.5
1954	3.85	86.3	32.0	5.44	155.4	53.8
1955	4.61	103.4	38.4	4.37	124.9	43.2
1956	4.04	90.6	33.6	6.04	172.6	59.7
1957	5.09	114.1	42.3	4.50	128.6	44.5
1958	4.46	100.0	37.1	3.50	100.0	34.6

Year	California Thompson Seedless Grapes (nontree weight = .213)			Pecans (nut weight = .070)			Price Index (1958 = 100)
	Price ($ per pkg.)	Price Relative (1958 = 100)	Weighted Relative	Price ($ per lb.)	Price Relative (1958 = 100)	Weighted Relative	
1952	3.38	76.0	16.2	.221	78.6	5.5	110.9
1953	4.10	92.1	19.6	.163	58.0	4.1	107.1
1954	4.26	95.7	20.4	.286	101.8	7.1	113.3
1955	3.57	80.2	17.1	.328	116.7	8.2	106.9
1956	3.85	86.5	18.4	.185	65.8	4.6	116.3
1957	4.09	91.9	19.6	.237	84.3	5.9	112.3
1958	4.45	100.0	21.3	.281	100.0	7.0	100.0

Source: Prices from *Agricultural Statistics, 1960* (Washington, D.C.: U.S. Department of Agriculture, 1961).

2. Many kinds of expenditure do not have well-defined physical units at all. Medical care and legal service are common examples. Because of their diversity and differentiation, there is no physical unit that is generally applicable. Price relatives can be obtained for a few relatively standardized items: general practitioner's office call, hospital bed and care for one day, appendectomy surgery, and so on. The behavior of these prices can then be weighted into the general index on the basis of expenditure by the average family for all medical care.

·10.3 APPLICATIONS OF PRICE INDEXES

10.3.1 Deflation

Price indexes serve as deflators to allow for changes in the purchasing power of money. For many purposes, income movements over long periods are meaningful only after adjustment for prices. This adjustment, known as *deflation*, consists of dividing the income figure by an appropriate price index. The resulting *deflated* or *"real"* income series shows the movement of the buying power of money income.

Deflation of average hourly earnings in manufacturing by the Consumer Price Index is shown in Table 10.7. The table shows that although dollar hourly earnings tripled between 1941 and 1960, when adjusted for increase in prices, the real purchasing power of an average hour of work had increased only about 50 per cent. Real hourly earnings occasionally decreased, as in 1945, 1946, and 1947. The modest setbacks during these three years were associated with the fact that prices, which had been closely controlled during World War II, were decontrolled at this time and rose more rapidly than wages.

10.3.2 Escalator Contracts

Cost of living adjustments in so-called escalator wage contracts are a related application of price indexes. Essentially such a contract entails an automatic adjustment in money wages in response to changes in the Consumer Price Index. This has the effect of increasing the stability of the buying power of wages and permits wage contracts to extend over longer periods.

10.3.3 Farm Price Supports

Price support legislation provides for government action to support the prices of specified farm commodities at given percentages of their *parity prices*. The parity price is a price that bears the same relationship to the current Index of Prices Paid by Farmers as it bore on the average during a designated base period.

If P_o is the average price of the commodity during the base period, when the Prices Paid Index was I_o, the current parity price $P^*{}_t$ is determined by the current Prices Paid Index to be

$$P^*{}_t = P_o \frac{I_t}{I_o}.$$

Table 10.7 Current and Deflated Hourly Earnings,[a] All U.S. Manufacturing, 1941–60

Year	Hourly Earnings (current $ per hour)	Consumer Price Index (1957–59 = 100)	Deflated Hourly Earnings (1957–59 $ per hour)
1941	.77	48.2	1.60
1942	.88	55.2	1.59
1943	.98	60.1	1.63
1944	1.03	60.8	1.69
1945	1.04	62.6	1.66
1946	1.12	69.4	1.61
1947	1.25	83.4	1.50
1948	1.37	89.4	1.53
1949	1.43	87.1	1.64
1950	1.48	87.6	1.69
1951	1.60	95.5	1.68
1952	1.70	96.7	1.76
1953	1.80	96.4	1.87
1954	1.86	95.4	1.95
1955	1.93	94.4	2.04
1956	2.03	95.3	2.13
1957	2.14	98.4	2.17
1958	2.23	100.7	2.21
1959	2.30	101.0	2.28
1960	2.38	101.7	2.34

[a] Exclusive of overtime earnings.
Source: Data from *Business Statistics*, *1961* (Washington, D.C.: U.S. Department of Commerce, Office of Business Economics, 1961).

For most commodities the original base period was 1910–14, and for this reason the Prices Paid Index is on the base 1910–14 = 100. Under the current law, base periods vary by commodity, and the calculation of base period prices requires a number of additional adjustments.

10.3.4 Price Indexes in the Study of Economic Relationships

Finally, as we have seen (section 7.15, above) price indexes can be used as deflators to introduce the average level of prices as an additional variable in the analysis of relationships.

10.4 SUMMARY

Quantity aggregates and quantity and price index numbers are helpful in reducing the complexity of economic reality to proportions that can be handled with available resources. Goods in the aggregate are treated in place of individual items.

Goods are seldom substitutes in terms of their conventional units, but they can be aggregated when they are expressed in value units carefully defined by a fixed set of prices. For some purposes the aggregate is converted to an index number expressing quantity as a percentage of some convenient base year.

Comparison of the current value of an aggregate of goods with the value of the same aggregate at constant prices yields a price index. If current quantities are used as weights, the result is a Paasche, or current weight, price index. If a fixed market basket is used, the result is a Laspeyres, or fixed weight, price index. A fixed weight price index can also be calculated as a weighted mean of price relatives.

Questions and Problems

1. From the data given in the table on page 242.

(a) Compile aggregate production of the three crops in 1954 prices.

(b) Express aggregate production as a quantity index, 1958 = 100.

(c) Calculate aggregate value of production in current prices and obtain the implicit deflator (Paasche price index).

(d) Calculate a fixed weight price index, using average annual production over the period as weights, and setting the base year as 1956 = 100.

2. In the data of Chapter VIII, problem 1, why were potato prices deflated by the Consumer Price Index? In Chapter IX, problem 1, what does the phrase "1954 dollars" mean? Why were the data presented this way?

1. Price and Production of Three Vegetables, 1954–59

	Green Lima Beans, Fresh Market		Celery		Lettuce	
Year	Production (thousands of cwt.)	Price ($ per cwt.)	Production (thousands of cwt.)	Price ($ per cwt.)	Production (thousands of cwt.)	Price ($ per cwt.)
1954	398	8.64	15,126	3.31	31,181	4.03
1955	372	7.15	14,903	3.95	32,093	4.34
1956	356	8.77	15,898	3.32	34,121	4.00
1957	324	9.03	14,774	3.90	33,137	4.29
1958	328	8.38	14,069	4.46	32,697	4.03
1959	276	10.03	15,227	3.24	33,011	3.95

Source: Data are from *Agricultural Statistics, 1960* (Washington, D.C.: U.S. Department of Agriculture, 1961).

References

1. *Techniques of Preparing Major BLS Statistical Series*. BLS Bulletin No. 1168. Washington, D.C.: U.S. Department of Labor, Bureau of Labor Statistics. A useful collection of short, but careful and fairly detailed summaries of the nature of many BLS series, including the Consumer Price Index and the Wholesale Price Index.

2. *Index Numbers of Industrial Production*. New York: Statistical Office of the United Nations, 1950. A short, thorough exposition of the technique of compiling quantity index numbers, intended as a practical guide.

3. *The Computation of Cost-of-Living Indexes*. Prepared by the U.S. Bureau of Labor Statistics for the International Cooperation Administration, Office of Labor Affairs, Washington, D.C., 1957 (mimeo.). This is a short, practical treatment of useful price indexes, intended "to assist statisticians, particularly those in less industrialized countries, who are beginning to develop a statistical series of cost-of-living indexes, or who are revising and improving existing series."

4. *Government Price Statistics*. Hearings before the Subcommittee on Economic Statistics, Joint Economic Committee, Eighty-seventh Congress, Part 2, May 1, 2, 3, 4, and 5, 1961. Testimony by a number of well-known government, business, labor, and academic economists on the nature, meaning, uses, and abuses of price indexes, especially the Consumer Price Index.

INDEX

Index

Index

independent, 80
numerical, 79

Variance, 38–51:
  among, 133
  of categorical variable, 42
  of combined distributions, 46
  of sum, 44
  properties of, 43–49
  within, 132

Variance, calculation of, 39–40:
  of classified data, 41
  short method, 40

Weights, selection of, 227, 233
Wentworth, G. P., 154
Wolf, F. L., 78, 153

$\bar{X}$. *See* **Mean**

PROPORTIONAL PARTS

Number	0	1	2	3	4	5	6	7	8	9	1 2 3	4 5 6	7 8 9
10	0000	0043	0086	0128	0170	0212	0253	0294	0334	0374	4 8 12	17 21 25	29 33 37
11	0414	0453	0492	0531	0569	0607	0645	0682	0719	0755	4 8 11	15 19 23	26 30 34
12	0792	0828	0864	0899	0934	0969	1004	1038	1072	1106	3 7 10	14 17 21	24 28 31
13	1139	1173	1206	1239	1271	1303	1335	1367	1399	1430	3 6 10	13 16 19	23 26 29
14	1461	1492	1523	1553	1584	1614	1644	1673	1703	1732	3 6 9	12 15 18	21 24 27
15	1761	1790	1818	1847	1875	1903	1931	1959	1987	2014	3 6 8	11 14 17	20 22 25
16	2041	2068	2095	2122	2148	2175	2201	2227	2253	2279	3 5 8	11 13 16	18 21 24
17	2304	2330	2355	2380	2405	2430	2455	2480	2504	2529	2 5 7	10 12 15	17 20 22
18	2553	2577	2601	2625	2648	2672	2695	2718	2742	2765	2 5 7	9 12 14	16 19 21
19	2788	2810	2833	2856	2878	2900	2923	2945	2967	2989	2 4 7	9 11 13	16 18 20
20	3010	3032	3054	3075	3096	3118	3139	3160	3181	3201	2 4 6	8 11 13	15 17 19
21	3222	3243	3263	3284	3304	3324	3345	3365	3385	3404	2 4 6	8 10 12	14 16 18
22	3424	3444	3464	3483	3502	3522	3541	3560	3579	3598	2 4 6	8 10 12	14 15 17
23	3617	3636	3655	3674	3692	3711	3729	3747	3766	3784	2 4 6	7 9 11	13 15 17
24	3802	3820	3838	3856	3874	3892	3909	3927	3945	3962	2 4 5	7 9 11	12 14 16
25	3979	3997	4014	4031	4048	4065	4082	4099	4116	4133	2 3 5	7 9 10	12 14 15
26	4150	4166	4183	4200	4216	4232	4249	4265	4281	4298	2 3 5	7 8 10	11 13 15
27	4314	4330	4346	4362	4378	4393	4409	4425	4440	4456	2 3 5	6 8 9	11 13 14
28	4472	4487	4502	4518	4533	4548	4564	4579	4594	4609	2 3 5	6 8 9	11 12 14
29	4624	4639	4654	4669	4683	4698	4713	4728	4742	4757	1 3 4	6 7 9	10 12 13
30	4771	4786	4800	4814	4829	4843	4857	4871	4886	4900	1 3 4	6 7 9	10 11 13
31	4914	4928	4942	4955	4969	4983	4997	5011	5024	5038	1 3 4	6 7 8	10 11 12
32	5051	5065	5079	5092	5105	5119	5132	5145	5159	5172	1 3 4	5 7 8	9 11 12
33	5185	5198	5211	5224	5237	5250	5263	5276	5289	5302	1 3 4	5 6 8	9 10 12
34	5315	5328	5340	5353	5366	5378	5391	5403	5416	5428	1 3 4	5 6 8	9 10 11
35	5441	5453	5465	5478	5490	5502	5514	5527	5539	5551	1 2 4	5 6 7	9 10 11
36	5563	5575	5587	5599	5611	5623	5635	5647	5658	5670	1 2 4	5 6 7	8 10 11
37	5682	5694	5705	5717	5729	5740	5752	5763	5775	5786	1 2 3	5 6 7	8 9 10
38	5798	5809	5821	5832	5843	5855	5866	5877	5888	5899	1 2 3	5 6 7	8 9 10
39	5911	5922	5933	5944	5955	5966	5977	5988	5999	6010	1 2 3	4 5 7	8 9 10
40	6021	6031	6042	6053	6064	6075	6085	6096	6107	6117	1 2 3	4 5 6	8 9 10
41	6128	6138	6149	6160	6170	6180	6191	6201	6212	6222	1 2 3	4 5 6	7 8 9
42	6232	6243	6253	6263	6274	6284	6294	6304	6314	6325	1 2 3	4 5 6	7 8 9
43	6335	6345	6355	6365	6375	6385	6395	6405	6415	6425	1 2 3	4 5 6	7 8 9
44	6435	6444	6454	6464	6474	6484	6493	6503	6513	6522	1 2 3	4 5 6	7 8 9
45	6532	6542	6551	6561	6571	6580	6590	6599	6609	6618	1 2 3	4 5 6	7 8 9
46	6628	6637	6646	6656	6665	6675	6684	6693	6702	6712	1 2 3	4 5 6	7 7 8
47	6721	6730	6739	6749	6758	6767	6776	6785	6794	6803	1 2 3	4 5 5	6 7 8
48	6812	6821	6830	6839	6848	6857	6866	6875	6884	6893	1 2 3	4 4 5	6 7 8
49	6902	6911	6920	6928	6937	6946	6955	6964	6972	6981	1 2 3	4 4 5	6 7 8
50	6990	6998	7007	7016	7024	7033	7042	7050	7059	7067	1 2 3	3 4 5	6 7 8
51	7076	7084	7093	7101	7110	7118	7126	7135	7143	7152	1 2 3	3 4 5	6 7 8
52	7160	7168	7177	7185	7193	7202	7210	7218	7226	7235	1 2 2	3 4 5	6 7 7
53	7243	7251	7259	7267	7275	7284	7292	7300	7308	7316	1 2 2	3 4 5	6 6 7
54	7324	7332	7340	7348	7356	7364	7372	7380	7388	7396	1 2 2	3 4 5	6 6 7
	0	1	2	3	4	5	6	7	8	9	1 2 3	4 5 6	7 8 9

PROPORTIONAL PARTS

Number	0	1	2	3	4	5	6	7	8	9	1 2 3	4 5 6	7 8 9
55	7404	7412	7419	7427	7435	7443	7451	7459	7466	7474	1 2 2	3 4 5	5 6 7
56	7482	7490	7497	7505	7513	7520	7528	7536	7543	7551	1 2 2	3 4 5	5 6 7
57	7559	7566	7574	7582	7589	7597	7604	7612	7619	7627	1 2 2	3 4 5	5 6 7
58	7634	7642	7649	7657	7664	7672	7679	7686	7694	7701	1 1 2	3 4 4	5 6 7
59	7709	7716	7723	7731	7738	7745	7752	7760	7767	7774	1 1 2	3 4 4	5 6 7
60	7782	7789	7796	7803	7810	7818	7825	7832	7839	7846	1 1 2	3 4 4	5 6 6
61	7853	7860	7868	7875	7882	7889	7896	7903	7910	7917	1 1 2	3 4 4	5 6 6
62	7924	7931	7938	7945	7952	7959	7966	7973	7980	7987	1 1 2	3 3 4	5 6 6
63	7993	8000	8007	8014	8021	8028	8035	8041	8048	8055	1 1 2	3 3 4	5 5 6
64	8062	8069	8075	8082	8089	8096	8102	8109	8116	8122	1 1 2	3 3 4	5 5 6
65	8129	8136	8142	8149	8156	8162	8169	8176	8182	8189	1 1 2	3 3 4	5 5 6
66	8195	8202	8209	8215	8222	8228	8235	8241	8248	8254	1 1 2	3 3 4	5 5 6
67	8261	8267	8274	8280	8287	8293	8299	8306	8312	8319	1 1 2	3 3 4	5 5 6
68	8325	8331	8338	8344	8351	8357	8363	8370	8376	8382	1 1 2	3 3 4	4 5 6
69	8388	8395	8401	8407	8414	8420	8426	8432	8439	8445	1 1 2	2 3 4	4 5 6
70	8451	8457	8463	8470	8476	8482	8488	8494	8500	8506	1 1 2	2 3 4	4 5 6
71	8513	8519	8525	8531	8537	8543	8549	8555	8561	8567	1 1 2	2 3 4	4 5 5
72	8573	8579	8585	8591	8597	8603	8609	8615	8621	8627	1 1 2	2 3 4	4 5 5
73	8633	8639	8645	8651	8657	8663	8669	8675	8681	8686	1 1 2	2 3 4	4 5 5
74	8692	8698	8704	8710	8716	8722	8727	8733	8739	8745	1 1 2	2 3 4	4 5 5
75	8751	8756	8762	8768	8774	8779	8785	8791	8797	8802	1 1 2	2 3 3	4 5 5
76	8808	8814	8820	8825	8831	8837	8842	8848	8854	8859	1 1 2	2 3 3	4 5 5
77	8865	8871	8876	8882	8887	8893	8899	8904	8910	8915	1 1 2	2 3 3	4 4 5
78	8921	8927	8932	8938	8943	8949	8954	8960	8965	8971	1 1 2	2 3 3	4 4 5
79	8976	8982	8987	8993	8998	9004	9009	9015	9020	9025	1 1 2	2 3 3	4 4 5
80	9031	9036	9042	9047	9053	9058	9063	9069	9074	9079	1 1 2	2 3 3	4 4 5
81	9085	9090	9096	9101	9106	9112	9117	9122	9128	9133	1 1 2	2 3 3	4 4 5
82	9138	9143	9149	9154	9159	9165	9170	9175	9180	9186	1 1 2	2 3 3	4 4 5
83	9191	9196	9201	9206	9212	9217	9222	9227	9232	9238	1 1 2	2 3 3	4 4 5
84	9243	9248	9253	9258	9263	9269	9274	9279	9284	9289	1 1 2	2 3 3	4 4 5
85	9294	9299	9304	9309	9315	9320	9325	9330	9335	9340	1 1 2	2 3 3	4 4 5
86	9345	9350	9355	9360	9365	9370	9375	9380	9385	9390	1 1 2	2 3 3	4 4 5
87	9395	9400	9405	9410	9415	9420	9425	9430	9435	9440	0 1 1	2 2 3	3 4 4
88	9445	9450	9455	9460	9465	9469	9474	9479	9484	9489	0 1 1	2 2 3	3 4 4
89	9494	9499	9504	9509	9513	9518	9523	9528	9533	9538	0 1 1	2 2 3	3 4 4
90	9542	9547	9552	9557	9562	9566	9571	9576	9581	9586	0 1 1	2 2 3	3 4 4
91	9590	9595	9600	9605	9609	9614	9619	9624	9628	9633	0 1 1	2 2 3	3 4 4
92	9638	9643	9647	9652	9657	9661	9666	9671	9675	9680	0 1 1	2 2 3	3 4 4
93	9685	9689	9694	9699	9703	9708	9713	9717	9722	9727	0 1 1	2 2 3	3 4 4
94	9731	9736	9741	9745	9750	9754	9759	9763	9768	9773	0 1 1	2 2 3	3 4 4
95	9777	9782	9786	9791	9795	9800	9805	9809	9814	9818	0 1 1	2 2 3	3 4 4
96	9823	9827	9832	9836	9841	9845	9850	9854	9859	9863	0 1 1	2 2 3	3 4 4
97	9868	9872	9877	9881	9886	9890	9894	9899	9903	9908	0 1 1	2 2 3	3 4 4
98	9912	9917	9921	9926	9930	9934	9939	9943	9948	9952	0 1 1	2 2 3	3 4 4
99	9956	9961	9965	9969	9974	9978	9983	9987	9991	9996	0 1 1	2 2 3	3 3 4
	0	1	2	3	4	5	6	7	8	9	1 2 3	4 5 6	7 8 9

Appendix B Table of Four-Place Antilogarithms

Log.	0	1	2	3	4	5	6	7	8	9	1 2 3	4 5 6	7 8 9
·00	1000	1002	1005	1007	1009	1012	1014	1016	1019	1021	0 0 1	1 1 1	2 2 2
·01	1023	1026	1028	1030	1033	1035	1038	1040	1042	1045	0 0 1	1 1 1	2 2 2
·02	1047	1050	1052	1054	1057	1059	1062	1064	1067	1069	0 0 1	1 1 1	2 2 2
·03	1072	1074	1076	1079	1081	1084	1086	1089	1091	1094	0 0 1	1 1 1	2 2 2
·04	1096	1099	1102	1104	1107	1109	1112	1114	1117	1119	0 1 1	1 1 2	2 2 2
·05	1122	1125	1127	1130	1132	1135	1138	1140	1143	1146	0 1 1	1 1 2	2 2 2
·06	1148	1151	1153	1156	1159	1161	1164	1167	1169	1172	0 1 1	1 1 2	2 2 2
·07	1175	1178	1180	1183	1186	1189	1191	1194	1197	1199	0 1 1	1 1 2	2 2 2
·08	1202	1205	1208	1211	1213	1216	1219	1222	1225	1227	0 1 1	1 1 2	2 2 3
·09	1230	1233	1236	1239	1242	1245	1247	1250	1253	1256	0 1 1	1 1 2	2 2 3
·10	1259	1262	1265	1268	1271	1274	1276	1279	1282	1285	0 1 1	1 1 2	2 2 3
·11	1288	1291	1294	1297	1300	1303	1306	1309	1312	1315	0 1 1	1 2 2	2 2 3
·12	1318	1321	1324	1327	1330	1334	1337	1340	1343	1346	0 1 1	1 2 2	2 2 3
·13	1349	1352	1355	1358	1361	1365	1368	1371	1374	1377	0 1 1	1 2 2	2 3 3
·14	1380	1384	1387	1390	1393	1396	1400	1403	1406	1409	0 1 1	1 2 2	2 3 3
·15	1413	1416	1419	1422	1426	1429	1432	1435	1439	1442	0 1 1	1 2 2	2 3 3
·16	1445	1449	1452	1455	1459	1462	1466	1469	1472	1476	0 1 1	1 2 2	2 3 3
·17	1479	1483	1486	1489	1493	1496	1500	1503	1507	1510	0 1 1	1 2 2	2 3 3
·18	1514	1517	1521	1524	1528	1531	1535	1538	1542	1545	0 1 1	1 2 2	2 3 3
·19	1549	1552	1556	1560	1563	1567	1570	1574	1578	1581	0 1 1	1 2 2	3 3 3
·20	1585	1589	1592	1596	1600	1603	1607	1611	1614	1618	0 1 1	1 2 2	3 3 3
·21	1622	1626	1629	1633	1637	1641	1644	1648	1652	1656	0 1 1	2 2 2	3 3 3
·22	1660	1663	1667	1671	1675	1679	1683	1687	1690	1694	0 1 1	2 2 2	3 3 3
·23	1698	1702	1706	1710	1714	1718	1722	1726	1730	1734	0 1 1	2 2 2	3 3 4
·24	1738	1742	1746	1750	1754	1758	1762	1766	1770	1774	0 1 1	2 2 2	3 3 4
·25	1778	1782	1786	1791	1795	1799	1803	1807	1811	1816	0 1 1	2 2 2	3 3 4
·26	1820	1824	1828	1832	1837	1841	1845	1849	1854	1858	0 1 1	2 2 3	3 3 4
·27	1862	1866	1871	1875	1879	1884	1888	1892	1897	1901	0 1 1	2 2 3	3 3 4
·28	1905	1910	1914	1919	1923	1928	1932	1936	1941	1945	0 1 1	2 2 3	3 4 4
·29	1950	1954	1959	1963	1968	1972	1977	1982	1986	1991	0 1 1	2 2 3	3 4 4
·30	1995	2000	2004	2009	2014	2018	2023	2028	2032	2037	0 1 1	2 2 3	3 4 4
·31	2042	2046	2051	2056	2061	2065	2070	2075	2080	2084	0 1 1	2 2 3	3 4 4
·32	2089	2094	2099	2104	2109	2113	2118	2123	2128	2133	0 1 1	2 2 3	3 4 4
·33	2138	2143	2148	2153	2158	2163	2168	2173	2178	2183	0 1 1	2 2 3	3 4 4
·34	2188	2193	2198	2203	2208	2213	2218	2223	2228	2234	1 1 2	2 3 3	4 4 5
·35	2239	2244	2249	2254	2259	2265	2270	2275	2280	2286	1 1 2	2 3 3	4 4 5
·36	2291	2296	2301	2307	2312	2317	2323	2328	2333	2339	1 1 2	2 3 3	4 4 5
·37	2344	2350	2355	2360	2366	2371	2377	2382	2388	2393	1 1 2	2 3 3	4 4 5
·38	2399	2404	2410	2415	2421	2427	2432	2438	2443	2449	1 1 2	2 3 3	4 4 5
·39	2455	2460	2466	2472	2477	2483	2489	2495	2500	2506	1 1 2	2 3 3	4 5 5
·40	2512	2518	2523	2529	2535	2541	2547	2553	2559	2564	1 1 2	2 3 4	4 5 5
·41	2570	2576	2582	2588	2594	2600	2606	2612	2618	2624	1 1 2	2 3 4	4 5 5
·42	2630	2636	2642	2649	2655	2661	2667	2673	2679	2685	1 1 2	2 3 4	4 5 6
·43	2692	2698	2704	2710	2716	2723	2729	2735	2742	2748	1 1 2	3 3 4	4 5 6
·44	2754	2761	2767	2773	2780	2786	2793	2799	2805	2812	1 1 2	3 3 4	4 5 6
·45	2818	2825	2831	2838	2844	2851	2858	2864	2871	2877	1 1 2	3 3 4	5 5 6
·46	2884	2891	2897	2904	2911	2917	2924	2931	2938	2944	1 1 2	3 3 4	5 5 6
·47	2951	2958	2965	2972	2979	2985	2992	2999	3006	3013	1 1 2	3 3 4	5 5 6
·48	3020	3027	3034	3041	3048	3055	3062	3069	3076	3083	1 1 2	3 4 4	5 6 6
·49	3090	3097	3105	3112	3119	3126	3133	3141	3148	3155	1 1 2	3 4 4	5 6 6
	0	1	2	3	4	5	6	7	8	9	1 2 3	4 5 6	7 8 9

PROPORTIONAL PARTS

Log.	0	1	2	3	4	5	6	7	8	9	1 2 3	4 5 6	7 8 9
·50	3162	3170	3177	3184	3192	3199	3206	3214	3221	3228	1 1 2	3 4 4	5 6 7
·51	3236	3243	3251	3258	3266	3273	3281	3289	3296	3304	1 2 2	3 4 5	5 6 7
·52	3311	3319	3327	3334	3342	3350	3357	3365	3373	3381	1 2 2	3 4 5	5 6 7
·53	3388	3396	3404	3412	3420	3428	3436	3443	3451	3459	1 2 2	3 4 5	6 6 7
·54	3467	3475	3483	3491	3499	3508	3516	3524	3532	3540	1 2 2	3 4 5	6 6 7
·55	3548	3556	3565	3573	3581	3589	3597	3606	3614	3622	1 2 2	3 4 5	6 7 7
·56	3631	3639	3648	3656	3664	3673	3681	3690	3698	3707	1 2 3	3 4 5	6 7 8
·57	3715	3724	3733	3741	3750	3758	3767	3776	3784	3793	1 2 3	3 4 5	6 7 8
·58	3802	3811	3819	3828	3837	3846	3855	3864	3873	3882	1 2 3	4 4 5	6 7 8
·59	3890	3899	3908	3917	3926	3936	3945	3954	3963	3972	1 2 3	4 5 5	6 7 8
·60	3981	3990	3999	4009	4018	4027	4036	4046	4055	4064	1 2 3	4 5 6	6 7 8
·61	4074	4083	4093	4102	4111	4121	4130	4140	4150	4159	1 2 3	4 5 6	7 8 9
·62	4169	4178	4188	4198	4207	4217	4227	4236	4246	4256	1 2 3	4 5 6	7 8 9
·63	4266	4276	4285	4295	4305	4315	4325	4335	4345	4355	1 2 3	4 5 6	7 8 9
·64	4365	4375	4385	4395	4406	4416	4426	4436	4446	4457	1 2 3	4 5 6	7 8 9
·65	4467	4477	4487	4498	4508	4519	4529	4539	4550	4560	1 2 3	4 5 6	7 8 9
·66	4571	4581	4592	4603	4613	4624	4634	4645	4656	4667	1 2 3	4 5 6	7 9 10
·67	4677	4688	4699	4710	4721	4732	4742	4753	4764	4775	1 2 3	4 5 7	8 9 10
·68	4786	4797	4808	4819	4831	4842	4853	4864	4875	4887	1 2 3	4 6 7	8 9 10
·69	4898	4909	4920	4932	4943	4955	4966	4977	4989	5000	1 2 3	5 6 7	8 9 10
·70	5012	5023	5035	5047	5058	5070	5082	5093	5105	5117	1 2 4	5 6 7	8 9 11
·71	5129	5140	5152	5164	5176	5188	5200	5212	5224	5236	1 2 4	5 6 7	8 10 11
·72	5248	5260	5272	5284	5297	5309	5321	5333	5346	5358	1 2 4	5 6 7	9 10 11
·73	5370	5383	5395	5408	5420	5433	5445	5458	5470	5483	1 3 4	5 6 8	9 10 11
·74	5495	5508	5521	5534	5546	5559	5572	5585	5598	5610	1 3 4	5 6 8	9 10 12
·75	5623	5636	5649	5662	5675	5689	5702	5715	5728	5741	1 3 4	5 7 8	9 10 12
·76	5754	5768	5781	5794	5808	5821	5834	5848	5861	5875	1 3 4	5 7 8	9 11 12
·77	5888	5902	5916	5929	5943	5957	5970	5984	5998	6012	1 3 4	5 7 8	10 11 12
·78	6026	6039	6053	6067	6081	6095	6109	6124	6138	6152	1 3 4	6 7 8	10 11 13
·79	6166	6180	6194	6209	6223	6237	6252	6266	6281	6295	1 3 4	6 7 9	10 11 13
·80	6310	6324	6339	6353	6368	6383	6397	6412	6427	6442	1 3 4	6 7 9	10 12 13
·81	6457	6471	6486	6501	6516	6531	6546	6561	6577	6592	2 3 5	6 8 9	11 12 14
·82	6607	6622	6637	6653	6668	6683	6699	6714	6730	6745	2 3 5	6 8 9	11 12 14
·83	6761	6776	6792	6808	6823	6839	6855	6871	6887	6902	2 3 5	6 8 9	11 13 14
·84	6918	6934	6950	6966	6982	6998	7015	7031	7047	7063	2 3 5	6 8 10	11 13 15
·85	7079	7096	7112	7129	7145	7161	7178	7194	7211	7228	2 3 5	7 8 10	12 13 15
·86	7244	7261	7278	7295	7311	7328	7345	7362	7379	7396	2 3 5	7 8 10	12 13 15
·87	7413	7430	7447	7464	7482	7499	7516	7534	7551	7568	2 3 5	7 9 10	12 14 16
·88	7586	7603	7621	7638	7656	7674	7691	7709	7727	7745	2 4 5	7 9 11	12 14 16
·89	7762	7780	7798	7816	7834	7852	7870	7889	7907	7925	2 4 5	7 9 11	13 14 16
·90	7943	7962	7980	7998	8017	8035	8054	8072	8091	8110	2 4 6	7 9 11	13 15 17
·91	8128	8147	8166	8185	8204	8222	8241	8260	8279	8299	2 4 6	8 9 11	13 15 17
·92	8318	8337	8356	8375	8395	8414	8433	8453	8472	8492	2 4 6	8 10 12	14 15 17
·93	8511	8531	8551	8570	8590	8610	8630	8650	8670	8690	2 4 6	8 10 12	14 16 18
·94	8710	8730	8750	8770	8790	8810	8831	8851	8872	8892	2 4 6	8 10 12	14 16 18
·95	8913	8933	8954	8974	8995	9016	9036	9057	9078	9099	2 4 6	8 10 12	15 17 19
·96	9120	9141	9162	9183	9204	9226	9247	9268	9290	9311	2 4 6	8 11 13	15 17 19
·97	9333	9354	9376	9397	9419	9441	9462	9484	9506	9528	2 4 7	9 11 13	15 17 20
·98	9550	9572	9594	9616	9638	9661	9683	9705	9727	9750	2 4 7	9 11 13	16 18 20
·99	9772	9795	9817	9840	9863	9886	9908	9931	9954	9977	2 5 7	9 11 14	16 18 20
	0	1	2	3	4	5	6	7	8	9	1 2 3	4 5 6	7 8 9

5% (ROMAN TYPE) AND 1% (BOLD FACE TYPE) POINTS FOR THE DISTRIBUTION OF F

n_1 degrees of freedom (for greater mean square)

Each cell: 5% point (roman) / 1% point (bold face).

n_2	1	2	3	4	5	6	7	8	9	10	11	12	14	16	20	24	30	40	50	75	100	200	500	∞
1	161 / 4,052	200 / 4,999	216 / 5,403	225 / 5,625	230 / 5,764	234 / 5,859	237 / 5,928	239 / 5,981	241 / 6,022	242 / 6,056	243 / 6,082	244 / 6,106	245 / 6,142	246 / 6,169	248 / 6,208	249 / 6,234	250 / 6,258	251 / 6,286	252 / 6,302	253 / 6,323	253 / 6,334	254 / 6,352	254 / 6,361	254 / 6,366
2	18.51 / 98.49	19.00 / 99.01	19.16 / 99.17	19.25 / 99.25	19.30 / 99.30	19.33 / 99.33	19.36 / 99.34	19.37 / 99.36	19.38 / 99.38	19.39 / 99.40	19.40 / 99.41	19.41 / 99.42	19.42 / 99.43	19.43 / 99.44	19.44 / 99.45	19.45 / 99.46	19.46 / 99.47	19.47 / 99.48	19.47 / 99.48	19.48 / 99.49	19.49 / 99.49	19.49 / 99.49	19.50 / 99.50	19.50 / 99.50
3	10.13 / 34.12	9.55 / 30.81	9.28 / 29.46	9.12 / 28.71	9.01 / 28.24	8.94 / 27.91	8.88 / 27.67	8.84 / 27.49	8.81 / 27.34	8.78 / 27.23	8.76 / 27.13	8.74 / 27.05	8.71 / 26.92	8.69 / 26.83	8.66 / 26.69	8.64 / 26.60	8.62 / 26.50	8.60 / 26.41	8.58 / 26.35	8.57 / 26.27	8.56 / 26.23	8.54 / 26.18	8.54 / 26.14	8.53 / 26.12
4	7.71 / 21.20	6.94 / 18.00	6.59 / 16.69	6.39 / 15.98	6.26 / 15.52	6.16 / 15.21	6.09 / 14.98	6.04 / 14.80	6.00 / 14.66	5.96 / 14.54	5.93 / 14.45	5.91 / 14.37	5.87 / 14.24	5.84 / 14.15	5.80 / 14.02	5.77 / 13.93	5.74 / 13.83	5.71 / 13.74	5.70 / 13.69	5.68 / 13.61	5.66 / 13.57	5.65 / 13.52	5.64 / 13.48	5.63 / 13.46
5	6.61 / 16.26	5.79 / 13.27	5.41 / 12.06	5.19 / 11.39	5.05 / 10.97	4.95 / 10.67	4.88 / 10.45	4.82 / 10.27	4.78 / 10.15	4.74 / 10.05	4.70 / 9.96	4.68 / 9.89	4.64 / 9.77	4.60 / 9.68	4.56 / 9.55	4.53 / 9.47	4.50 / 9.38	4.46 / 9.29	4.44 / 9.24	4.42 / 9.17	4.40 / 9.13	4.38 / 9.07	4.37 / 9.04	4.36 / 9.02
6	5.99 / 13.74	5.14 / 10.92	4.76 / 9.78	4.53 / 9.15	4.39 / 8.75	4.28 / 8.47	4.21 / 8.26	4.15 / 8.10	4.10 / 7.98	4.06 / 7.87	4.03 / 7.79	4.00 / 7.72	3.96 / 7.60	3.92 / 7.52	3.87 / 7.39	3.84 / 7.31	3.81 / 7.23	3.77 / 7.14	3.75 / 7.09	3.72 / 7.02	3.71 / 6.99	3.69 / 6.94	3.68 / 6.90	3.67 / 6.88
7	5.59 / 12.25	4.74 / 9.55	4.35 / 8.45	4.12 / 7.85	3.97 / 7.46	3.87 / 7.19	3.79 / 7.00	3.73 / 6.84	3.68 / 6.71	3.63 / 6.62	3.60 / 6.54	3.57 / 6.47	3.52 / 6.35	3.49 / 6.27	3.44 / 6.15	3.41 / 6.07	3.38 / 5.98	3.34 / 5.90	3.32 / 5.85	3.29 / 5.78	3.28 / 5.75	3.25 / 5.70	3.24 / 5.67	3.23 / 5.65
8	5.32 / 11.26	4.46 / 8.65	4.07 / 7.59	3.84 / 7.01	3.69 / 6.63	3.58 / 6.37	3.50 / 6.19	3.44 / 6.03	3.39 / 5.91	3.34 / 5.82	3.31 / 5.74	3.28 / 5.67	3.23 / 5.56	3.20 / 5.48	3.15 / 5.36	3.12 / 5.28	3.08 / 5.20	3.05 / 5.11	3.03 / 5.06	3.00 / 5.00	2.98 / 4.96	2.96 / 4.91	2.94 / 4.88	2.93 / 4.86
9	5.12 / 10.56	4.26 / 8.02	3.86 / 6.99	3.63 / 6.42	3.48 / 6.06	3.37 / 5.80	3.29 / 5.62	3.23 / 5.47	3.18 / 5.35	3.13 / 5.26	3.10 / 5.18	3.07 / 5.11	3.02 / 5.00	2.98 / 4.92	2.93 / 4.80	2.90 / 4.73	2.86 / 4.64	2.82 / 4.56	2.80 / 4.51	2.77 / 4.45	2.76 / 4.41	2.73 / 4.36	2.72 / 4.33	2.71 / 4.31
10	4.96 / 10.04	4.10 / 7.56	3.71 / 6.55	3.48 / 5.99	3.33 / 5.64	3.22 / 5.39	3.14 / 5.21	3.07 / 5.06	3.02 / 4.95	2.97 / 4.85	2.94 / 4.78	2.91 / 4.71	2.86 / 4.60	2.82 / 4.52	2.77 / 4.41	2.74 / 4.33	2.70 / 4.25	2.67 / 4.17	2.64 / 4.12	2.61 / 4.05	2.59 / 4.01	2.56 / 3.96	2.55 / 3.93	2.54 / 3.91
11	4.84 / 9.65	3.98 / 7.20	3.59 / 6.22	3.36 / 5.67	3.20 / 5.32	3.09 / 5.07	3.01 / 4.88	2.95 / 4.74	2.90 / 4.63	2.86 / 4.54	2.82 / 4.46	2.79 / 4.40	2.74 / 4.29	2.70 / 4.21	2.65 / 4.10	2.61 / 4.02	2.57 / 3.94	2.53 / 3.86	2.50 / 3.80	2.47 / 3.74	2.45 / 3.70	2.42 / 3.66	2.41 / 3.62	2.40 / 3.60
12	4.75 / 9.33	3.88 / 6.93	3.49 / 5.95	3.26 / 5.41	3.11 / 5.06	3.00 / 4.82	2.92 / 4.65	2.85 / 4.50	2.80 / 4.39	2.76 / 4.30	2.72 / 4.22	2.69 / 4.16	2.64 / 4.05	2.60 / 3.98	2.54 / 3.86	2.50 / 3.78	2.46 / 3.70	2.42 / 3.61	2.40 / 3.56	2.36 / 3.49	2.35 / 3.46	2.32 / 3.41	2.31 / 3.38	2.30 / 3.36
13	4.67 / 9.07	3.80 / 6.70	3.41 / 5.74	3.18 / 5.20	3.02 / 4.86	2.92 / 4.62	2.84 / 4.44	2.77 / 4.30	2.72 / 4.19	2.67 / 4.10	2.63 / 4.02	2.60 / 3.96	2.55 / 3.85	2.51 / 3.78	2.46 / 3.67	2.42 / 3.59	2.38 / 3.51	2.34 / 3.42	2.32 / 3.37	2.28 / 3.30	2.26 / 3.27	2.24 / 3.21	2.22 / 3.18	2.21 / 3.16

The function, $F = e$ with exponent $2z$ is computed in part from Fisher's Table VI (7). Additional entries are by interpolation, mostly graphical.
Source: Reprinted from Table 10.5.3, pp. 246–49, Snedecor, *Statistical Methods*, Fifth Edition, copyright 1956, published by the Iowa State University Press, by permission.

5% (ROMAN TYPE) AND 1% (BOLD FACE TYPE) POINTS FOR THE DISTRIBUTION OF *F*

n_1 degrees of freedom (for greater mean square)

n_2	1	2	3	4	5	6	7	8	9	10	11	12	14	16	20	24	30	40	50	75	100	200	500	∞
27	4.21 / **7.68**	3.35 / **5.49**	2.96 / **4.60**	2.73 / **4.11**	2.57 / **3.79**	2.46 / **3.56**	2.37 / **3.39**	2.30 / **3.26**	2.25 / **3.14**	2.20 / **3.06**	2.16 / **2.98**	2.13 / **2.93**	2.08 / **2.83**	2.03 / **2.74**	1.97 / **2.63**	1.93 / **2.55**	1.88 / **2.47**	1.84 / **2.38**	1.80 / **2.33**	1.76 / **2.25**	1.74 / **2.21**	1.71 / **2.16**	1.68 / **2.12**	1.67 / **2.10**
28	4.20 / **7.64**	3.34 / **5.45**	2.95 / **4.57**	2.71 / **4.07**	2.56 / **3.76**	2.44 / **3.53**	2.36 / **3.36**	2.29 / **3.23**	2.24 / **3.11**	2.19 / **3.03**	2.15 / **2.95**	2.12 / **2.90**	2.06 / **2.80**	2.02 / **2.71**	1.96 / **2.60**	1.91 / **2.52**	1.87 / **2.44**	1.81 / **2.35**	1.78 / **2.30**	1.75 / **2.22**	1.72 / **2.18**	1.69 / **2.13**	1.67 / **2.09**	1.65 / **2.06**
29	4.18 / **7.60**	3.33 / **5.42**	2.93 / **4.54**	2.70 / **4.04**	2.54 / **3.73**	2.43 / **3.50**	2.35 / **3.33**	2.28 / **3.20**	2.22 / **3.08**	2.18 / **3.00**	2.14 / **2.92**	2.10 / **2.87**	2.05 / **2.77**	2.00 / **2.68**	1.94 / **2.57**	1.90 / **2.49**	1.85 / **2.41**	1.80 / **2.32**	1.77 / **2.27**	1.73 / **2.19**	1.71 / **2.15**	1.68 / **2.10**	1.65 / **2.06**	1.64 / **2.03**
30	4.17 / **7.56**	3.32 / **5.39**	2.92 / **4.51**	2.69 / **4.02**	2.53 / **3.70**	2.42 / **3.47**	2.34 / **3.30**	2.27 / **3.17**	2.21 / **3.06**	2.16 / **2.98**	2.12 / **2.90**	2.09 / **2.84**	2.04 / **2.74**	1.99 / **2.66**	1.93 / **2.55**	1.89 / **2.47**	1.84 / **2.38**	1.79 / **2.29**	1.76 / **2.24**	1.72 / **2.16**	1.69 / **2.13**	1.66 / **2.07**	1.64 / **2.03**	1.62 / **2.01**
32	4.15 / **7.50**	3.30 / **5.34**	2.90 / **4.46**	2.67 / **3.97**	2.51 / **3.66**	2.40 / **3.42**	2.32 / **3.25**	2.25 / **3.12**	2.19 / **3.01**	2.14 / **2.94**	2.10 / **2.86**	2.07 / **2.80**	2.02 / **2.70**	1.97 / **2.62**	1.91 / **2.51**	1.86 / **2.42**	1.82 / **2.34**	1.76 / **2.25**	1.74 / **2.20**	1.69 / **2.12**	1.67 / **2.08**	1.64 / **2.02**	1.61 / **1.98**	1.59 / **1.96**
34	4.13 / **7.44**	3.28 / **5.29**	2.88 / **4.42**	2.65 / **3.93**	2.49 / **3.61**	2.38 / **3.38**	2.30 / **3.21**	2.23 / **3.08**	2.17 / **2.97**	2.12 / **2.89**	2.08 / **2.82**	2.05 / **2.76**	2.00 / **2.66**	1.95 / **2.58**	1.89 / **2.47**	1.84 / **2.38**	1.80 / **2.30**	1.74 / **2.21**	1.71 / **2.15**	1.67 / **2.08**	1.64 / **2.04**	1.61 / **1.98**	1.59 / **1.94**	1.57 / **1.91**
36	4.11 / **7.39**	3.26 / **5.25**	2.86 / **4.38**	2.63 / **3.89**	2.48 / **3.58**	2.36 / **3.35**	2.28 / **3.18**	2.21 / **3.04**	2.15 / **2.94**	2.10 / **2.86**	2.06 / **2.78**	2.03 / **2.72**	1.98 / **2.62**	1.93 / **2.54**	1.87 / **2.43**	1.82 / **2.35**	1.78 / **2.26**	1.72 / **2.17**	1.69 / **2.12**	1.65 / **2.04**	1.62 / **2.00**	1.59 / **1.94**	1.56 / **1.90**	1.55 / **1.87**
38	4.10 / **7.35**	3.25 / **5.21**	2.85 / **4.34**	2.62 / **3.86**	2.46 / **3.54**	2.35 / **3.32**	2.26 / **3.15**	2.19 / **3.02**	2.14 / **2.91**	2.09 / **2.82**	2.05 / **2.75**	2.02 / **2.69**	1.96 / **2.59**	1.92 / **2.51**	1.85 / **2.40**	1.80 / **2.32**	1.76 / **2.22**	1.71 / **2.14**	1.67 / **2.03**	1.63 / **2.00**	1.60 / **1.97**	1.57 / **1.90**	1.54 / **1.86**	1.53 / **1.84**
40	4.08 / **7.31**	3.23 / **5.18**	2.84 / **4.31**	2.61 / **3.83**	2.45 / **3.51**	2.34 / **3.29**	2.25 / **3.12**	2.18 / **2.99**	2.12 / **2.88**	2.07 / **2.80**	2.04 / **2.73**	2.00 / **2.66**	1.95 / **2.56**	1.90 / **2.49**	1.84 / **2.37**	1.79 / **2.29**	1.74 / **2.20**	1.69 / **2.11**	1.66 / **2.05**	1.61 / **1.97**	1.59 / **1.94**	1.55 / **1.88**	1.53 / **1.84**	1.51 / **1.81**
42	4.07 / **7.27**	3.22 / **5.15**	2.83 / **4.29**	2.59 / **3.80**	2.44 / **3.49**	2.32 / **3.26**	2.24 / **3.10**	2.17 / **2.96**	2.11 / **2.86**	2.06 / **2.77**	2.02 / **2.70**	1.99 / **2.64**	1.94 / **2.54**	1.89 / **2.46**	1.82 / **2.35**	1.78 / **2.26**	1.73 / **2.17**	1.68 / **2.08**	1.64 / **2.02**	1.60 / **1.94**	1.57 / **1.91**	1.54 / **1.85**	1.51 / **1.80**	1.49 / **1.78**
44	4.06 / **7.24**	3.21 / **5.12**	2.82 / **4.26**	2.58 / **3.78**	2.43 / **3.46**	2.31 / **3.24**	2.23 / **3.07**	2.16 / **2.94**	2.10 / **2.84**	2.05 / **2.75**	2.01 / **2.68**	1.98 / **2.62**	1.92 / **2.52**	1.88 / **2.44**	1.81 / **2.32**	1.76 / **2.24**	1.72 / **2.15**	1.66 / **2.06**	1.63 / **2.00**	1.58 / **1.92**	1.56 / **1.88**	1.52 / **1.82**	1.50 / **1.78**	1.48 / **1.75**
46	4.05 / **7.21**	3.20 / **5.10**	2.81 / **4.24**	2.57 / **3.76**	2.42 / **3.44**	2.30 / **3.22**	2.22 / **3.05**	2.14 / **2.92**	2.09 / **2.82**	2.04 / **2.73**	2.00 / **2.66**	1.97 / **2.60**	1.91 / **2.50**	1.87 / **2.42**	1.80 / **2.30**	1.75 / **2.22**	1.71 / **2.13**	1.65 / **2.04**	1.62 / **1.98**	1.57 / **1.90**	1.54 / **1.86**	1.51 / **1.80**	1.48 / **1.76**	1.46 / **1.72**
48	4.04 / **7.19**	3.19 / **5.08**	2.80 / **4.22**	2.56 / **3.74**	2.41 / **3.42**	2.30 / **3.20**	2.21 / **3.04**	2.14 / **2.90**	2.08 / **2.80**	2.03 / **2.71**	1.99 / **2.64**	1.96 / **2.58**	1.90 / **2.48**	1.86 / **2.40**	1.79 / **2.28**	1.74 / **2.20**	1.70 / **2.11**	1.64 / **2.02**	1.61 / **1.96**	1.56 / **1.88**	1.53 / **1.84**	1.50 / **1.78**	1.47 / **1.73**	1.45 / **1.70**

Appendix C (continued)   Table of F

5% (ROMAN TYPE) AND 1% (BOLD FACE TYPE) POINTS FOR THE DISTRIBUTION OF F

n_1 degrees of freedom (for greater mean square)

n_2	1	2	3	4	5	6	7	.8	9	10	11	12	14	16	20	24	30	40	50	75	100	200	500	∞	n_2
14	4.60 / **8.86**	3.74 / **6.51**	3.34 / **5.56**	3.11 / **5.03**	2.96 / **4.69**	2.85 / **4.46**	2.77 / **4.28**	2.70 / **4.14**	2.65 / **4.03**	2.60 / **3.94**	2.56 / **3.86**	2.53 / **3.80**	2.48 / **3.70**	2.44 / **3.62**	2.39 / **3.51**	2.35 / **3.43**	2.31 / **3.34**	2.27 / **3.26**	2.24 / **3.21**	2.21 / **3.14**	2.19 / **3.11**	2.16 / **3.06**	2.14 / **3.02**	2.13 / **3.00**	14
15	4.54 / **8.68**	3.68 / **6.36**	3.29 / **5.42**	3.06 / **4.89**	2.90 / **4.56**	2.79 / **4.32**	2.70 / **4.14**	2.64 / **4.00**	2.59 / **3.89**	2.55 / **3.80**	2.51 / **3.73**	2.48 / **3.67**	2.43 / **3.56**	2.39 / **3.48**	2.33 / **3.36**	2.29 / **3.29**	2.25 / **3.20**	2.21 / **3.12**	2.18 / **3.07**	2.15 / **3.00**	2.12 / **2.97**	2.10 / **2.92**	2.08 / **2.89**	2.07 / **2.87**	15
16	4.49 / **8.53**	3.63 / **6.23**	3.24 / **5.29**	3.01 / **4.77**	2.85 / **4.44**	2.74 / **4.20**	2.66 / **4.03**	2.59 / **3.89**	2.54 / **3.78**	2.49 / **3.69**	2.45 / **3.61**	2.42 / **3.55**	2.37 / **3.45**	2.33 / **3.37**	2.28 / **3.25**	2.24 / **3.18**	2.20 / **3.10**	2.16 / **3.01**	2.13 / **2.96**	2.09 / **2.89**	2.07 / **2.86**	2.04 / **2.80**	2.02 / **2.77**	2.01 / **2.75**	16
17	4.45 / **8.40**	3.59 / **6.11**	3.20 / **5.18**	2.96 / **4.67**	2.81 / **4.34**	2.70 / **4.10**	2.62 / **3.93**	2.55 / **3.79**	2.50 / **3.68**	2.45 / **3.59**	2.41 / **3.52**	2.38 / **3.45**	2.33 / **3.35**	2.29 / **3.27**	2.23 / **3.16**	2.19 / **3.08**	2.15 / **3.00**	2.11 / **2.92**	2.08 / **2.86**	2.04 / **2.79**	2.02 / **2.76**	1.99 / **2.70**	1.97 / **2.67**	1.96 / **2.65**	17
18	4.41 / **8.28**	3.55 / **6.01**	3.16 / **5.09**	2.93 / **4.58**	2.77 / **4.25**	2.66 / **4.01**	2.58 / **3.85**	2.51 / **3.71**	2.46 / **3.60**	2.41 / **3.51**	2.37 / **3.44**	2.34 / **3.37**	2.29 / **3.27**	2.25 / **3.19**	2.19 / **3.07**	2.15 / **3.00**	2.11 / **2.91**	2.07 / **2.83**	2.04 / **2.78**	2.00 / **2.71**	1.98 / **2.68**	1.95 / **2.62**	1.93 / **2.59**	1.92 / **2.57**	18
19	4.38 / **8.18**	3.52 / **5.93**	3.13 / **5.01**	2.90 / **4.50**	2.74 / **4.17**	2.63 / **3.94**	2.55 / **3.77**	2.48 / **3.63**	2.43 / **3.52**	2.38 / **3.43**	2.34 / **3.36**	2.31 / **3.30**	2.26 / **3.19**	2.21 / **3.12**	2.15 / **3.00**	2.11 / **2.92**	2.07 / **2.84**	2.02 / **2.76**	2.00 / **2.70**	1.96 / **2.63**	1.94 / **2.60**	1.91 / **2.54**	1.90 / **2.51**	1.88 / **2.49**	19
20	4.35 / **8.10**	3.49 / **5.85**	3.10 / **4.94**	2.87 / **4.43**	2.71 / **4.10**	2.60 / **3.87**	2.52 / **3.71**	2.45 / **3.56**	2.40 / **3.45**	2.35 / **3.37**	2.31 / **3.30**	2.28 / **3.23**	2.23 / **3.13**	2.18 / **3.05**	2.12 / **2.94**	2.08 / **2.86**	2.04 / **2.77**	1.99 / **2.69**	1.96 / **2.63**	1.92 / **2.56**	1.90 / **2.53**	1.87 / **2.47**	1.85 / **2.44**	1.84 / **2.42**	20
21	4.32 / **8.02**	3.47 / **5.78**	3.07 / **4.87**	2.84 / **4.37**	2.68 / **4.04**	2.57 / **3.81**	2.49 / **3.65**	2.42 / **3.51**	2.37 / **3.40**	2.32 / **3.31**	2.28 / **3.24**	2.25 / **3.17**	2.20 / **3.07**	2.15 / **2.99**	2.09 / **2.88**	2.05 / **2.80**	2.00 / **2.72**	1.96 / **2.63**	1.93 / **2.58**	1.89 / **2.51**	1.87 / **2.47**	1.84 / **2.42**	1.82 / **2.38**	1.81 / **2.36**	21
22	4.30 / **7.94**	3.44 / **5.72**	3.05 / **4.82**	2.82 / **4.31**	2.66 / **3.99**	2.55 / **3.76**	2.47 / **3.59**	2.40 / **3.45**	2.35 / **3.35**	2.30 / **3.26**	2.26 / **3.18**	2.23 / **3.12**	2.18 / **3.02**	2.13 / **2.94**	2.07 / **2.83**	2.03 / **2.75**	1.98 / **2.67**	1.93 / **2.58**	1.91 / **2.53**	1.87 / **2.46**	1.84 / **2.42**	1.81 / **2.37**	1.80 / **2.33**	1.78 / **2.31**	22
23	4.28 / **7.88**	3.42 / **5.66**	3.03 / **4.76**	2.80 / **4.26**	2.64 / **3.94**	2.53 / **3.71**	2.45 / **3.54**	2.38 / **3.41**	2.32 / **3.30**	2.28 / **3.21**	2.24 / **3.14**	2.20 / **3.07**	2.14 / **2.97**	2.10 / **2.89**	2.04 / **2.78**	2.00 / **2.70**	1.96 / **2.62**	1.91 / **2.53**	1.88 / **2.48**	1.84 / **2.41**	1.82 / **2.37**	1.79 / **2.32**	1.77 / **2.28**	1.76 / **2.26**	23
24	4.26 / **7.82**	3.40 / **5.61**	3.01 / **4.72**	2.78 / **4.22**	2.62 / **3.90**	2.51 / **3.67**	2.43 / **3.50**	2.36 / **3.36**	2.30 / **3.25**	2.26 / **3.17**	2.22 / **3.09**	2.18 / **3.03**	2.13 / **2.93**	2.09 / **2.85**	2.02 / **2.74**	1.98 / **2.66**	1.94 / **2.58**	1.89 / **2.49**	1.86 / **2.44**	1.82 / **2.36**	1.80 / **2.33**	1.76 / **2.27**	1.74 / **2.23**	1.73 / **2.21**	24
25	4.24 / **7.77**	3.38 / **5.57**	2.99 / **4.68**	2.76 / **4.18**	2.60 / **3.86**	2.49 / **3.63**	2.41 / **3.46**	2.34 / **3.32**	2.28 / **3.21**	2.24 / **3.13**	2.20 / **3.05**	2.16 / **2.99**	2.11 / **2.89**	2.06 / **2.81**	2.00 / **2.70**	1.96 / **2.62**	1.92 / **2.54**	1.87 / **2.45**	1.84 / **2.40**	1.80 / **2.32**	1.77 / **2.29**	1.74 / **2.23**	1.72 / **2.19**	1.71 / **2.17**	25
26	4.22 / **7.72**	3.37 / **5.53**	2.98 / **4.64**	2.74 / **4.14**	2.59 / **3.82**	2.47 / **3.59**	2.39 / **3.42**	2.32 / **3.29**	2.27 / **3.17**	2.22 / **3.09**	2.18 / **3.02**	2.15 / **2.96**	2.10 / **2.86**	2.05 / **2.77**	1.99 / **2.66**	1.95 / **2.58**	1.90 / **2.50**	1.85 / **2.41**	1.82 / **2.36**	1.78 / **2.28**	1.76 / **2.25**	1.72 / **2.19**	1.70 / **2.15**	1.69 / **2.13**	26

5% (Roman Type) and 1% (Bold Face Type) Points for the Distribution of F

n_1 degrees of freedom (for greater mean square)

(Roman type = 5% point; **bold face type = 1% point**)

n_2	1	2	3	4	5	6	7	8	9	10	11	12	14	16	20	24	30	40	50	75	100	200	500	∞
50	4.03 / **7.17**	3.18 / **5.06**	2.79 / **4.20**	2.56 / **3.72**	2.40 / **3.41**	2.29 / **3.18**	2.20 / **3.02**	2.13 / **2.88**	2.07 / **2.78**	2.02 / **2.70**	1.98 / **2.62**	1.95 / **2.56**	1.90 / **2.46**	1.85 / **2.39**	1.78 / **2.26**	1.74 / **2.18**	1.69 / **2.10**	1.63 / **2.00**	1.60 / **1.94**	1.55 / **1.86**	1.52 / **1.82**	1.48 / **1.76**	1.46 / **1.71**	1.44 / **1.68**
55	4.02 / **7.12**	3.17 / **5.01**	2.78 / **4.16**	2.54 / **3.68**	2.38 / **3.37**	2.27 / **3.15**	2.18 / **2.98**	2.11 / **2.85**	2.05 / **2.75**	2.00 / **2.66**	1.97 / **2.59**	1.93 / **2.53**	1.88 / **2.43**	1.83 / **2.35**	1.76 / **2.23**	1.72 / **2.15**	1.67 / **2.06**	1.61 / **1.96**	1.58 / **1.90**	1.52 / **1.82**	1.50 / **1.78**	1.46 / **1.71**	1.43 / **1.66**	1.41 / **1.64**
60	4.00 / **7.08**	3.15 / **4.98**	2.76 / **4.13**	2.52 / **3.65**	2.37 / **3.34**	2.25 / **3.12**	2.17 / **2.95**	2.10 / **2.82**	2.04 / **2.72**	1.99 / **2.63**	1.95 / **2.56**	1.92 / **2.50**	1.86 / **2.40**	1.81 / **2.32**	1.75 / **2.20**	1.70 / **2.12**	1.65 / **2.03**	1.59 / **1.93**	1.56 / **1.87**	1.50 / **1.79**	1.48 / **1.74**	1.44 / **1.68**	1.41 / **1.63**	1.39 / **1.60**
65	3.99 / **7.04**	3.14 / **4.95**	2.75 / **4.10**	2.51 / **3.62**	2.36 / **3.31**	2.24 / **3.09**	2.15 / **2.93**	2.08 / **2.79**	2.02 / **2.70**	1.98 / **2.61**	1.94 / **2.54**	1.90 / **2.47**	1.85 / **2.37**	1.80 / **2.30**	1.73 / **2.18**	1.68 / **2.09**	1.63 / **2.00**	1.57 / **1.90**	1.54 / **1.84**	1.49 / **1.76**	1.46 / **1.71**	1.42 / **1.64**	1.39 / **1.60**	1.37 / **1.56**
70	3.98 / **7.01**	3.13 / **4.92**	2.74 / **4.08**	2.50 / **3.60**	2.35 / **3.29**	2.23 / **3.07**	2.14 / **2.91**	2.07 / **2.77**	2.01 / **2.67**	1.97 / **2.59**	1.93 / **2.51**	1.89 / **2.45**	1.84 / **2.35**	1.79 / **2.28**	1.72 / **2.15**	1.67 / **2.07**	1.62 / **1.98**	1.56 / **1.88**	1.53 / **1.82**	1.47 / **1.74**	1.45 / **1.69**	1.40 / **1.62**	1.37 / **1.56**	1.35 / **1.53**
80	3.96 / **6.96**	3.11 / **4.88**	2.72 / **4.04**	2.48 / **3.56**	2.33 / **3.25**	2.21 / **3.04**	2.12 / **2.87**	2.05 / **2.74**	1.99 / **2.64**	1.95 / **2.55**	1.91 / **2.48**	1.88 / **2.41**	1.82 / **2.32**	1.77 / **2.24**	1.70 / **2.11**	1.65 / **2.03**	1.60 / **1.94**	1.54 / **1.84**	1.51 / **1.78**	1.45 / **1.70**	1.42 / **1.65**	1.38 / **1.57**	1.35 / **1.52**	1.32 / **1.49**
100	3.94 / **6.90**	3.09 / **4.82**	2.70 / **3.98**	2.46 / **3.51**	2.30 / **3.20**	2.19 / **2.99**	2.10 / **2.82**	2.03 / **2.69**	1.97 / **2.59**	1.92 / **2.51**	1.88 / **2.43**	1.85 / **2.36**	1.79 / **2.26**	1.75 / **2.19**	1.68 / **2.06**	1.63 / **1.98**	1.57 / **1.89**	1.51 / **1.79**	1.48 / **1.73**	1.42 / **1.64**	1.39 / **1.59**	1.34 / **1.51**	1.30 / **1.46**	1.28 / **1.43**
125	3.92 / **6.84**	3.07 / **4.78**	2.68 / **3.94**	2.44 / **3.47**	2.29 / **3.17**	2.17 / **2.95**	2.08 / **2.79**	2.01 / **2.65**	1.95 / **2.56**	1.90 / **2.47**	1.86 / **2.40**	1.83 / **2.33**	1.77 / **2.23**	1.72 / **2.15**	1.65 / **2.03**	1.60 / **1.94**	1.55 / **1.85**	1.49 / **1.75**	1.45 / **1.68**	1.39 / **1.59**	1.36 / **1.54**	1.31 / **1.46**	1.27 / **1.40**	1.25 / **1.37**
150	3.91 / **6.81**	3.06 / **4.75**	2.67 / **3.91**	2.43 / **3.44**	2.27 / **3.14**	2.16 / **2.92**	2.07 / **2.76**	2.00 / **2.62**	1.94 / **2.53**	1.89 / **2.44**	1.85 / **2.37**	1.82 / **2.30**	1.76 / **2.20**	1.71 / **2.12**	1.64 / **2.00**	1.59 / **1.91**	1.54 / **1.83**	1.47 / **1.72**	1.44 / **1.66**	1.37 / **1.56**	1.34 / **1.51**	1.29 / **1.43**	1.25 / **1.37**	1.22 / **1.33**
200	3.89 / **6.76**	3.04 / **4.71**	2.65 / **3.88**	2.41 / **3.41**	2.26 / **3.11**	2.14 / **2.90**	2.05 / **2.73**	1.98 / **2.60**	1.92 / **2.50**	1.87 / **2.41**	1.83 / **2.34**	1.80 / **2.28**	1.74 / **2.17**	1.69 / **2.09**	1.62 / **1.97**	1.57 / **1.88**	1.52 / **1.79**	1.45 / **1.69**	1.42 / **1.62**	1.35 / **1.53**	1.32 / **1.48**	1.26 / **1.39**	1.22 / **1.33**	1.19 / **1.28**
400	3.86 / **6.70**	3.02 / **4.66**	2.62 / **3.83**	2.39 / **3.36**	2.23 / **3.06**	2.12 / **2.85**	2.03 / **2.69**	1.96 / **2.55**	1.90 / **2.46**	1.85 / **2.37**	1.81 / **2.29**	1.78 / **2.23**	1.72 / **2.12**	1.67 / **2.04**	1.60 / **1.92**	1.54 / **1.84**	1.49 / **1.74**	1.42 / **1.64**	1.38 / **1.57**	1.32 / **1.47**	1.28 / **1.42**	1.22 / **1.32**	1.16 / **1.24**	1.13 / **1.19**
1000	3.85 / **6.66**	3.00 / **4.62**	2.61 / **3.80**	2.38 / **3.34**	2.22 / **3.04**	2.10 / **2.82**	2.02 / **2.66**	1.95 / **2.53**	1.89 / **2.43**	1.84 / **2.34**	1.80 / **2.26**	1.76 / **2.20**	1.70 / **2.09**	1.65 / **2.01**	1.58 / **1.89**	1.53 / **1.81**	1.47 / **1.71**	1.41 / **1.61**	1.36 / **1.54**	1.30 / **1.44**	1.26 / **1.38**	1.19 / **1.28**	1.13 / **1.19**	1.08 / **1.11**
∞	3.84 / **6.64**	2.99 / **4.60**	2.60 / **3.78**	2.37 / **3.32**	2.21 / **3.02**	2.09 / **2.80**	2.01 / **2.64**	1.94 / **2.51**	1.88 / **2.41**	1.83 / **2.32**	1.79 / **2.24**	1.75 / **2.18**	1.69 / **2.07**	1.64 / **1.99**	1.57 / **1.87**	1.52 / **1.79**	1.46 / **1.69**	1.40 / **1.59**	1.35 / **1.52**	1.28 / **1.41**	1.24 / **1.36**	1.17 / **1.25**	1.11 / **1.15**	1.00 / **1.00**

Appendix D   Table of Chi Square

PROBABILITY

n	.99	.98	.95	.90	.80	.70	.50	.30	.20	.10	.05	.02	.01	.001
1	$.0^3157$	$.0^3628$	$.0^3393$	.0158	.0642	.148	.455	1.074	1.642	2.706	3.841	5.412	6.635	10.827
2	.0201	.0404	.103	.211	.446	.713	1.386	2.408	3.219	4.605	5.991	7.824	9.210	13.815
3	.115	.185	.352	.584	1.005	1.424	2.366	3.665	4.642	6.251	7.815	9.837	11.341	16.268
4	.297	.429	.711	1.064	1.649	2.195	3.357	4.878	5.989	7.779	9.488	11.668	13.277	18.465
5	.554	.752	1.145	1.610	2.343	3.000	4.351	6.064	7.289	9.236	11.070	13.388	15.086	20.517
6	.872	1.134	1.635	2.204	3.070	3.828	5.348	7.231	8.558	10.645	12.592	15.033	16.812	22.457
7	1.239	1.564	2.167	2.833	3.822	4.671	6.346	8.383	9.803	12.017	14.067	16.622	18.475	24.322
8	1.646	2.032	2.733	3.490	4.594	5.527	7.344	9.524	11.030	13.362	15.507	18.168	20.090	26.125
9	2.088	2.532	3.325	4.168	5.380	6.393	8.343	10.656	12.242	14.684	16.919	19.679	21.666	27.877
10	2.558	3.059	3.940	4.865	6.179	7.267	9.342	11.781	13.442	15.987	18.307	21.161	23.209	29.588
11	3.053	3.609	4.575	5.578	6.989	8.148	10.341	12.899	14.631	17.275	19.675	22.618	24.725	31.264
12	3.571	4.178	5.226	6.304	7.807	9.034	11.340	14.011	15.812	18.549	21.026	24.054	26.217	32.909
13	4.107	4.765	5.892	7.042	8.634	9.926	12.340	15.119	16.985	19.812	22.362	25.472	27.688	34.528
14	4.660	5.368	6.571	7.790	9.467	10.821	13.339	16.222	18.151	21.064	23.685	26.873	29.141	36.123
15	5.229	5.985	7.261	8.547	10.307	11.721	14.339	17.322	19.311	22.307	24.996	28.259	30.578	37.697
16	5.812	6.614	7.962	9.312	11.152	12.624	15.338	18.418	20.465	23.542	26.296	29.633	32.000	39.252
17	6.408	7.255	8.672	10.085	12.002	13.531	16.338	19.511	21.615	24.769	27.587	30.995	33.409	40.790
18	7.015	7.906	9.390	10.865	12.857	14.440	17.338	20.601	22.760	25.989	28.869	32.346	34.805	42.312
19	7.633	8.567	10.117	11.651	13.716	15.352	18.338	21.689	23.900	27.204	30.144	33.687	36.191	43.820
20	8.260	9.237	10.851	12.443	14.578	16.266	19.337	22.775	25.038	28.412	31.410	35.020	37.566	45.315
21	8.897	9.915	11.591	13.240	15.445	17.182	20.337	23.858	26.171	29.615	32.671	36.343	38.932	46.797
22	9.542	10.600	12.338	14.041	16.314	18.101	21.337	24.939	27.301	30.813	33.924	37.659	40.289	48.268
23	10.196	11.293	13.091	14.848	17.187	19.021	22.337	26.018	28.429	32.007	35.172	38.968	41.638	49.728
24	10.856	11.992	13.848	15.659	18.062	19.943	23.337	27.096	29.553	33.196	36.415	40.270	42.980	51.179
25	11.524	12.697	14.611	16.473	18.940	20.867	24.337	28.172	30.675	34.382	37.652	41.566	44.314	52.620
26	12.198	13.409	15.379	17.292	19.820	21.792	25.336	29.246	31.795	35.563	38.885	42.856	45.642	54.052
27	12.879	14.125	16.151	18.114	20.703	22.719	26.336	30.319	32.912	36.741	40.113	44.140	46.963	55.476
28	13.565	14.847	16.928	18.939	21.588	23.647	27.336	31.391	34.027	37.916	41.337	45.419	48.278	56.893
29	14.256	15.574	17.708	19.768	22.475	24.577	28.336	32.461	35.139	39.087	42.557	46.693	49.588	58.302
30	14.953	16.306	18.493	20.599	23.364	25.508	29.336	33.530	36.250	40.256	43.773	47.962	50.892	59.703

For larger values of n, the expression $\sqrt{2\chi^2} - \sqrt{2n-1}$ may be used as a normal deviate with unit variance, remembering that the probability for χ^2 corresponds with that of a single tail of the normal curve.

Source: Reprinted from Table IV of Fisher and Yates, *Statistical Tables for Biological, Agricultural, and Medical Research*, published by Oliver and Boyd Ltd., Edinburgh, by permission of the authors and publishers.

Appendix E   Table of Student's *t*   two TAILED TEST

Degrees of Freedom (*n*)	Probability				
	0.50	0.10	0.05	0.02	0.01
1	1.000	6.34	12.71	31.82	63.66
2	0.816	2.92	4.30	6.96	9.92
3	.765	2.35	3.18	4.54	5.84
4	.741	2.13	2.78	3.75	4.60
5	.727	2.02	2.57	3.36	4.03
6	.718	1.94	2.45	3.14	3.71
7	.711	1.90	2.36	3.00	3.50
8	.706	1.86	2.31	2.90	3.36
9	.703	1.83	2.26	2.82	3.25
10	.700	1.81	2.23	2.76	3.17
11	.697	1.80	2.20	2.72	3.11
12	.695	1.78	2.18	2.68	3.06
13	.694	1.77	2.16	2.65	3.01
14	.692	1.76	2.14	2.62	2.98
15	.691	1.75	2.13	2.60	2.95
16	.690	1.75	2.12	2.58	2.92
17	.689	1.74	2.11	2.57	2.90
18	.688	1.73	2.10	2.55	2.88
19	.688	1.73	2.09	2.54	2.86
20	.687	1.72	2.09	2.53	2.84
21	.686	1.72	2.08	2.52	2.83
22	.686	1.72	2.07	2.51	2.82
23	.685	1.71	2.07	2.50	2.81
24	.685	1.71	2.06	2.49	2.80
25	.684	1.71	2.06	2.48	2.79
26	.684	1.71	2.06	2.48	2.78
27	.684	1.70	2.05	2.47	2.77
28	.683	1.70	2.05	2.47	2.76
29	.683	1.70	2.04	2.46	2.76
30	.683	1.70	2.04	2.46	2.75
35	.682	1.69	2.03	2.44	2.72
40	.681	1.68	2.02	2.42	2.71
45	.680	1.68	2.02	2.41	2.69
50	.679	1.68	2.01	2.40	2.68
60	.678	1.67	2.00	2.39	2.66
70	.678	1.67	2.00	2.38	2.65
80	.677	1.66	1.99	2.38	2.64
90	.677	1.66	1.99	2.37	2.63
100	.677	1.66	1.98	2.36	2.63
125	.676	1.66	1.98	2.36	2.62
150	.676	1.66	1.98	2.35	2.61
200	.675	1.65	1.97	2.35	2.60
300	.675	1.65	1.97	2.34	2.59
400	.675	1.65	1.97	2.34	2.59
500	.674	1.65	1.96	2.33	2.59
1000	.674	1.65	1.96	2.33	2.58
∞	.674	1.64	1.96	2.33	2.58

The greater portion of this table is abridged from Table III of Fisher and Yates, *Statistical Tables for Biological, Agricultural and Medical Research*, published by Oliver and Boyd Ltd., Edinburgh, and by permission of the authors and publishers.

Source: Reproduced by permission from C. H. Goulden, *Methods of Statistical Analysis* (New York: John Wiley & Sons, 1939).

Appendix F Table of Areas of the Normal Curve

$t = \frac{x}{\sigma}$	.00	.01	.02	.03	.04	.05	.06	.07	.08	.09
0.0	.0000	.0040	.0080	.0120	.0159	.0199	.0239	.0279	.0319	.0359
0.1	.0398	.0438	.0478	.0517	.0557	.0596	.0636	.0675	.0714	.0753
0.2	.0793	.0832	.0871	.0910	.0948	.0987	.1026	.1064	.1103	.1141
0.3	.1179	.1217	.1255	.1293	.1331	.1368	.1406	.1443	.1480	.1517
0.4	.1554	.1591	.1628	.1664	.1700	.1736	.1772	.1808	.1844	.1879
0.5	.1915	.1950	.1985	.2019	.2054	.2088	.2123	.2157	.2190	.2224
0.6	.2257	.2291	.2324	.2357	.2389	.2422	.2454	.2486	.2518	.2549
0.7	.2580	.2612	.2642	.2673	.2704	.2734	.2764	.2794	.2823	.2852
0.8	.2881	.2910	.2939	.2967	.2995	.3023	.3051	.3078	.3106	.3233
0.9	.3159	.3186	.3212	.3238	.3264	.3289	.3315	.3340	.3365	.3389
1.0	.3413	.3438	.3461	.3485	.3508	.3531	.3554	.3577	.3599	.3621
1.1	.3643	.3665	.3686	.3718	.3729	.3749	.3770	.3790	.3810	.3830
1.2	.3849	.3869	.3888	.3907	.3925	.3944	.3962	.3980	.3997	.4015
1.3	.4032	.4049	.4066	.4083	.4099	.4115	.4131	.4147	.4162	.4177
1.4	.4192	.4207	.4222	.4236	.4251	.4265	.4279	.4292	.4306	.4319
1.5	.4332	.4345	.4357	.4370	.4382	.4394	.4406	.4418	.4430	.4441
1.6	.4452	.4463	.4474	.4485	.4495	.4505	.4515	.4525	.4535	.4545
1.7	.4554	.4564	.4573	.4582	.4591	.4599	.4608	.4616	.4625	.4633
1.8	.4641	.4649	.4656	.4664	.4671	.4678	.4686	.4693	.4699	.4706
1.9	.4713	.4719	.4726	.4732	.4738	.4744	.4750	.4758	.4762	.4767
2.0	.4773	.4778	.4783	.4788	.4793	.4798	.4803	.4808	.4812	.4817
2.1	.4821	.4826	.4830	.4834	.4838	.4842	.4846	.4850	.4854	.4857
2.2	.4861	.4865	.4868	.4871	.4875	.4878	.4881	.4884	.4887	.4890
2.3	.4893	.4896	.4898	.4901	.4904	.4906	.4909	.4911	.4913	.4916
2.4	.4918	.4920	.4922	.4925	.4927	.4929	.4931	.4932	.4934	.4936
2.5	.4938	.4940	.4941	.4943	.4945	.4946	.4948	.4949	.4951	.4952
2.6	.4953	.4955	.4956	.4957	.4959	.4960	.4961	.4962	.4963	.4964
2.7	.4965	.4966	.4967	.4968	.4969	.4970	.4971	.4972	.4973	.4974
2.8	.4974	.4975	.4976	.4977	.4977	.4978	.4979	.4980	.4980	.4981
2.9	.4981	.4982	.4983	.4984	.4984	.4984	.4985	.4985	.4986	.4986
3.0	.49865	.4987	.4987	.4988	.4988	.4988	.4989	.4989	.4989	.4990
3.1	.49903	.4991	.4991	.4991	.4992	.4992	.4992	.4992	.4993	.4993
3.2	.49931									
3.3	.49952									
3.4	.49966									
3.5	.49977									
3.6	.49984									
3.7	.49989									
3.8	.49993									
3.9	.49995									
4.0	.49997									

Source: Herbert Arkin and Raymond R. Colton, *An Outline of Statistical Methods* (4th ed.; New York: Barnes & Noble, 1939), p. 110.

PRINTED IN U.S.A.

180-1